TECHNICAL ASSISTANCE AND INNOVATION IN SCIENCE EDUCATION

by

ROBERT H. MAYBURY

TECHNICAL ASSISTANCE AND INNOVATION IN SCIENCE EDUCATION

BY

ROBERT H. MAYBURY

Deputy Head, UNESCO
Field Science Office for Africa
Nairobi, Kenya

A critical and comparative appraisal of five projects for science education improvement supported by the Ford Foundation.

Argentina
Brazil
Lebanon and other Arab Countries in the Middle East
Philippines
Turkey

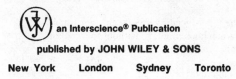 an Interscience® Publication

published by JOHN WILEY & SONS

New York   London   Sydney   Toronto

III

TECHNICAL ASSISTANCE AND INNOVATION IN SCIENCE EDUCATION
is published by

SCIENCE EDUCATION

an Interscience® Publication of John Wiley & Sons
605 Third Avenue, New York, New York 10016

This report was prepared with the help of a grant from the Ford Foundation and is distributed free of charge to subscribers to SCIENCE EDUCATION. Additional copies may be obtained from the publisher.

Ford Foundation Foreword

In the course of reviewing some twenty years of its assistance to educational development in Asia, Africa and the Middle East, and Latin America, the Ford Foundation singled out for early attention its support to science education in all three areas. The Foundation's interest in the improvement of science education had emerged in the fifties and had been sustained throughout the sixties. Therefore, the record of effort was relatively long. Moreover, the question, "How much is enough?," is still very much before us in this as in other fields. Whether or not we should decide to continue to be active on the scale and in the manner of the past, it seemed to us to be important to provide for a public review of five principal projects undertaken to date, hoping not only that we might learn from a study of them but that development planners and science educators in the developing world and elsewhere and other "agencies" assisting education would find such a review of value.

To make the study, we looked for someone who was thoroughly and professionally conversant with science education in the developing world, and with technical assistance in that field, but who also had not been a participant in the Foundation's work. We were fortunate in identifying a scientist and educator who fully filled this bill in Robert Maybury, in discovering that he would find the task congenial, and in being permitted by UNESCO to interrupt his regular duties for what proved to be more than a year's time. We are grateful for this arrangement, to UNESCO and even more to Dr. Maybury himself, who has given to the study more of his time and energy than any mere contract could have required of anyone.

Although those who took part in the projects Dr. Maybury recounts and discusses will not necessarily share all of his interpretative conclusions, I am sure that they share my own gratitude to him for recovering so carefully the histories of projects in which the Ford Foundation has invested limited funds and much concern, and for saying so forthrightly what he believes those histories can teach those who took part in them and others who believe in the importance of improved education in science.

F. Champion Ward
Program Advisor in Education
International Division
The Ford Foundation

V

Author's Preface

This study examines five remarkable programs for improving science teaching in the schools of Argentina, Brazil, Lebanon, the Philippines and Turkey. Its aim is to give a wide public view to the record of the experiences of these programs—an aim set by the Ford Foundation in reviewing a decade or two of its international assistance mission to education in developing countries. Indeed, these five programs have participated in that mission—receiving substantial grants of assistance from the Ford Foundation from their inception to the present.

To give that record as wide a public view as possible, I present the study in two parts. The first contains five case histories—descriptive and uninterpreted accounts of the events as they have unfolded over time in these programs. Those accounts trace the two strands of effort which are intertwined throughout the history of the programs—that by the scientists, educators and government authorities in each country collaborating to bring about innovation and change in the teaching of science in their schools—and that of the Ford Foundation in meeting the technical assistance requirements of those innovators.

The second part of the study presents my attempt to compare, analyze and interpret the experiences of these programs in a search for the two sets of lessons they teach: on innovating in science education and on meeting the technical assistance needs that arise in that innovating.

The Ford Foundation gave generous support to my work of preparing this study. They made it possible for me to travel to each of the countries where the programs are located. While in each, I was able to devote many weeks to examining relevant files and documents, to interviewing the directors and staff members of the projects, as well as government authorities, educators and scientists, to observing the projects at work in the schools and among teachers, and in general, to acquire the information needed in writing accurate and full accounts.

Two basic reasons moved me to accept the Foundation invitation to take on this study. First was my belief in the importance of science education in all countries—developed and devoloping—in an age of growing influence of science and technology on human life and affairs. At the same time, a decade of work with UNESCO has shown me some of the difficulties afflicting science education in so many developing countries. Therefore, I saw, in carrying on the study, a chance to learn more about the improvement of science education by looking closely at the accomplishments of five projects with a reputation for success along this line.

The second reason was my conviction that the time was ripe for a review of the technical assistance mission to education in the developing countries—that of

UNESCO's as well as of other international agencies. The invitation from The Ford Foundation offered me just the chance I had been looking for to step down from operating in order to enter a "study" mode in which to examine operations and reflect upon their successes and difficulties.

No study of this kind would be possible without the cooperation of the directors and staff members of these five projects during my visits to their countries. They shared many hours of their busy working days with me in a generous and interested effort to help me grasp the nature of their educational mission. To each of them, I express genuine gratitude, not only for their time but also for taking me in as colleague.

Moreover, no study of this kind could succeed in the absence of contributions —substantive and critical—from loyal assistants. The Ford Foundation generosity enabled me to seek the assistance of four capable graduate students: Albert Medvitz at the Center for Studies in Education and Development, Harvard University; Cary Sneider at the Lawrence Hall of Science, University of California, Berkeley; Ersin Asarkaya at the Middle East Technical University, Ankara, Turkey; and Samir Makzume at the American University of Beirut. Moreover, Jeanne McCormack held us together as a team at Harvard University* and tended a lifeline to me during my global perigrinations. To this team, then, I express gratitude and appreciation.

Finally, no study of this kind is carried on without a price being paid— invariably by the author's family who, through his need to give single-minded attention to his material, knew many months of relative neglect. To Helen, my wife, and our school-aged children, then, I express gratitude for support and understanding through a seemingly never-ending period.

I alone am to be held responsible for the accuracy of the facts reported in the case histories and the soundness of the judgments and interpretations offered in the analysis. I have, of course, shared the case histories with Ford Foundation officers and with the relevant project directors to seek their assistance in eliminating errors and filling in the gaps. Also, I benefited greatly from discussions with Ford Foundation officers who showed an interest in the various conclusions I reach. These talks were stimulating and open—but they left the final judgment on each issue up to me.

Robert H. Maybury

*I thank Dr. Charles Myers of the Center for Studies in Education and Development at Harvard University for his kindness in providing me a delightful office during the year of this study which, in turn, placed me in a most helpful and critical milieu for the task I was carrying out.

Contents

Ford Foundation Foreword V
Author's Preface VII

PART I
Case Histories in the
Improvement of Education in Science
    Argentina... 1
    Brazil 25
    Lebanon and Other Arab Countries 55
    The Philippines 79
    Turkey 107

PART II
Analysis and Conclusions
    Introduction 147
    1. Lessons on Innovating in
        Science Education 149
    2. Lessons on Meeting the
        Technical Assistance Requirements of
        Innovation in Education 181

Epilogue.. 209

PART I
Case Histories in the Improvement
of Education in Science

ARGENTINA

1.   *Argentine scientists decide to improve science education in their country*
    Early in 1960, an elite corps of Argentina's scientists, associated as the National Council for Scientific and Technical Research (CONICYT), took stock of the outdated and inadequate science teaching in the schools of their country and decided to attack the problem. Under the leadership of that country's Nobel laureate, Bernardo Houssay, those scientists had earlier taken several bold steps to modernize their scientific and educational institutions. Shortly after founding the Council in 1958, they had embarked upon a program of repatriating Argentine scientists from abroad, providing them privileges and financial support to enable them to start new research careers at home. The Council had also sent hundreds of Argentine scholars abroad for advanced study in a wide range of fields including the social and political sciences. Under yet another program, one designed to strengthen and develop the educational system of Argentina, the Council had provided fellowships for advanced study abroad to teachers and administrators from universities and from the Ministry of Education.
    Although none of those activities had been aimed specifically at secondary school science teaching, the experience with programs focussing on more advanced scientific training and research soon convinced Council members that inadequate science instruction at the secondary school level was holding back the development of high-level scientific manpower in Argentina. They saw the flaws in that instruction: its dependence on rote memorization of formulas and facts; the outdated textbooks and lack of teaching aids; little or no opportunity for students to carry out laboratory work; poorly trained teachers with neither the time nor the incentive to keep abreast of new developments in their subjects; student-teacher contact limited to the lecture room and, because of low salary scales, teachers frequently assigned to two or more schools, resulting in failure to identify and encourage talented students.
    The Council viewed its 1960 decision to exert leadership in the area of secondary school science education as a modest one that would trigger future action on a broad scale by the Ministry of Education. It wanted its initial thrust to stimulate the interest and enthusiasm of the teachers themselves for thorough-going reform and reorientation of secondary school science programs. To get this initial effort underway, the Council established an office for the improvement of secondary school education and, in November 1960, appointed Ing. Andres Valeiras, a former mathematics teacher and public high school principal, as full-time director. As the first step in launching the Council's secondary school science program, Ing. Valeiras organized a summer seminar for 35 physics teachers from high schools throughout the country. A committee of university professors and a delegate from the Ministry of Education planned and

1

supervised the four-week seminar in 1961 at Rio Tercero in the province of Cordoba. The professors themselves taught in the seminar, which focused on experimental and modern physics. The basic objectives were to interest teachers in the application of modern scientific criteria to secondary school physics and to demonstrate the possibilities of using low-cost science equipment in the classroom.[1]

2. *The Foundation makes its first grant for science education improvement*

The success of the Council's initial effort in conducting in-service courses encouraged Professor Houssay to request support from the Ford Foundation representative in Buenos Aires to expand these in-service activities:

> The Council has started on a program which aims at raising the standards of science teaching at high school level in Argentina.
>
> As a first step, a committee of Argentina physicists (recommended) summer courses for secondary school teachers so they may freshen up their general knowledge of the subject and get acquainted with the new aspects of science from the latest research, simultaneously acquainting and encouraging the use of experimental techniques through simple teaching aids, which any teacher with an average manual ability may prepare when the material available in the school laboratory proves insufficient or obsolete.
>
> The pilot course was a complete success. In view of the success attained, it is proposed to hold further summer courses for high school science teachers next January and February, repeating and improving the Physics course, to which it is intended to invite Physics high school teachers from neighboring countries and also holding similar courses in mathematics, chemistry and biology.[2]

In this request to the Ford Foundation, Professor Houssay presented an itemized budget covering, among other things, the cost of stipends for the teachers attending the in-service courses, the cost of putting a Spanish-language sound track on 141 science films donated to the Council by the Ford Foundation, and fares for selected teachers to travel to the U.S. to participate in National Science Foundation courses there.

On receiving this request from Professor Houssay, the Ford Foundation office in Buenos Aires prepared the usual formal document, the Request for Grant Action (RGA), in which the field office sets forth the merits of the prospective recipient's case for consideration by the Foundation headquarters in New York. In October 1961, the Ford Foundation then awarded a grant of $400,000 to the Council, out of which $75,000 was allocated to a greatly expanded program of in-service courses for science teachers.

In addition to this grant, the Ford Foundation provided a series of travel grants to the Council so that it could send five selected teachers to the National Science Foundation summer institutes in the U.S. The Foundation also awarded a special travel grant to Ing. Valeiras so that he could spend two months in the U.S. observing in-service courses at the University of Colorado, Massachusetts Institute of Technology and Columbia University. During that trip, he also visited representatives of the National Science Foundation in Washington as well as other educational and scientific organizations related to his work with the Council.

Under this first grant from the Ford Foundation, the Council brought more than 300 science teachers, supervisors and Ministry of Education officials in Argentina into in-service courses. Through this intimate contact with the realities of the educational system, the Council saw even more clearly how poor were conditions for science teaching in the nation's schools. They grew determined to mount a comprehensive attack on the problem.

3. *The Council seeks Foundation assistance for a comprehensive program*

At a meeting held in October 1963, the Executive Committee of the Council appointed a commission of three of its members, Dr. Rolanda Garcia, Dean of the Faculty of Exact and Natural Sciences, University of Buenos Aires, and Vice President of the Council, Dr. Luis A. Santalo, Professor of Mathematics at the University of Buenos Aires, and Ing. Valeiras, to study preliminary plans for an organization that could assume full and continuing responsibility for promoting reform of school science education in Argentina. They envisaged such an organization proceeding along the following lines:

a. Contributing to better preparation of teachers;
b. Developing summer courses for teacher up-grading;
c. Developing academic-year in-service courses for teachers;
d. Reforming the school science curriculum and syllabus;
e. Designing and producing laboratory equipment for the schools;
f. Preparing and publishing textbooks and other materials for students and teachers.

This special commission of the Council drew up a proposal for a large-scale project of science education improvement along these above lines and, in September 1963 submitted this, along with a budget request in the amount of $240,000, to the Ford Foundation as a formal proposal for support.

On receiving this from the Council, the Ford Foundation specified the following conditions that would have to be fulfilled before the Foundation could act further on the proposal:

1. A more detailed costing of the proposal.
2. A description of the administrative structure to be used for the implementation of this program. Because of the Consejo's demonstrated ability to carry through its projects it would appear that administrative control should be directly under the Consejo.
3. A commitment from the Ministry of Education indicating its interest in the program and its willingness to commit substantial financial resources to the implementation of the curricula and the purchase of the equipment developed by the Consejo.
4. Involvement by a member of the Ministry in the progress of the program, possibly in the form of a member in the senior body of the service organization being studied by the Consejo.[3]

The Foundation explained its insistence upon full participation by the Ministry of Education in any large-scale effort to upgrade science teaching in the schools of the country in this way:

3

Ultimate effectiveness on a broad scale would depend to a substantial extent on the interest and support of the Ministry of Education. In the Foundation's view, it seemed evident that the Council's efforts to develop new curricula, textbooks, and model, low-cost equipment would have very limited impact without the institutional means—which only the Ministry could provide—for systematically channeling these new science materials to the secondary schools. In addition, even if initial financing were to be obtained from outside sources, over the long run only the Ministry of Education, with its annual budget appropriation for equipment and teaching materials, could underwrite the production of equipment, manuals and science texts on a scale adequate to ensure their distribution throughout the national school system. While the Foundation therefore encouraged the Council to develop a firm project proposal, it was stipulated that the Foundation would require an official commitment to the project by the Ministry.[4]

The Council accepted the conditions set by the Foundation and proceeded to carry out the costing, to prepare the description of the proposed structure, and to seek the Ministry commitment to the proposed plan. The general political instability of the country at that time rendered negotiations with the Ministry exceedingly difficult and caused them to extend over a protracted period. Then, in the midst of conducting these difficult negotiations, Ing. Valeiras received an invitation from the Organization of American States to become director of its Latin American Program in Science Education. To accept this invitation, he had to resign as Director of the Council's science education program, which left that post vacant. The Council then needed to find a new Director.

4.   *Angel Hernaiz takes over as Director of the Council's science education program*

The Council's extensive canvas of prospective candidates for the post vacated by Ing. Valeiras led eventually to Professor Angel Hernaiz, the Head Inspector of the National Council for Technical Education. After graduating from the Instituto Nacional del Profesorado Secundario and the Faculty of Chemistry and Pharmacy of the National University of La Plata, Hernaiz had entered secondary school teaching of chemistry. From that he rose through various memberships on commissions for education to his post as Head Inspector. In selecting Hernaiz to be the new Director of the science education program, the Council gained a leader who was familiar with the procedures and personnel of the Ministry of Education, an asset sorely needed at that time of difficult negotiations with the Ministry.

Although it was late in 1964 (August) when the Council finally appointed Hernaiz to the Directorship of the science education program, and although little progress had been made in the negotiations with the Ministry related to the proposal before the Ford Foundation, nevertheless, that year included some notable achievements by the program. In particular, the mathematics advisory committee completed its drafting of a new six-year mathematics curriculum and prepared instructional materials and accompanying teacher's guides for the first three years of the sequence. Dr. Oscar Varsavsky, Professor of Mathematics of the University of Buenos Aires, authored the algebra textbook for these trial programs. A group of 25 pilot schools put the new materials to test under a trial program supervised by the Ministry of Educa-

tion. The mathematics committee then revised the materials on the basis of this trial use in the classrooms.

Two additional achievements marked the mathematics group's efforts that year. First, circulation of a journal for secondary school mathematics teachers initiated by Ing. Valeiras as, "Elementas Revista de Matematica para la Enseñanza Media" reached a circulation of 3,000 in 1964. Second, the Council's in-service course in mathematics took on a new aspect, when it was used as a demonstration of new curriculum materials for 80 teachers of mathematics.

Progress during 1964 was less rapid in the other disciplines. The Council's advisory committee in chemistry prepared new course materials in chemistry, but were unable to reach the pilot testing phase. The chemistry group also organized a seminar to familiarize a group of teachers with the CHEM-Study materials, one of the U.S. National Science Foundation supported curriculum projects. In the following year, 1965, this group received an inspirational boost when it served as host to the Third Latin American Conference on Chemistry Teaching in Latin America, an event which brought scientists and educators from Europe, North America, and other Latin American countries to Buenos Aires for a week-long review of the state of curriculum reform in chemistry.

The Council's work in physics that year centered on Dr. Felix Cernuschi and his colleagues at the Faculty of Engineering of the University of Buenos Aires and on Professor Alberto Maiztegui, director of the Institute of Mathematics, Astronomy, and Physics (IMAF) at the National University of Cordoba. The Buenos Aires group developed a set of manuals to guide physics teachers in the use of equipment based on the Physical Science Study Committee (PSSC) in the U.S. They conducted in-service courses to acquaint teachers with the manuals and to encourage them to employ low-cost equipment in their school laboratories.

Professor Maiztegui's group (IMAF) initiated a quite different interest among the physics teachers, one based upon inexpensive kits of physics equipment developed by Latin American physics teachers working collaboratively during 1964 in a year-long pilot project organized by UNESCO in São Paulo, Brazil. In 1965, under the National Council auspices, IMAF conducted a six-week seminar that acquainted 21 Argentine physics teachers with the UNESCO pilot project kits. The Council provided funds for each teacher to receive a complete set of the kits to take back to his school at the close of the seminar.

Because the biology group showed relatively little activity that year, Council members pressed for the more comprehensive program outlined by Houssay to the Ford Foundation.

As an interim measure, the Council decided to broaden its base for action in behalf of science teachers. It set up four national commissions with representatives from the Ministry of Education, the Council, the universities and the teacher-training colleges (Institutos de Profesorado).

This reorganization of the commissions brought immediate results. For example, the newly organized Biology commission prepared a guide for the improvement of instruction in biology which was distributed to biology teachers by the Ministry of Education. The commission next revised the five-year biology course sequence at the Secondary level. One of its members, Dr. del Ponte, completed a Spanish translation of the ecological oriented text developed by the Biological Sciences Curriculum Study in the United States (BSCS green version). And, finally, the commission organized a regional course for secondary school teachers in January and February 1965 that included 24 Argentinian teachers and 22 participants from other South American countries.

5.   *The Ministry and the Council cooperate in developing
      a proposal to the Foundation*

As the year 1965 opened, and with still no response from the Ministry of Education, Professor Houssay decided to contact the Minister of Education directly. In discussions with the Minister, Houssay outlined the proposed plan of the Council for reform of science education and explained the Ford Foundation insistence that the Council be given assurance by the Ministry of Education of its cooperation with the Council in the implementation of the program. Houssay followed his visit with a letter in which he again outlined the salient issues awaiting the Ministry's response. In that letter he warned that "the philanthropic organization (the Ford Foundation) has for quite some time earmarked a sum of money for the financing of this project, and there is a very serious risk of losing such a significant contribution . . . (unless government acts)." Houssay went on to request that the Minister appoint a high-level representative who could meet with the Council and other participating groups in studying the administrative problems of setting up the proposed project.

The Minister replied to Houssay almost immediately. In his reply, the Minister granted the required assurance of Ministry support and willingness to participate in the proposed project and designated the high level representative requested by Professor Houssay. The Minister followed up his letter by issuing Ministerial Decree No. 1029, dated 26 July 1965, in which he appointed the Inspector-in-Chief of the Ministry's Department of Instruction, Professor Hellmuth Volker, as the Ministry representative in the negotiations with the Council.

The Council, led by Professor Hernaiz, now engaged the Ministry's designated representative in an intensive series of discussions that led straight-away to a plan for a comprehensive program of reform of science education in Argentina's secondary schools. The principal objectives of that program were four-fold:

1) the development of new curricula in the four basic sciences at the secondary level.
2) writing and publication of teachers' manuals and textbooks corresponding to the new science curricula.
3) design, production and distribution of modern, low-cost laboratory equipment and of the corresponding experiment manuals for students.
4) teacher training—both in-service and within the Institutos de Profesorado.

To achieve these objectives, the framers of the plan concluded that a strong institutional base would be necessary and proposed the formation of a National Institute for Science Teaching (Instituto Nacional para el Mejoramiento de la Enseñanza de las Ciencias (INEC). This new institution, INEC, was to be placed administratively under the auspices of the Council to protect it from political and bureaucratic pressures. At the same time, to ensure that the Ministry of Education would implement reforms emanating from INEC, the Ministry was asked to assign staff members to it as well as to allocate funds to it from the Ministry budget. Finally, overall planning, supervision and coordination of the program of INEC was placed in the hands of national commissions composed of representatives of the Council, the Ministry of Education, the Institutos de Profesorado, and the national universities of Argentina.

After reviewing the estimated costs of conducting the programs foreseen over the first several years of the life of INEC, the framers of the plan outlined a budget that itemized costs for development of curriculum materials, preparation of prototype laboratory apparatus, stipends for teachers to participate in in-service courses, and pilot production of the newly prepared instructional materials for the schools. The Council then drafted a proposal which they brought to the Ford Foundation, seeking a grant of $250,000 to meet half of the costs of setting up and operating the new institution. After appropriate study of the proposal, the Ford Foundation awarded (on 22 September 1965) a grant of $250,000 to the Council and thereby set the stage for the anticipated upsurge in science education improvement in Argentina. But before work on this larger scale could get under way, fate intervened in a most cruel manner. On 28 June 1966, Argentine military leaders carried out a bloodless coup. They ousted the nation's president who had been elected in 1963, dissolved the national and provincial legislatures, and placed all executive and legislative power in the office of their appointed executive.

In the changed political atmosphere following the coup, police and military personnel made massive intrusions on university campuses throughout the country, causing the exodus from Argentina of over six hundred university professors. This had disastrous consequences, of course, for those national commissions on science education which the Council had just created, by draining off much of their intellectual strength. So gravely did this political situation interfere with the Council's efforts to organize the new institute for science education, that nearly two years passed before INEC could eventually be organized.

In January, 1967, a full sixteen months after the award of the grant to the Council under which INEC was to have been set up, the Ford Foundation was obliged by its own regulations to issue the following warning to the Council:

> As we all know, the Ford Foundation grant of $250,000 to the National Council for Scientific and Technical Research for the improvement of secondary science teaching has not yet been able to function despite the valiant efforts of yourself, Dr. Hernaiz and many others in and out of the Government. Sixteen months have passed since the grant was approved but due to circumstances which were, and I believe still are, largely beyond the control of either the Council or the Foundation staff, the following actions necessary to secure the release of funds under the grant have not yet been taken:
>
> 1. Signing of the convenio between the Council and the education authorities of the national government for the creation and operation of a national institute of science teaching, which would administer the Foundation grant funds as intended.
>
> 2. The commitment and release of peso funds by the national government for program operations to the equivalent of US$250,000, under the matching terms of the grant.
>
> 3. The constitution of four national commissions of teachers and scholars in physics, chemistry, biology and mathematics, qualified and able to provide leadership and action toward accomplishing the objectives of the Foundation's grant.
>
> Under Ford Foundation regulations, grants which remain inactive for a period of more than 18 months are subject to cancellation so that the earmarked funds may be released for other Foundation projects.

It therefore appears likely that the Foundation will find it necessary to request the release from its commitment of the $250,000 under the grant for the secondary science project on the date of March 15, 1967.[6]

During that sixteen months interval, although conditions produced by the military coup prevented progress on obtaining the formal government agreement for the proposed institution, nevertheless much was achieved by Hernaiz and his Council-led program by way of providing services to Argentine science teachers. Hundreds of these teachers participated in the Council-supported in-service courses conducted in Buenos Aires and throughout the provinces. However, the need for the comprehensive kind of program called for in the plan of INEC remained as great as ever. The thought of losing the Ford Foundation grant opened the Council to fresh initiatives in its behalf.

6.   *A consultant appointed to advise Argentine educators and the Foundation*

Thus, in May, 1967, the Foundation invited Abraham Fischler, a science educator at the University of California at Berkeley (and now the President of Nova University in Florida), to serve as a consultant to Hernaiz and his colleagues and to advise the Foundation on what it should do about its inactive grant. Fischler travelled to schools and universities throughout the country and met with Ministry of Education officials, including Professor Volker. He strongly recommended a formal decree from the government as the only certain way to place INEC on a firm legal footing. Moreover, he argued, a decree would establish the necessary relationship between the executive branch of the government and the Council and thereby permit the Ministry of Education to provide funds in its budget for support of INEC's program. Fischler also recommended that a national meeting be convened to bring scientists, secondary school teachers, and Ministry officials together to discuss and agree upon the philosophy and basic objectives of the National Institute for Science Education and the necessary commitment of the time and talents of Argentine educators to assure INEC's success. His other recommendations included the formation of subject groups and writing teams, the decentralization of curriculum development activities to regional centers such as Cordoba and the establishment of a library and documentation center for use by the working groups.[7]

He then advised the Foundation to delay release of grant funds until the Ministry of Education issued the formal decree on INEC. He also recommended that more grant funds be directed toward the support of indigenous and creative curriculum development and less toward the conduct of in-service courses for teachers. He argued that materials developed in Argentina by Argentine educators should be placed in the hands of students as soon as possible. He also argued that in-service teacher training courses would be more meaningful when based on materials developed within the country rather than on those developed abroad.

Fischler's visit encouraged the Foundation representative in Argentina to expect a breakthrough in the long-stalled negotiations with the Ministry. A "Convenio" (agreement) between the Council and Ministry specifying the legal, organizational and technical dimensions of INEC was indeed developed, but bureaucratic procedures delayed the signing of the "Convenio" for yet another six months. While waiting for this final signing of the Convenio, Hernaiz decided to move ahead on Fischler's recommendation that a major conference on science education policy matters be convened:

Meanwhile, Hernaiz has been setting the stage for the implementation of Fischler's second recommendation, namely, "a

8

meeting of scientists, secondary school teachers, and Ministry officials, in order to establish the philosophy and basic objectives of INEC ..." The meeting is tentatively scheduled for October and will probably be held in Rio Tercero in the province of Cordoba. Hernaiz has already talked with Cordoba's Minister of Education, as well as with the scientists at the National University of Cordoba, and has been promised full cooperation.

Hernaiz has also been busy on other fronts. Attached for your information is a list of science seminars scheduled for 1967, and the first draft of a physics laboratory guide for students.[8]

One Foundation officer gave this assessment of the delay in the signing:

We are all suffering from this delay, the Foundation, Hernaiz, and his group, Ministry officials and, of course, in the meantime students and teachers. But INEC will be formed—and soon, says Hernaiz, and this year has not entirely been lost since Hernaiz' department has been as active as ever.[9]

On 27 December 1967, the long-awaited Presidential decree creating INEC was signed. The Council reported this information to the Ford Foundation and requested immediate activation of the grant which had been awarded twenty-six months earlier.

7.   *INEC enters its first full year of operation*
INEC entered the year 1968 fully anticipating that its new legal relationship to the Ministry would speed up its work. Much to Hernaiz' dismay, however, this did not turn out to be the case. Instead, he found a frustratingly slow pace on the part of the Ministry of Education in handling basic issues related to INEC's position and structure. The official steps taken by the Ministry to clarify INEC's relationships to the National Council of Scientific and Technical Research and the Ministry of Education followed a two-year time table as shown below:

Ministry Action	Date	Purpose
Decree No. 9317	27 Dec. 1967	Created INEC and outlined the terms of the "Convenio" of 15 March 1967 prepared by Volker of the Ministry and Hernaiz of the National Council.
Decree No. 2,704	17 May 1968	Established position of INEC in Ministry.
Decree No. 699	28 Feb. 1969	Further clarified INEC structure.
Resolution 512	5 June 1968	Constituted a new National Commission for the teaching of mathematics under Ministry auspices.
Resolution 615	1 July 1968	Constituted National Commission for teaching of Biology, Physics, and Chemistry.
Resolution 484	22 May 1969	Corroborated the missions and functions of INEC set forth originally in Article 3 of the Convenio (15 March 1967).

In spite of this slow pace on the government's part, Hernaiz drew up an ambitious program of activities for INEC in 1968. That program ranged from a long list of in-service courses through convening the first National Symposium for the Improvement of Science Education to organization of the National Commissions in Biology, Physics, Mathematics and Chemistry. It included promoting and planning science fairs and clubs. At the level of creative developmental work, it called for preparation of prototype kits in physics and biology and for writing of laboratory guides. Finally at the informational level, it included organization of a specialized library and exhibition of teacher materials, mass distribution of information on science education to teachers organizations, public offices, institutions both public and private, and training of mobile science education groups.

To bolster Hernaiz and the young INEC organization in its determination to undertake a workload of this magnitude, the Ford Foundation requested Fischler to make two additional consultant visits to Argentina during that year. His first visit took place in May, 1968 while Hernaiz was planning the forthcoming National Symposium of Science Education. During that visit, Fischler paid special attention to the burgeoning activities of the discipline-oriented groups at INEC:

> I first met with the physics group. (They worked with) twenty-four teachers coming in on Saturdays for an introductory physics seminar and utilizing the IPS program developed by Educational Services Incorporated in Massachusetts. This program is a laboratory-oriented program for first-year physics. Each teacher was given all the necessary materials so that every two students could work together. Every Saturday, the teachers came to discuss the problems as well as to perform the following week's work. They work a minimum of four hours on Saturday. They did not start teaching their own students until they were three weeks into the IPS program. Six hundred and thirty students are being taught through this method.
>
> I met next with the biology group. They had just translated the BSCS Green version. I should use the word, "adapted" rather than translated. I introduced the Learning Activity Packets to them in order to indicate that adapting the BSCS books is only the first step towards the necessary problem of individualizing instruction and allowing for students to pace themselves and to select from a rich series of resources, those resources which are compatible with students' learning styles.[10]

The mathematics group carried on a particularly extensive program that year. In fact, the story of seven years of its work in mathematics, carried on under National Council auspices, appears in a special report, "A Contribution of INEC to the Teaching of Mathematics."[11] That report records that 100 mathematics teachers participated in a National Mathematics Course organized by the mathematics group in January, 1968, as the fifth annual national course for mathematics teachers in Argentina. Earlier in 1965, that group had also initiated annual courses for teachers in the interior regions of Argentina. (See p. 3 and p. 8 of the report.)

During his May visit, Fischler gained much insight into the task before INEC by going directly into classrooms and laboratories:

> With Dr. Ariel Guerrero, Dean of Faculty of Exact and
> Natural Sciences, University of Buenos Aires (I) visited the

chemistry and physics laboratories of Colegio Nacional, Buenos Aires. There we learned, as I expected, that the students in physics spend two hours once a month in the laboratory, and in chemistry only one hour, once a month. This is the reality of their world. This particular high school is probably the best high school in Argentina, but students experience very little actual manipulation of the equipment. The teachers do some demonstration work and they do have a well-equipped demonstration laboratory.

This is the problem of the seminars for science teachers. Unless they are given the materials to take back to their classrooms in the quantities that are necessary so that two students can work with one set-up, we shall not produce very much change in the actual teaching. This is no different from the problem which (I saw) in Chile. They had 3,000 eighth-grade teachers for seminars in science instruction and gave them no equipment. If you go to the classrooms, you will see that there is absolutely no change taking place. Teachers know what they would like to do, but find it impossible to do it.[12]

In a report prepared at the close of his May visit, Fischler recommended measures for upgrading INEC's ability to bring reform directly into classrooms:

1. That INEC move to new quarters in order to accommodate people who will work full-time. . . .

2. That the Ministry supply additional funds so that personnel will be paid at a rate which would encourage them to devote all of their energies to the project.

3. That each commission must establish realistic goals utilizing performance language in order to determine whether they are achieving at a rate commensurate with expectations. . . .[13]

Fischler's second visit of that year to Argentina occurred in October at the time of the First National Symposium on Science Education which convened in Cordoba. More than 1200 secondary school teachers attended the Symposium; 800 paid their own way. The Symposium directed one set of recommendations to the Ministry of Education and a second set to INEC. The latter set referred to general and specific objectives for the teaching of science, suggested the basic orientation this teaching should take, and specified appropriate science content for each level and branch of the school curriculum. Additional recommendations referred to the need for out-of-school stimulation of science among students.

Under Hernaiz' leadership, INEC opened two vital new areas of its program in 1968. First, it organized a division concerned with conducting science fairs and stimulating the organization of science clubs in schools; and second, it created a division on testing and evaluation. The out-of-school division proceeded to conduct the first National Science Fair in Buenos Aires during September of that year and drew over one hundred exhibitors to the fair. That division also sponsored a series of regional science fairs throughout the country.

In connection with setting up the testing and evaluation division, Hernaiz requested funds from the Ford Foundation to send an appropriate individual to the

Educational Testing Service at Princeton in the U.S. for training related to leading the new division. He conceived the testing division as a technical assistance service to the schools, offering them help in test construction, on-going evaluation of their programs, curriculum and statistical studies, and analysis of various educational problems which they might face.

Upon her appointment as chief of the new testing and evaluation division, Señora Marta Maraschi, together with her small staff, then organized a course on educational evaluation for 96 science teachers in the Buenos Aires area during the month of May, 1968. Abraham Fischler, who was there at that time, took special interest in the work of the fledgling division. With his encouragement, the division began publishing an important series of bulletins on educational measurements and statistics, essentially a primer on the subject for teachers in the schools. Over the following year or two, the Ministry of Education mailed out seven issues of the bulletin entitled "Medicion Educativa," (Educational Measurements) to over 3000 science teachers throughout Argentina. Later, INEC prepared a collection of these bulletins in a single volume.

8.   *Conflicting tugs pull INEC in two directions*

At the close of 1968, Hernaiz prepared a report on the first full year of INEC's operations and submitted this to the Council. Professor Houssay then transmitted this report to the Ford Foundation along with his assurance that solutions would soon be found to the problems of INEC's inadequate quarters and its shortage of personnel. Very soon thereafter, the Ministry of Education did in fact provide space for INEC in the newly-built headquarters building of the Ministry and assigned eight additional staff members to INEC.

On receiving this report on INEC, one of the Ford Foundation officers in New York, Dr. K. N. Rao, drew up a detailed analysis of the INEC activities. He found praiseworthy Hernaiz' "quiet leadership" and his ability to obtain Ministry of Education cooperation with INEC's program. However, he expressed dissatisfaction over the limited extent of INEC's involvement with creative work in curriculum development and research. In a determined effort to encourage Hernaiz to increase activity along these lines, Rao proposed to his Foundation colleagues that they re-direct the Foundation's grant funds to support this creative emphasis in INEC's future work plan:

> The most active program of the Council to date is the series
> of courses organized by INEC in the provincial centers. These
> *cursillos.* and *cursos de verano* appear to attract a large number
> of secondary teachers in Argentina. During my recent conversa-
> tions with Dr. Angel Hernaiz, he told me that there are approxi-
> mately 20,000 science teachers in Argentina, and during 1967 and
> 1968 INEC has, through these courses and through mailings of
> its publications, contacted approximately 5,000 of these teachers.
> The activity of INEC should pick up in 1970 and 1971 now that
> the organizational phases of INEC have reached a steady state
> after a faltering start. . . .
>   A variety of activities contemplated under our original grant
> to INEC have now begun to receive support from other sources.
> INEC and the Foundation have now an opportunity to evaluate
> the accomplishments to date and to direct the Foundation grant

to more innovative purposes and programs than have been supported until this time.

There is quite a bit of work to be done yet in the development of prototype laboratory equipment and producing them in large enough quantities for trying them out in the school system at large. INEC has translated and adapted several U.S. and European texts. These are now in the form of experimental editions and some in the form of mimeographed notes. Teams of classroom teachers and university scientists will need to be organized to evaluate these texts and move them to the stage of commercialization. . . .

The work of INEC has not yet extended to teacher training institutions in the country. It is important that INEC begin to work in the normal schools and faculties of education so that the next generation of teachers could be exposed to the new methods and materials.[14]

To convince Hernaiz to pay greater attention to research and development, Rao decided to visit Argentina. During that visit, Rao learned of an interest at the Center for Educational Research (CICE) in collaborating with INEC in suitable educational research studies. A Foundation colleague describes the outcome of that visit to Argentina by Rao in these words:

I had a recent visit with Hernaiz and I am pleased to report that Rao's good offices have borne fruit and INEC is now prepared to enter into a joint project with CICE for an evaluation of INEC's program. In a recent letter Hernaiz has laid out the details for a joint working group to include three of the CICE research staff and two from INEC, for a total of five. INEC is prepared to support the working group with an allocation from its grant of $17,000 annually totalling $51,000 over a three-year period. Of the annual allocation $10,000 is earmarked for CICE and $6,700 for the INEC staff.[15]

Hernaiz did in fact put forward a plan as indicated and requested Ford Foundation approval of it. By late 1969, a joint team of INEC and CICE members began evaluating the IPS (Introductory Physical Science) course in 45 Argentine schools. They published a final report of that study in 1970.

Opposing the Ford Foundation effort that year to draw INEC toward greater involvement in research and curriculum development was a tug by the Organization of American States pulling INEC into greater attention to in-service training for teachers. The OAS awarded INEC a large grant of $530,000 out of its Regional Program for Education Development under which INEC organized in-service courses of six-months' duration for science educators from throughout Latin America. INEC staff members cooperated with the National Commissions in providing instructional services for the participants of these courses which covered biology, chemistry, physics, mathematics, psychology and sociology, and educational measurements. Seventeen teachers from five Latin American countries (Bolivia, Chile, Paraguay, Peru, and Venezuela) enrolled in the courses that first year (1969) along with 50 Argentine teachers. The OAS grant provided funds to meet the costs of travel and upkeep of the participants and to pay for equipment, instructional materials, and technical assistants for the courses. The Ministry of Education contributed generously to the courses by

13

providing costs of administering and financing the instruction provided to the teachers from within Argentina. Not only did the Ministry pay travel and living costs for these Argentine participants, but it also paid a substitute teacher to fill the classroom of each Argentine participant during his time away.

9. *The Ford Foundation modifies its grant terms to enlarge*
the innovative component in INEC's program

As INEC entered 1969, its second year of service to Argentina science teachers, it possessed a complement of four subject-matter National Commissions and two or three specialized divisions. In that year, the National Commission on Physics Teaching conducted trial use of the IPS course in 45 Argentine schools and distributed over 1500 kits of the IPS apparatus to those schools. INEC also prepared a new physics course for the fourth year of the secondary school and introduced it into 20 schools.

The biology staff of INEC cooperated with the National Commission on Biology Teaching that year in presenting an intensive training course to biology teachers to familiarize them with the Argentine adaptation of the BSCS Green Version. The biology group also initiated an important new program in secondary school biology based on ecological principles which spanned the entire secondary school period in a sequence of five separate courses.

The mathematics and the chemistry commissions both conducted in-service courses in 1969 for their respective groups of teachers at various centers throughout the country. The evaluation division of INEC continued its publication of the information bulletin on educational measurements and mailed them to hundreds of teachers in the schools. The out-of-school division maintained an aggressive program of stimulating school science clubs and promoting science fairs. INEC also extended its service to teachers by setting up a permanent exhibition of modern textbooks and teaching aids, preparing a bibliography of science books and mailing this to over 5000 teachers, and providing films, film loops, slides and projectors on loan to schools.

Although Rao could recognize in these activities a commendable pattern of stability on INEC's part, especially following the fitful developments and long periods of delays of the recent past, he continued to be dissatisfied over what he believed to be the relatively scant attention to indigenous curriculum development and research in the INEC program. As the year 1969 wore on and he saw little change at INEC in this respect, K. N. Rao wrote to his Foundation colleagues in Buenos Aires:

> It may be possible to come to terms (with Hernaiz) on specific program activities for which our grant funds would be needed. These would include such things as the development of new texts in the sciences for the secondary and elementary levels, the development of training kits and their commercial production, development of teachers' manuals, the field evaluation of the materials that have already been produced by INEC and seminars involving subject area specialists from inside and outside of Argentina which his own budget cannot adequately support.
>
> I see an opportunity here to redirect the INEC efforts, or at least those which the Foundation would be asked to support, along the lines of innovative work of Isaias Raw in Brazil. Then, of course, there is the further definition of the research collaboration between INEC and CICE for which the grant funds now available in 65-357 could be applied.[16]

Rao finally decided that he would again travel to Argentina for yet another direct attempt to influence Hernaiz in the direction of greater use of the Ford Foundation grant funds for innovative activities within INEC. He went to Argentina in October, 1969, where he talked not only to Hernaiz but also to the then Sub-secretary of Education, Dr. Emilio Mignone who had only recently initiated a national program of educational reform. Rao reports that he found the Sub-Secretary "most anxious to make rapid positive moves in curriculum innovation to support the reform program."[17] Rao then did his best to persuade Hernaiz to relate science education innovation at INEC to this national program of reform, discussing with him possible re-allocation of some of the Ford Foundation grant funds to specific projects of a truly innovative character. Rao argued that since both the Ministry of Education support to INEC and that coming from the OAS were underwriting INEC's programs for teacher training it would make sense for INEC to avail itself of the flexibility provided by the Ford Foundation funds in the interest of initiating experiments in education.

Rao returned from that visit persuaded that he should enlist the support of Abraham Fischler in the attempts to draw Hernaiz and INEC into greater innovative activity. He again prevailed upon Fischler who had, in fact, not visited the program in Argentina for over a year, and, in November 1969, Fischler finally paid a four-day visit to Argentina, calling on Hernaiz and on Mignone. Fischler summarized his observations of that visit in these words:

1. INEC has spent a great deal of its energy on giving courses for teachers. For example, they ran 45 model courses for teachers; many training courses for second-level biology teachers, as well as courses for teachers in other subjects. There is a great deal of pressure on INEC from the Ministry to run professional courses for the improvement of science teaching. Professor Hernaiz has not spent any Ford Foundation money for these courses and does not plan to. The Ministry has told INEC that they would assume the cost for running these professional courses.

2. Four (educational evaluation) bulletins have been published and distributed to 3,000 teachers in Argentina.

3. The IPS evaluation is proceeding through cooperation between INEC and CICE. The design calls for comparison between experimental schools and twenty control schools, making allowance for teacher variability.

4. In the manufacture of kits, INEC is producing prototypes. They have arrangements to manufacture the kits in large quantities. The royalties from these kits will be fed back to INEC for future kit development.

5. INEC (is) manufacturing some closed-circuit TV science programs. These were tested in schools. The TV program was used in 20 schools as an aid to teachers in both physics and biology.

6. INEC has assumed the responsibility for the coordination of all science fairs in Argentina. IMAF (Ferreyra and Maiztequi) are attempting to cooperate with INEC in this.

7. Through a series of visiting consultants, INEC had organized

courses for teachers in the provinces. In these courses, INEC supplies materials and publications for teachers to take back with them. The in-service courses serve as a clearinghouse for ideas and keeps people in the provinces aware of what is going on and committed to the program. Until now the Ministry has provided most of the funds for the courses and will soon provide all funding.

8. Due to the reform, INEC has been given the responsibility of developing the total math and science program from grades 1 through 12.

9. I must say that I was most impressed with Professor Hernaiz, who is attempting to get the Ministry to support as much of the INEC activities as possible. Until now, he has used very little Ford Foundation funds. Also, often after a Ford financed trial, the Ministry returns the money to him. Therefore he uses Ford Foundation money as seed money to get ideas tested for the Ministry. Thus, they see its effectiveness and become willing to support the activity themselves. Hernaiz realizes that when Ford withdraws support, the only funds he will have will be those supplied by the Minister and other organizations. Therefore, he is fully aware that Ford money should be used only to support the fringes of the activity in the hope of enlarging the Ministry's commitment to the activities of INEC.[18]

Fischler also attempted to assist Hernaiz in practical ways to intensify the INEC effort along the direction of indigenous curriculum development. In one discussion with the INEC staff Fischler presented the following model for development of classroom materials:

(1) each writer prepare one lesson lasting 3 or 4 days;

(2) the writer then teaches the lesson in a classroom. He must do this to get a feeling for the children and to be in a better position to revise what he wrote initially;

(3) the writer rewrites on the basis of his own experience and then finds a teacher who will teach it for him;

(4) the evaluation team member works with the writer all this time to develop items for the test;

(5) the lesson is finally typed and tested in twenty schools. The evaluation team produces tests for this stage.[19]

In his report of that visit, Fischler pleaded with the Foundation to permit Hernaiz wide freedom in the use of his grant funds from the Ford Foundation:

I would give Professor Hernaiz the freedom he needs to use Ford funds effectively. I did, of course, exclude support of in-service activity. However, once the development of new texts and guides is finished, I feel that it would be appropriate for him to use some Ford funds for the experimental versions. Since I do not see that Professor Hernaiz is spending our money foolishly and I tend to agree with his philosophy, I would rather have a budget proposed as the initial one in the grant and allow him the use of the money as long as it is within some line item.

A careful review shows he spent $13,700 of Ford funds in 1968. During 1969, it seems as though he will spend $25,000. Therefore, by this new method we will be saving quite a sum of money from the original $250,000 and we would still have an opportunity to be part of the effort. I suggest we give INEC $50,000 to use at the discretion of Dr. Mignone for further development of projects in science and mathematics. This would have to come as a request from Dr. Mignone to INEC. This would also bring INEC even closer to the Ministry.[20]

Philosophical differences now arose between Rao, the Foundation officer and Fischler, an external consultant, on the best strategy for advancing the work of INEC to which both had become strongly committed over the several years of their association with that program. To illustrate, Fischler's proposal of a general revolving fund for INEC clashed with Rao's determination to direct Foundation support to specific innovative projects whose progress could be assessed periodically both by the Foundation and INEC. Moreover, shrinking budgets and changes in procedures for grant development and closer monitoring within the Foundation also appear to have influenced the Foundation to move for a modification of the budget provisions under the grant to INEC.

Consultations among Rao, his Foundation colleagues in Buenos Aires, and Hernaiz yielded a formal proposal for grant modification which called for re-directing funds to specific curriculum development projects, to continuing INEC collaboration in research with CICE, and to initiating research with units of the Ministry of Education. The largest shift of funds under the modification was to take $80,000 from the original allocation to in-service courses and to re-distribute it among three other activities: full-time staff expansion, INEC–CICE collaboration on evaluation studies, and special research projects in collaboration with Dr. Mignone and the Ministry.

The New York office of the Foundation approved the modification of the original grant to INEC in May, 1970, and extended the termination date to the end of 1972. The total financial resources available to INEC for the year 1970 were as follows:

Source of Funds	Amount	Percentage of INEC Budget
OAS	US$ 48,600	30.1
Ford Foundation	42,695	26.4
National Council	32,000	19.8
Argentine Ministry of Education	38,300	23.7
	US$161,595	100.0

10. *INEC consolidates its program of educational services to Argentina; the years 1970 to 1973*

The effort by the Ford Foundation to encourage INEC to place greater emphasis on creative curriculum development was only partially successful, as the history of its activities over the following three years reveals. By this time, INEC had managed to diversify its sources of support and had committed itself to programs of teacher training and technical assistance to the Latin American region, which taxed the ener-

17

gies of its specialist staff. The Foundation contribution to INEC represented a little more than one-fourth of its total budget. Thus, in spite of the flexibility provided by its grant funds, the Foundation's leverage on the INEC program was at best limited.

Throughout the three-year period 1970–1973, INEC pressed steadily ahead under the OAS-supported Regional Program for Educational Development, enlarging its program of in-service courses both at INEC headquarters and throughout Latin America. Its courses in Buenos Aires drew science educators from Guatemala, Honduras, Nicaragua and Panama, while INEC staff travelled to Paraguay and to Ecuador to organize and conduct courses there.

Throughout this period, INEC also continued to provide important educational services to Argentina through the activities of its National Commissions and its specialized divisions. In 1970, for example, the chemistry staff of INEC, in collaboration with the National Commission on Chemistry Education, initiated an experimental course in chemistry for the fourth and fifth years of the secondary school. This course, given the title "Chemistry Project 30," includes elementary physical chemistry and basic ideas from inorganic chemistry in its first year. In its second year, the course includes a study of co-valency, characteristic of the carbon atom, and leads into organic and even biological chemistry.

At that time, INEC's out-of-school division, in collaboration with the mathematics division, set up a unique program known as the Mathematics Olympiad. During 1970, INEC laid the groundwork for the first nation-wide Olympiad scheduled for 1971, including organization of the Superior Council composed of leading professors of mathematics and naming a director of the Council. The objectives of the Olympiad were to discover students with special abilities to learn mathematics, and to promote interest in the study of mathematics. The infrastructure for the 1971 Olympiad included 12 zonal centers, 48 coordinating schools, 4 regional secretaries and contact with over 1000 interested schools throughout the country. The Council for the Olympiad conducted a nation-wide pre-Olympiad contest under the title "Youth for Understanding," drawing in 1200 students from 200 schools to the contest. The winner received a round-trip ticket for travel to the United Stated. The pre-Olympiad evaluation test involved over 3000 students in 431 schools.

The evaluation division of INEC opened this three-year period with preparation of a major report on its several years of work in evaluating the IPS trial program. The division then turned its energies to an evaluation of the in-service courses under the OAS Regional Program for Educational Development. The division staff specialists travelled to other Latin American countries where they interviewed about two-thirds of the 40 science educators who had participated in the OAS courses in Buenos Aires from 1969 to 1972. The results of this overview appear in a report entitled "Follow-up of Fellowships–OAS Regional Program for Educational Development," available from the OAS office in Washington, D.C. The information obtained in the study of the OAS fellows was supplied to the directors of the OAS courses to assist them in introducing modifications in their courses.

The evaluation division also commenced an evaluation of each of the operational divisions of INEC itself during this three-year period. Professional staff of INEC, CICE and other research specialists became involved in this undertaking. Sra. Maraschi, Chief of the Division, wrote concerning this evaluation:

> The concept of evaluation employed here considers evaluation as the analysis and interpretation of our experience; its pur-

pose is to offer an orientation necessary for the improvement of program planning and execution. . . . Such improvement may include the abandoning of ideas which once seemed beneficial but proved inadequate.

Being a useful tool for better management of INEC, evaluation should be one of the responsibilities of the Directorate shared by all those along the hierarchical chain. The emphasis is placed largely, although not exclusively, on the fact that evaluation improves the execution of projects. A 'good' project well executed probably gives better results than the 'better' project executed in a mediocre fashion, and evaluation correctly carried out has influence on such execution.[21]

An analysis of Hernaiz' annual reports to the Ford Foundation during that three-year period reveals the continuing heavy commitments by INEC to in-service teacher training. For example, the analysis of a six-page list of the principal activities of INEC during 1970, numbering 80 in all, showed that almost fifty percent of those were in in-service courses and seminars, twenty percent in out-of-school activities and less than ten percent in new initiatives in curriculum development and experimentation. Understandably, then, this distribution of effort at INEC which showed little movement toward an emphasis on research or curriculum development, drew critical comments from Ford Foundation officers at Buenos Aires and New York.

Their criticisms centered on the slow rate of expenditure by INEC of their grant funds:

One of the points we stressed at the time of the modification, a year ago, was the need for increasing the core staff, financed, if necessary, from the grant. Yet (Hernaiz) shows only three half-time people on his list which absorbed only US$750 of grant funds in 1970. Consequently, most of the US$20,000 for staff expansion remains untouched.[22]

At the same time, they tempered those criticisms by acknowledging the increased overall level of activity in the INEC program:

One also gets the impression of a better organization of the activities themselves and a greater sense of mission than in the earlier years. INEC now is being asked to serve the region as a training center. (Also), from the table of distribution of sources of support, a better balance between national and outside courses is evident. In his own quiet way, Mr. Hernaiz has shown a surprising ability to muster the resources he needs. He cannot be faulted for his conservative use of the resources so obtained.

On the substantive side, I am pleased with the vitality of the evaluation group within INEC. Their evaluation of the IPS curriculum was well conceived. Argentina and Brazil are the only two countries in the region starting on the evaluation of the new curriculum materials. The idea of tying the CICE researchers to the INEC effort is proving to be an excellent one. I am suggesting to FUNBEC in São Paulo to involve INEC in some aspect of the biology evaluation that the former is mounting in collaboration with BSCS of Boulder, Colorado.[23]

19

11.   *The Ford Foundation conducts a terminal evaluation*
        of its grant to INEC

The end of 1972 had been designated as the time for terminating the Ford Foundation grant to INEC. As this time drew near, the Foundation decided to review the impact of its grant funds on science education in Argentina. As part of this review, the Foundation asked one of its officers who had a scientific training, Mr. Peter Hakim, stationed at the Foundation office in Chile, to visit Argentina and INEC and to prepare a report based upon his observations and reflections. To his task Hakim brought insight as a scientist and knowledge of and experience with science curriculum improvement programs in Brazil and Chile. He was especially knowledgeable about the procedures and products of FUNBEC of Brazil, another Ford Foundation supported project. (See Case History on the Brazil Project.)

Hakim's analysis of the INEC program led him to conclude that the Foundation's grant to INEC was largely ineffective in achieving its general objectives. He conceded that the general objectives themselves were sound, but faulted the Ministry of Education for its half-hearted cooperation and the National Council for its failure to apply high standards to INEC's performance. He made a special point of the paucity of support given INEC by university scientists in Argentina. He blamed the Foundation for its initial insistence upon INEC's placement in the Ministry of Education, asserting: "that ties to the Ministry have not resulted in the effective distribution of its materials, but may have had a stifling effect on its creativity."[24] In spite of these negative reactions, Hakim complimented INEC's management on its ability to muster financial support from a variety of sources and husband the resources so obtained with great care. In common with previous reviewers, Hakim was enthusiastic about the work of the evaluation department of INEC and its leadership.

Upon receipt of Hakim's report, Ford Foundation officers in New York, particularly K. N. Rao, prepared their own assessment of the net accomplishments of INEC and the part played by the Foundation's grant. Rao viewed the INEC record in relatively sympathetic terms, stating:

> Probably because of the better base of science training in the universities and relatively well-established secondary education system, the INEC's program in Argentina has taken a different course than in Brazil. Whereas Brazil went first through the adaptation of foreign models of curriculum development and is now well on its way to developing indigenous innovations, the Argentine program started off through a program of "concentizisation" through workshops and regional meetings and has not thus been as productive as FUNBEC in its kits and other aids to better science education. Nevertheless, the list of accomplishments that Peter lists in the third paragraph of his memo are substantial. Peter may be underestimating the number of science teachers exposed over the past seven years to INEC's training courses.[25]

The two reports of INEC from these Foundation officers expressed considerably divergent views on several points while at the same time agreeing on others. Thus, Rao disagreed with Hakim on the role of the Ministry of Education and contended that it had provided sufficient freedom of action to INEC in curriculum development. The INEC program emphasized in-service teacher training because one of the Ministry's biggest constituencies is its teachers. On the other hand, he agreed with

Hakim on two points: that INEC did not benefit from the contributions of the substantial number of Argentinian scientists and that INEC's development program did not emphasize the training of a corps of its own young specialists to provide continuing leadership to its several programs. Both reviewers felt that the Foundation's contribution to INEC was only marginally effective.

These were conclusions, of course, of officers of an outside donor agency who look for changes wrought through their particular contributions to a project. At best, with the Ford Foundation grant amounting to a little more than 25% of the resources available to INEC, the kind of changes wished for by the Foundation officers were not likely to have been dominant in the INEC record.

In contrast, then, to the conclusions drawn by the Ford Foundation officers are those reported by Hernaiz who in 1972 also looked back over the accomplishments of INEC to that time, not in terms of changes wrought through use of just the Ford Foundation resources but through use of the total range of resources available to him. Hernaiz' summary of INEC achievements appears in a report he presented before a 1972 UNESCO meeting of leaders of science education improvement projects. His report includes an impressive list of accomplishments:

"Science Teaching Reform in the Argentine Republic has drawn inspiration from International Congresses, from studies, projects and initiatives of the National Commissions; from the teacher training courses organized by the National Institute for the Improvement of Science Teaching (INEC) and from the recommendations of the 1st National Science Teaching Symposium held in 1968.

INEC in collaboration with leading educators, is preparing Curricular Projects in which a change in scientific content is introduced to Argentine schools, specially as regards methodology assigning pupils an active part and teachers one of guidance and counsel.

The Curricular Project for Integrated Sciences at Elementary School level began in 1970 at 5 schools, extended in 1971 to 60 schools.

The Curricular Project in Biology for 1st through 5th years of secondary school began in 1968; in 1972 now includes 193 courses with a total of 7,800 pupils and 70 teachers in 105 schools. Note: Specialist teachers often teach at more than one school.

In 1968, INEC initiated the IPS course for 3rd and 4th years at Secondary School level. In 1969 further modifications in the spirit of IPS were introduced in the Physics (Mechanics) programme for 4th year secondary school level. By 1972 this project includes 106 courses, 2,735 pupils, 90 schools and 96 teachers.

The Curricular Project in Mathetmatics for 3rd year Secondary School Level was begun in 1971 at 5 schools with a total of 7 courses involving 220 pupils and 6 teachers.

The Curricular Project in Chemistry for 4th and 5th years at Secondary School level "Project 30" has been under way since 1970 and at present includes 90 courses at 49 schools with a total of 1,850 pupils and 61 teachers.

INEC contributes to these projects in supervising the courses, training the teachers, providing teaching-aid material on loan (optical instruments for Biology courses, laboratory equipment for Chemistry. For the Physics courses INEC designed and built 2,500 sets of IPS equipment, 400 Ripple tanks and 400 modular equipment sets for Mechanics. It also prepared 600 low cost kits for Biology and Physics.)

INEC has stressed the need for Out-of-School Scientific Activities. In this respect INEC mainly co-ordinates those activities corresponding to secondary school level, including Scientific Clubs, Science Fairs, Math Olympiads, Math Circles, Youth Science Meetings and courses for Leader-Teachers in out-of-school scientific activities. In the Math-Olympiads 31,000 students and over 1,500 teachers took part and at the 6th National Fair in 1971, 150 items of work were exhibited selected from 24 provincial fairs. We estimated that the out-of-school scientific activities now reach over 80,000 pupils and about 1,800 secondary schools.

The teacher-training referred to in this report corresponds to the in-service courses organized and directed by INEC over the years 1969 to 1972. In this period, there have been 23 Latin American courses (intensive study for 6 months), with a total of 121 participants in Biology; 120 in Physics; 110 in Chemistry; 110 in Math; 461 in Courses in Measurement, Statistics and Probability for Educators; and 314 in Courses of Fundamental Psycho-Sociology for Educators). These courses were also attended by teachers from neighboring Latin-American countries holding OAS fellowships.

Furthermore, INEC has conducted National and Regional courses, Methodological seminars, Courses for laboratory assistants; training courses for teachers in charge of experimental courses, and courses for primary school teachers.

INEC has carried out Evaluation Surveys of the Curricular Projects: "Introduction to the Physical Sciences–IPS" and "Project 30 for Chemistry Teaching." The evaluation of Math and Biology projects is carried out by the divisions in charge of these areas.

A follow-up study has been made on 49 teachers from 9 neighboring countries who had held OAS scholarships in the Latin American courses.

INEC has organized International Meetings such as the 4th General Assembly of the International Coordinating Council recently held in Buenos Aires in September 1972 and the 3rd Inter-American Conference on Mathematics Education in November, 1972.

INEC prepares and edits several publications among which may be mentioned: laboratory guides, booklets on out-of-school scientific activities, bibliographies, modern scientific essays, recommendations for science teaching and the Information Bulletins of Educational Measurement. Moreover it promotes the distribution of OAS monographs, of the BSCS green version on Biology, and of other text books, and subscriptions of the RIDEQ journal for Chemistry Teaching, the Journal of Math Concepts and the ICC Journal on Out-of-School Scientific Activities. It also lends out films and projectors to secondary schools and universities."[26]

12.   *The Ministry of Education establishes a new national curriculum directorate (DIEPE) which includes INEC*
    In early 1973, the Argentine Ministry of Education established a larger and more comprehensive organization for the development and diffusion of educational innovations than that represented by INEC. This new organization known as the Dirección Nacional de Investigación, Experimentación y Perfeccionamiento Educativo (National Directorate of Research, Experimentation and Educational Improvement, DIEPE) is to be concerned with curriculum and in-service training in *all* subject areas in the schools, including science and mathematics. The new directorate, organized along functional lines, is designed to serve as the research and development arm of the Ministry of Education, a new trend in several countries of Latin America seeking solutions to the urgent educational problems of their societies. Professor Herraiz de Ortiz was designated as the Director of DIEPE. The appointment of Angel Hernaiz as the Chief of Coordination of the new agency provides continuity of leadership for science and mathematics improvement in Argentina and hopefully for the transfer of that experience to other subject areas as well.

REFERENCES

1. Adapted from a 30 July 1965 memorandum by Mrs. Nita Rous Manitzas, Ford Foundation, Buenos Aires.

2. 12 May 1961 memorandum, Bernardo Houssay to Alfred Wolf, Ford Foundation.

3. 7 November 1963 memorandum, Robert A. Mayer, Ford Foundation in Buenos Aires to Harry E. Wilhelm, Ford Foundation, New York.

4. Ibid.

5. Letter of April 2, 1965 from Bernardo Houssay to Dr. Carlos Alconada Aramburu, Minister of Education, Argentina.

6. 19 January 1967 letter from John S. Nagel, Buenos Aires, to Bernardo Houssay, Buenos Aires.

7. These recommendations appear in a report submitted by Fischler to the Foundation on 29 May 1967.

8. 16 June 1967 report from Nita Rous Manitzas to John S. Nagel.

9. 5 December 1967 letter, Cristina Garay to Fischler.

10. 23 May memo of Fischler to John Nagel, Ford Foundation, Buenos Aires.

11. Presented at the Third Inter-American Conference on Mathematics Education, Buenos Aires (1972).

12. 23 May 1968 memorandum, Fischler to Nagel.

13. 13 November 1968 memorandum, Fischler to Ford Foundation.

14. July 31, 1969 memorandum from K. N. Rao to R. E. Carlson, Ford Foundation, Buenos Aires.

15. Reynold E. Carlson to John S. Nagel, July 11, 1969.

16. K. N. Rao to Dr. Reynold E. Carlson, September 25, 1969.

17. Letter of 6 November 1969 from K. N. Rao to Abraham Fischler.

18. 3 December 1969 Report to Ford Foundation by Abraham Fischler.

19. 3 December 1969 Report to Ford Foundation by Abraham Fischler.

20. 3 December 1969 Report by Abraham S. Fischler submitted to Ford Foundation, New York.

21. 1973 Evaluation of INEC's Operating Divisions 1968–1972, Sra. Marta Maraschi, Chief, Educational Testing and Evaluation Division, INEC.

22. 8 May, 1971 memorandum from R. E. Carlson (Ford Foundation, Bueno Aires) to K. N. Rao.

23. June 16, 1971 letter from K. N. Rao to R. E. Carlson.

24. March 3, 1972 report by Peter Hakim submitted to R. E. Carlson.

25. April 26, 1972 memorandum from K. N. Rao to R. E. Carlson.

26. 1972 UNESCO, Paris, Report presented by Hernaiz to the Meeting of Leaders of Science Education Improvement Projects, "Organization and Development of Science Education Reform in the Argentine Republic."

BRAZIL

1.   *Isaias Raw establishes the IBECC science education program*
From the only medical school in Latin America holding class A status with the American Medical Association, a 25-year old Brazilian received his doctor of medicine degree in 1945 and turned around to join its teaching and research ranks. Reflecting upon his privileged position, that young medical doctor, Isaias Raw, asked himself—characteristically:

> What should I do under these circumstances? Try to do my
> little job? Try to produce scientific knowledge in order to become
> part of the international family of scientists? Attract attention of
> the authorities?[1]

Although writers and thinkers of that time held out a vision of Brazil as the "Country of Tomorrow,"[2] Isaias Raw believed that vision could become reality only when large numbers of young people could gain access to education and especially when schools adopted modern instructional methods starting with the sciences. He felt instinctively that the scientists should play a role in bringing about these changes:

> Undoubtedly, there is lack of understanding and apprecia-
> tion of the value of science and its impact on society. The value of
> science education must be emphasized to our leaders. *This
> should be one of the roles of the scientist.*[3] (Emphasis added.)

Twenty years later, looking back on that earlier moment in 1949 as he had stood at the threshold of his life devoted to science education improvement, Isaias Raw recalls the ideas that gripped him then:

> The basic assumption I made then is, it is the social role of
> the man of science to evaluate the impact of science in human
> society and its implications for education. He should review con-
> tinuously the evolution of scientific achievements and its relation
> to the conditions within his country, and take it upon himself to
> guide science education from the primary school on. One should
> not risk the future by leaving the bureaucratic authorities to
> decide upon content or methods of science education. The teacher
> and general educator has an important contribution to make, but
> the scientist has an integral part in education by judging the
> values and relevance of science education.[4]

Raw also asked himself the question: "How is one to start?" He knew that a direct assault on the officially determined curriculum would be unproductive. He saw a much more promising approach to change, through the minds of teachers and students:

> This handicap was in a way our strength, because I was not diverted by the need of proposing to the authorities any new curricula. The aim was to change, not the curriculum, but the approach and the understanding of what science education meant.[5]

Isaias Raw then took the first step toward carrying out the convictions he held so deeply on how to bring livelier science to pupils in Brazil: He began publishing a magazine, "Cultus," and sending it to science teachers and their students. Through the pages of this magazine, he urged teachers to introduce experiments in their science classes and challenged students to perform experiments at home with available materials. This first step soon led him to take the bolder steps of putting scientific equipment directly into the hands of the students.

As he continued to apply his mind to the problem of stimulating students and teachers to "practice" live science, he soon realized how modest his means and measures were for such work. Therefore, he turned to the university professor who had befriended him from his earliest student days to seek advice on ways to put his program on a sounder footing. That professor, Professor Jaime Cavalcanti, held a rare perception of Raw's potential and value to Brazilian science education:

> I was trying to find a way to start, when one day I discussed the problem with the head of my department. This was a special man, who not only was, but still is, young in mind. He was always open to new ideas and ready to help execute them. Professor Jaime Cavalcanti was then on leave, directing the University Research Fund, created during the Second World War to stimulate the research that was needed. He told me then that there was an international institution, UNESCO, with a national committee, the Brazilian Institute for Education, Science and Culture—IBECC. The branch in São Paulo was being organized by the University. He was glad to have me present my ideas at their meeting.
>
> During an afternoon in 1952, I gave the members of the board, which included Professor Cavalcanti, Professor Noel de Azevedo (a famous lawyer and professor of law) and Professor Mendes da Rocha (from the School of Engineering), copies of a long list of possible activities. They included science fairs, science museum, science clubs, curriculum design and research, teachers training, production of laboratory equipment, and a few other minor things.
>
> They offered five hundred dollars a year for a budget, a room in the Medical School, a librarian as a secretary, and an official status. The last two were really the key for success—status, and the cooperation through the years of Mrs. J. Ormastroni.[6]

Raw found in this IBECC affiliation and support the required base to begin translating his zeal and vision into a program of concrete action:

> In the corridors (of the Medical School), we assembled a
> chemistry kit in specially made suitcases. It contained glassware
> and chemicals in small amounts. Students who purchased the kits
> received a monthly issue of a four page journal. Soon, a small
> group was assembling kits not only for chemistry, but also
> physics and biology—and writing the related journals.
>
>   Two other ideas were developed at the same time—a science
> museum and a science club. We obtained funds from the city to
> demonstrate that a science exhibit that would teach could be set
> up with small funds.[7]

These early ventures of Raw's, particularly the science museum and the science clubs, quickly aroused public interest. Raw soon found himself caught up in intense activity, not only in Brazil, but in other Latin American countries as well. For a variety of reasons, however, the museum and club ideas soon ceased to prosper, so that only the work of producing and distributing the kits survived this initial period of enthusiasm. Before long, the production of kits blossomed into a major industry through which Raw put science kits and apparatus by the thousands into schools and homes throughout Brazil. His team of designers and shop workers became highly skilled in fashioning inexpensive and pedogogically sound apparatus, with the result that, in 1954, the educational authorities of São Paulo State asked him to supply science apparatus to the schools of the State.

Raw's work soon came to the attention of a representative of the Rockefeller Foundation, Harry M. Miller, who had come to Brazil to identify projects and initiatives with promise for improving scientific research and medical education. Miller was so impressed with the kit production scheme that he awarded a grant of $10,000 to Raw for the purchase of machinery and raw materials. Three years later, Miller provided additional support to increase the production of kits.

Raw continued to expand his workshop. In 1960, so great had its volume of production become that he was forced to seek larger quarters. The University of São Paulo Medical School then responded to his request for space by providing him several university buildings into which he moved his equipment and materials, now worth $500,000, and a group of 40 workshop employees. At that time, the IBECC workshop was receiving an annual budget of $10,000 from the state of São Paulo for manufacturing equipment and providing services to the schools. The Federal Ministry of Education was also providing IBECC an annual budget of $20,000 for the production of science equipment which the Ministry distributed free to secondary schools throughout Brazil. Some of the other state Ministries of Education were also beginning to request IBECC equipment. By 1960, under Raw's direction, IBECC had placed science equipment in over 2,000 Brazilian schools.

This large-scale endeavor to supply equipment to schools did not in any way reduce Isaias Raw's determination to reach out directly to students and provide them, through inexpensive science kits, the experience of handling equipment and performing experiments. Raw wrote as follows in a report of that time:

> To achieve quick results and not to abandon the present
> generation of students completely, we decided to work directly
> with them. This approach has the advantage of avoiding all the
> school problems. The method employed is, again, laboratory ex-
> periment. Students are supplied, at cost price, with small
> laboratory kits.

These kits are not used as toys but to conduct experiments and help good students to develop a scientific mind; to enable them to conduct experiments and reach conclusions by themselves, the kit is supplied with a free monthly journal that contains experiments.[8]

Mounting requests from the schools for scientific equipment brought Isaias Raw and his IBECC colleagues into active contact with classroom teachers and their needs:

Teachers are an important element of our program. We have been dealing with the present staff of teachers.

Laboratory instructions in chemistry, physics, biology and general science are being published and mailed to all secondary schools free. A laboratory was assembled, with some financial help of the Division of Secondary Education of the Ministry of Education, permanently open for teachers use and training. Saturday afternoons a laboratory lecture is given for the teachers, by our staff. The teachers repeat experiments and discuss results. In summer and winter, courses are given. Special courses are prepared under contract. About 30 science teachers from the State of Minas Gerais stayed one month. A course for chemistry teachers of industrial schools is in progress.[9]

Other programs began to fill the agenda of IBECC in those first years: a national science talent search, a science fair which, in its first year drew over 100,000 people to the exhibits, and production of a weekly television program in which teachers and students participated. These soon brought IBECC into national prominence:

The important and widespread activities transformed IBECC to an authority in science education in Brazil. This project is revolutionizing teaching in Brazil.

The organization that is supporting this project—IBECC, State Committee of São Paulo—is an official national agency, organized to develop UNESCO's program in Brazil. The State Committee is directed by a board consisting of Professors of the University and industry leaders. It operates in the University of São Paulo, at the School of Medicine, and has complete administrative and financial freedom. It has the resources of an official agency and the freedom of a private organization. It can act in matters where a private organization could operate and with an efficiency impossible to a regular official agency. This progressive program awoke the consciousness of the whole country to the problem and its importance, for the first time. By surmounting the barrier of apathy in the educational systems, we have persuaded more than 2,000 schools to start using our services.[10]

The Ford Foundation awards its first grant to IBECC

In 1959, preparatory to opening a program of technical assistance in Latin America, the Ford Foundation sent one of its officers, Alfred Wolf, on an exploratory visit to Brazil. He made it a point, while in Brazil, to observe Raw's activities. Wolf then reported to his Ford Foundation colleagues in New York:

I was able to observe some very impressive work in the field of low-cost science teaching equipment being carried out by Dr. Isaias Raw. In addition to his work in the area of science teaching equipment, Dr. Raw has been very active generally in promoting improvement in secondary school science teaching in Brazil.[11]

Following Wolf's visit and in response to a request from Raw, the Ford Foundation sent a team of scientists to Brazil in July 1960 which included Dr. Arthur Roe (National Science Foundation), Dr. Karl Dittmer (American Chemical Society) and Prof. Paul Klinge (Indiana Univeristy). Their report to the Ford Foundation described IBECC and Raw's leadership in these words:

> The setup of this organization has been rather well explained in communications from Dr. Raw, but our group wanted to go on record as finding this organization to be one which can be praised very highly. Its activities have grown by leaps and bounds, and in our many visits to the offices, laboratories, and workshops, we were convinced that IBECC is doing an outstanding job for the improvement of science education in Brazil. Dr. Raw has a keen perception of the problems facing the secondary school science teacher and is able to implement many of his ideas into practical reality through the agency of IBECC. It is an organization which any foundation would be well advised to use in any major development in the program in this area.
>
> This organization (IBECC) deserves a great deal of support for its fine role and initiative in improving science education in secondary schools. Its organization, staff, and general spirit indicate that it is one of the most encouraging developments we have observed.
>
> Isaias Raw is one of the most encouraging developments in the secondary school science picture. His knowledge of the secondary school picture is quite extensive. His energy, persistence, and initiative are qualities which should be used in any development program in the country.[12]

They went on to give recommendations for improvement of secondary school science in Brazil:

> Three general criteria will be important in judging the value of any proposed program:
> (1) men to get the job done in the way in which it must be done. Dr. Isaias Raw is one person on whom a great deal of reliance may be placed.
> (2) the *catalytic influence of a foundation* as a starter; and,
> (3) many of the things which are suggested, the people of Brazil will do anyway.
>
> However, the catalyst is the necessary ingredient in initiating and speeding up the changes which must take place.
>
> The most obvious and certainly the primary source organization which must be used for any program to improve secondary school science will be IBECC. Desperately needed is stabilization

of its operations so that it is not completely dependent on the fluctuation in the type of orders which it receives from many of the Federal and State schools. IBECC also is in need of some administrative reorganization for the purposes of stabilizing the operation in future years.[13]

The Ford Foundation officers, following the advice of these consultants, invited Raw to prepare a statement of his basic philosophy and to outline the needs of his program for science education improvement in Brazil. He submitted such a list to them, specifying the following needs:

1. Higher revolving fund and enlargement of IBECC's production means
2. Building Fund
3. Publication Fund to translate and publish American projects in science
4. Science Films Fund
5. Travelling Teachers Program
6. Industrial Arts Science Teaching
7. Exchange Fund[14]

Foundation officers then examined the recommendations from the team of scientists and the statement of needs and plans submitted by Raw:

Both Raw and the team were in agreement on the importance of enlarging the working capital fund. In fact, the team feels there would be no point in helping to stabilize the management of IBECC unless the working capital fund is enlarged. While this may not be the case of this institution, which is working on a shoestring, so to speak.

Raw did not ask for help for a deputy. This is, however, a real weakness in the organization, in the view of the team. The amount recommended may not be realistic. What is needed is a sum of money to get IBECC to take on a full-time responsible deputy to Raw.

The effectiveness of much of IBECC's work depends, obviously, on how well it is disseminated throughout Brazil. In addition, IBECC is playing an important role in introducing new materials from abroad.

Finally, $10,000 is recommended to promote teacher training efforts. The team was convinced that IBECC itself was not in a position to undertake teacher training programs. This is the role of the universities. At the same time, there is a coordinating and stimulating role to be performed, and for this IBECC is ideal.[15]

Discussions with Raw soon led those officers to terms of a grant that would direct their technical assistance to priority needs in his rapidly growing IBECC enterprises. The Request for Grant Action (RGA) prepared by the Brazil office of the Foundation specified those terms as follows:

In view of the Institute's unique role in developing scientific and technical manpower in Brazil, a Foundation grant of $125,000 is recommended for a period of approximately three years with the following objectives:

(1) To increase the working capital fund of the Institute, so that it might enlarge its production lines of science equipment.

(2) To help stabilize the management of the Institute, by providing support for three years on a declining basis for a full-time responsible deputy to Dr. Raw, who also serves as a professor of biochemistry in the medical faculty of the University of São Paulo.

(3) To support a coordinate extension program including publication of printed materials and translations of works from other languages. Use will be made of American high-school science films and a fund will be established for development of a low-cost film projector to be manufactured in Brazil, in cooperation with the State Ministry of Education. Two traveling advisers, with automobiles fully equipped for scientific demonstrations, provided by the state of São Paulo, will visit schools to help overcome equipment difficulties, and to show them how to improve their science teaching generally.

(4) A small fund to help coordinate and stimulate teacher-training efforts in Brazilian universities, by supporting workshops and conferences for present and future secondary science teachers of Brazil.[16]

3. *IBECC accomplishments under that first grant*
In January 1961, the Ford Foundation awarded IBECC a grant in the amount of $125,000 for a three-year period. That action proved particularly timely, for in that same year, the Brazilian government passed a landmark Law of Directives and Bases that freed the school curriculum from centralized control and opened it to influences for reform. The grant enabled Raw and IBECC to move with vigor in introducing modern science teaching materials and practices in Brazilian schools along three principal directions: distribution of kits, both directly to young people through commercial sales, and to schools through the official educational channels; upgrading of science teachers through annual summer institutes; and, translation and distribution of selected U.S. science curriculum materials.

That grant also enabled IBECC to translate and distribute the U.S. science curriculum materials on a large scale. Raw enlisted the cooperation of both public and private sectors in Brazil in this effort:

Among the many activities carried on by IBECC, none has been more significant than the translation and publication of textual materials in the sciences and mathematics, especially those based on the new curriculum developments in the United States. Professor Isaias Raw, Scientific Director of IBECC, has demonstrated unusual initiative in arranging for permission to translate, publish, and use these materials, and then in following with his organization to see that this work was carried out.

The remaining texts were sold through commerical channels by contract between private publishers and IBECC and the University of Brasilia Press. At the beginning no private publisher

31

would gamble on these publications, so arrangements were made with the University of Brasilia Press to advance the necessary capital, the guarantee of USAID to pay for 36,000 copies being the decisive factor in this arrangement. After first printing, royalty arrangements were made, with 10% being returned to IBECC, who then handled the royalty payments of about 5% to the copyright holders in the United States.[17]

Under this first Foundation grant IBECC also stepped up its direct assistance to teachers through organizing suitable training courses with them:

> Placing science kits in a secondary school is, of course, only one part of the problem, for new methods will never be adopted until the teachers of those courses have themselves been exposed to the use of this new approach. One method whereby an increasing number of secondary school teachers may be reached is the device of a summer institute, which meets during the long school holiday. A careful selection process identifies potential leaders among the secondary science teachers who may be brought together and taught in a systematic fashion designed to excite their enthusiasm for new methods of teaching science.

> Accordingly, two sessions were organized in São Paulo during the early part of 1962, one in physics and one in biology, with some 40 teachers participating for six weeks in these summer institutes. Of the total, approximately one-half came from Brazilian schools and the other half were drawn from other countries in Latin America with the support of the Organization of American States. The success of these institutes has led to a proposal that they be repeated and, indeed, expanded in number for the coming summer session in early 1963, when three institutes are planned, one in physics to be held in Rio de Janeiro, one in chemistry in Piracicaba, State of São Paulo, and one in biology in the city of São Paulo, each with 40 student participants with the continued attendance form other parts of Latin America.[18]

"Summer" courses conducted by IBECC for teachers in January 1962 brought 50 teachers together in a PSSC physics course and a similar number in a BSCS biology course. The following table summarizes IBECC's outreach to teachers through these in-service courses over the years 1961 to 1964:

IBECC TEACHER TRAINING COURSES

1961   94 teachers (30 colegio, 60 industrial schools and 4 vocational)

1962   122 teachers (35 normal school, 42 PSSC Summer Institute, 42 BSCS Summer Institute)

1963   566 teachers (37 in BSCS Summer Institute, 38 in PSSC Summer Institute, 21 in CBA Summer Institute, 20 S. Paulo teachers, 100 normal school teachers, 39 ministry of education leaders; and 11 leaders and 300 teachers were trained in Parana by IBECC trainers in 1962)

1964   1018 teachers trained (200 in small institute in Parana, and through indirect courses in 94 in Goias, 238 in S. Paulo, 32 in St. Catarina, 28 in Minas, 49 R. Grande do Sul, 85 in Pernambuco, 36 in Alagoas, 98 in Ceara, 10 in Amazonas, 28 in Paraiba, 120 in Rio).[19]

Despite the huge scale on which IBECC operations proceeded in that early period, Raw never lost sight of the need to maintain standards of excellence in IBECC's activities and materials for educational use. To illustrate, regarding the spread of the U.S. curriculum materials he wrote:

In the last three years we have introduced the BSCS (green), PSSC, CBA. We are now ready, and the school system was made ready by us (preparing the teachers, as well as making the University understand the new curriculum and its results), to fully introduce CBS, BSSC (green and blue) SMSG, and PSSC. As we do not want them to become the new "official" curriculum, alternatives are being worked upon, such as CHEM Study.

When I said we are introducing—it means more than just asking some publishing house to print a translation. It means, first, selecting the right men, with the proper background, to study and understand the new approach. Training him abroad, as close to the people that design the approach as possible (some of our staff people have worked with PSSC in its preparation, or in BSCS).

Translation of text and lab guide, with some adaptation, is then carried out, lab equipment is produced and made available. Teachers are trained and equipment introduced in schools. Even the entrance examination at some Universities (São Paulo) are used as a tool to actually introduce the curriculum. It is a very complex operation that is succeeding by the way it is being handled. When it is completed—we have the new curriculum being taught as they ought to be—not as some are being used, or misused—elsewhere, like any other book.[20]

4.   *IBECC receives additional resources for fresh needs arising in its program:*

Officers of the Brazil office of the Ford Foundation remained alert to IBECC's growing range of activities. They encouraged Raw to report to them any new needs or difficulties as they arose. Thus, when inflation began to assume runaway proportions in Brazil, Raw described to Foundation officers the effects of inflation on his grant funds and sought their advice on how to cope with them:

1961 was a very busy year. The resignation of Janio and the tremendous inflation have produced an impact. For some of the activities, we shall need more money. I would like to have your advice, especially on:

(a) funds to produce on large scale;

(b) teaching by TV;

(c) publication of books, preparation of equipment for supply and maintenance of pilot projects for PSSC and BSCS courses. New funds are necessary due to the loss of the purchasing power of our present fund and to the losses incurred last year, when prices changed.

The advice I need is: Shall I request a new grant from the Foundation? Shall I make an effort with your help to obtain a large loan from the Interamerican Development Bank? Can I obtain some help from the Bank or Federal Government?

I would like to receive personal and informal advice that will help me in the judgement I have to make on the future steps to take.[21]

This plea triggered discussions that led to a Foundation decision, in October 1962, to award IBECC a supplementary grant of $45,000 largely to pay for translation and distribution of the U.S. science curriculum materials so that IBECC could respond rapidly to demands being made on it. The University of São Paulo also came to IBECC's rescue at that time, making available a greatly enlarged workshop on the new University campus. The expansion in IBECC's workshop space, from 4,000 sq. ft. to over 18,000 sq. ft., aided IBECC greatly in raising its output to match the growing demand for science equipment.

The 1962 law that decentralized the school curriculum specified that general science should be taught at the ginasio (lower secondary) level, creating an additional opportunity. He saw that at that level, science materials could reach twice as many students as IBECC had been reaching at the colegio, or upper secondary, level. In the wake of that legal requirement for a new course at the ginasio level, Raw immediately pressed his entire staff at IBECC into producing general science materials:

The high priority project is the preparation of a *general science text* to be introduced in a new course now being set up at the first-year ginasio under the new legislation. The whole IBECC staff has been diverted from other tasks and is now at work on this general science text. It will be designed to cover all four years of the ginasio course in general science.

The new educational legislation presents an unparalleled opportunity for a change in the character of science teaching at the ginasio level and Raw is probably sound in his judgment, that, unless new texts can be produced within a year, the commercial publishers will bring out "new editions" of old material and the opportunity to change will be lost.[22]

As part of an effort sponsored by the Emergency Plan of the Ministry of Education, IBECC prepared 3000 copies of pamphlets for the first seven units of a general science course. A kit for small group use was produced in a cardboard box for each one of the units. By 1965 IBECC had produced over 140,000 copies of the texts and over 25,000 units of the kits.

These very rapid and large increases in the level of IBECC activity caused considerable anxiety among the Foundation officers, however. They had been watching the program attentively and knew that despite Raw's imagination and dynamic leadership, a growing and complex enterprise such as IBECC required greater and more efficient management than they considered him to be giving it. They brought their concern to Raw's attention through a series of discussions but were unable to

34

prevail in convincing him to introduce changes in the management of IBECC. Raw maintained against all their efforts that "We will not have any longer one man to direct all—it is now and will remain a collegiate."[23]

5. *Creation of the network of science teacher training centers (CECI's)*
IBECC's energetic program continued to reach out to more and more Brazilian schools and teachers. Nevertheless, the Ford Foundation office in Brazil saw that in a country as large as Brazil additional centers of innovatory action would have to be set up to meet the demand adequately. Accordingly, Dr. John Baxter, a science educator on the staff of the Foundation office in Rio de Janeiro, opened negotiations with scientists at the University of Pernambuco in Recife in the northeast region of Brazil on the subject of establishing a center for science education improvement there modeled after the IBECC program but oriented toward serving schools and teachers in that northeast region. These negotiations led quickly to a Foundation grant of $150,000 to the Unitersity of Recife for the development of a Secondary Science Teaching Center on its campus under the leadership of Dr. Marcionilo Lins, Chair professor of Bio-chemistry in the Medical School and Director of the Institute of Chemistry of the University. This center would serve the northeast of Brazil, paralleling IBECC in the populous south central and south.
A year later, in 1965, the Ministry of Education then set up additional centers of the CECINE type to form a national network of six such centers that could provide in-service training opportunities to science teachers throughout Brazil. These six centers and their locations are listed below:

STATE	CENTER	CITY
Bahia	CECIBA	Salvador
Guanabara	CECIGUA	Rio de Janeiro
Minas Gerais	DECIMIG	Belo Horizonte
Pernambuco	CECINE	Recife
	NE = Northeast	
Rio Grande do Sul	CECIRGS	Porto Alegre
São Paulo	CECISP	São Paulo

(CECI = Centros de Treinamento para Professores de Ciencias)
All the new centers were modeled after IBECC. Each undertook similar activities including: (a) teacher retraining, (b) production and distribution of experimental equipment and supplies, (c) publication and distribution of textual materials, and (d) related efforts designed to stimulate improvements in secondary science teaching.

6. *IBECC introduces training of leaders for Brazilian education*
The Ministry's attempts to blanket the country with centers to provide in-service opportunities for science teachers soon created a need for adequately trained leaders for the courses provided by the centers. Raw saw in this a fresh opportunity for IBECC to engage in training leadership for Brazil. He drew up a plan for an IBECC program in training of leaders and forwarded the proposal to the Ford Foundation with a request for a suitable grant of funds:

> Summer institutes are being multiplied at a fast rate incompatible with its quality due to lack of leaders with understanding and experience. Previous work of IBECC has not resulted in providing a large enough multiplication factor.
> Presently we propose to provide one year fellowships to

35

bring personnel of University level and some outstanding secondary school teachers, to work in IBECC, they will be involved in collaborating with our innovation program, will participate in a summer institute, and learn how to run it.[24]

Correspondence between Foundation officers at that time bears witness to the fact that Raw's leadership training scheme attracted the attention of the Ministry of Education:

> From the beginning it was evident that there was a dearth of informed leadership for these new CECI centers. The Ministry and the center directors see the problem and are anxious to do something about it. They want to carry on an active Institute program and the Ministry is willing to help finance it. They now realize how small the leadership pool is. Each will welcome trained leaders to help provide through this project with IBECC. It is a *Brazilian* solution for the problem. It could have a multiplying effect by interesting more University professors in the problem of Secondary Science Teaching, and one might hope, in all secondary teaching.[25]

> We have been working for the past six months with Dr. Isaias Raw, the energetic biochemist at the University of São Paulo and the moving force behind the well-known programs of IBECC in secondary science, on a proposal to assist in the training of leaders and directors for vacation period institutes in the sciences in Brazil.
>
> It should be noted that this project has the enthusiastic support of the Director of Secondary Education of the Federal Ministry of Education and his top science aides. It also has the full support of the Directors of these Science Institutes, which, as you know, are modeled in many ways on the original Summer Institutes of IBECC itself.[26]

As clearly pleased as Foundation officers were with Raw's scheme, however, they found it necessary to question some of his cost estimates as well as the size of groups he wanted to handle. Such differences of opinion precipitated a series of negotiations that delayed a decision on the grant for many months. Only in September of that year did Raw submit a revised proposal that was acceptable to the Foundation:

> We propose a revision of the initial proposal made by IBECC, with a major emphasis on the teacher's guide. The large effort started by IBECC, with help of the Foundation, on training of teachers in Summer Institutes, is now multiplied by the regional science teachers' centers (the CECI's). The availability of the teacher's guide is of utmost importance for that program.
>
> The publication of the proposed series of high level teacher's guides will open the eyes of the publishers and the Government (now involved more and more in supporting the publishers) on the value and importance of well-made teacher's guides.[27]

The Foundation expressed its satisfaction with this revised plan from Raw in these terms:

The recommendation by Mr. Stacey Widdicombe for a grant of $86,000 to the Brazilian Institute of Education, Science and Culture (IBECC) over a three-year period for leadership training and translation of teachers' manuals is the culmination of discussions and negotiations on proposals which Isaias Raw made to the Foundation during January 1966. In the process the original proposals have undergone considerable modification.

The total effort (translation and leadership training) has now been spread over a period of three years. Baxter, Rey and I shared the view that it will be difficult to assemble 20 top scientists in a year and have them spend five months in this activity. The revised proposals call for the training of 6 to 7 "leaders" per year. This is certainly more realistic and manageable.

The final consolidated proposal and the time allotted for the realization of the project objectives appear to me to be much more realistic than the individual projects presented earlier.

The major purpose of the present grant is to expand the cadre of "leaders" to shoulder the burden of strengthening the program of the six centers that the Ministry of Education has designated and has made budgetary provisions to support.

What started as a "center" with financial support from outside agencies is now beginning to assume a national character and becoming part of a system of "centers" with national government support.[28]

In November 1966, the Foundation awarded a grant of $86,000 to IBECC for the internship program and for preparation of teacher's guides to accompany the translated U.S. science curriculum materials. But another long delay then set in, before the new program began while Isaias Raw opened negotiations in Brazil towards placing IBECC on a more secure legal footing to protect its institutional integrity. When the new legal status was granted, IBECC was re-named the Brazilian Foundation for Science Education Development and came to be known by its current acronym, FUNBEC.[29]

In addition to placing the former IBECC (now FUNBEC) on a new legal footing, Raw also set up a series of advisory and policy-setting organs:

Higher Council — Meets once a year for general approval of FUNBEC's program. It is composed of industrial leaders, university professors, scientists and educators.

Board of Directors — Most important of the directing bodies. It meets once a week to discuss plans and programs, analyze activities, and approve purchases and hiring of personnel. The members of the Board are:

President — Professor A. Ulhoa Cintra, President of FAPESP[30] and State Secretary of Education (on leave).

Vice President — Jaime Cavalcanti, President of the Executive Board of FAPESP and retired University Professor.

Financial Director — Rubens de Melo, industrial director of the State Federation of Industries.

Directors — Ernesto Giesbrecht, Professor of Chemistry, University of São Paulo; Jose Reis, a science writer for a São Paulo newspaper.

Board of science advisors — Composed of professors, representatives of the other centers, representatives of the University, and of the National Research Council. It meets once a year to discuss the general program and future plans. Members are called upon separately when needed.[31]

Public recognition of the newly constituted FUNBEC came quickly when the Brazilian Minister of Education visited the offices and workshops of FUNBEC and gave his official support to its leadership training program.

A Ford Foundation consultant who visited FUNBEC in June of that year (1968) found much to praise in FUNBEC's handling of the new leadership training program:

> The supervisors of training are experienced and well selected. They include two scientists from the University of São Paulo and one each from the Faculty of Santo Andre and the Technical Institute of Aeronautics. It is worth noting that both supervisors and students become involved not only in the training program but also in the work of translating U.S. teachers guides into Portuguese and in the experimental and developmental work constantly under way in FUNBEC for the improvement of science instruction.
>
> The five trainees were well selected, they receive excellent individual supervision and have had great opportunity to work on their own. Those that I met briefly seemed to be enthusiastic and alert. The curriculum vitae for each trainee gives some reason to believe that they are competent professionals.[32]

FUNBEC progressed steadily toward its goals of training leadership for the CECI centers and preparing teachers guides to accompany the Brazilian versions of the U.S. science curriculum materials. By the end of 1970, Raw was able to write:

> Thirty-seven teachers guides have been recently planned, fifteen have been published, eight are ready for the publisher or already in press, the first drafts of seven have been completed and are in various stages of revision, and seven others are currently being written or translated. Sales have not yet reached the first press runs of 3,000 copies, but three guides have sold more than 2,200 copies, and seven others have sold more than 700 copies.
>
> To date twenty trainees have been awarded internships, fifteen have completed the five-month program, four others are within a month or two of completion, and only one withdrew early. Eleven of the interns are exclusively university professors, seven teach at both universities and secondary schools, and two others are high school teachers. Eight trainees (including both high school teachers) are staff members of five of the six regional science centers.

38

FUNBEC staff consider the internship program to have been highly successful. A good deal of time and effort was dedicated to the program, the trainees were carefully selected on the basis of their capacity and prospective contribution to science teaching, and the training was tailored to meet their individual needs, interests, and capabilities. The trainees integrated well —to the extent that several supervisors considered them an integral part of the FUNBEC staff. Over the period of the grant the scientific production of FUNBEC was assisted by the contribution of the interns, and strong personal and professional relationships were established among FUNBEC staff and prospective leaders of educational innovation at other institutions.[33]

7. *The Ford Foundation encourages Raw to set priorities, improve services, and introduce evaluation into FUNBEC*

Raw recognized in this rapidly growing program a clear need to chart a more adequate long-term course for FUNBEC. Accordingly, he outlined a set of future plans for FUNBEC that included curriculum development covering the entire gamut of education from primary through university levels:

Some time ago I discussed with you the future of IBECC, and other initiatives we are taking. For a while, I was considering withdrawing a number of activites ... after a number of considerations, and a number of discussions, I have decided to go ahead, and even enlarge our area of action.

My experience in the Office of Education has pointed out that FUNBEC still has a role in Brazilian education development. I do not expect to replace the Governmental activities by the foundations, but I feel that we can point out a number of new ways to the authorities, that will slowly move to displace us. That is beginning to happen in the teachers training at the secondary school, but even there we still have to prepare the leaders and programs. They do not yet realize that the same thing can be done at the primary and higher education (levels). We were only concerned with the secondary school science, and now we are moving to the primary and college, and from exact sciences into social sciences...

So, we are planning even wider programs. We are approaching at the moment the State Research Foundation (FAPESP) to help us, (and) we are thinking in approaching the Interamerican Development Bank.[34]

Raw submitted these plans for expansion to the Ford Foundation officers. But because they held some reservation regarding FUNBEC's institutional capacity to carry out such expanded plans, they suggested to Raw that he join them in a critical study of FUNBEC's many activities that could clarify his purposes and help him assign priorities among his rapidly developing enterprises. To initiate the study, Peter Hakim of the Brazil office prepared a series of comprehensive reports in which he described the history, scope of activities, and accomplishments of the FUNBEC and CECI Northeast centers. Meanwhile, the New York Office submitted the FUNBEC proposals to thoughtful analytical study. As part of that analytical study, K. N. Rao of the New York Office brought Raw's program under critical examination with respect to the following major questions:

I. *Division of labor and setting of priorities:*
   1. Science and Mathematics for Primary Schools
   2. Physics and Chemistry for *Colegios*
   3. Exact and Social Sciences for *Ginasios*
   4. Sciences and Handicrafts for *Ginasios*
   5. Sciences for the Basic Course for Higher Education
   6. Survey of Teachers of Science and Mathematics
   7. Working Capital and Re-Equipment

II. *Distinction between translation and genuine innovation:*
   I believe this is also the time for us to begin the difficult taks of discrimination of translation, translation with adaptation, and genuine innovation in curriculum development in Latin America.

III. *Decision on size and purpose:*
   FUNBEC has entered the phase where it will need to keep its small size and be concerned with genuinely innovative activity or become a service and training center for the very large needs of Brazil and for international assignments which it might be asked to undertake.

   There is certainly no dearth of projects where Isaias Raw's innovative and entrepreneurial abilities are now needed. His own proposals are evidences of this great need. I am somewhat sympathetic with his predicament, but when he asks for an annual working capital of $400,000 and capital investment of $100,000 in new machines and tools for production, finishing, and packaging, his operation seems to be moving away from the classification of a center for innovation in education and is rapidly taking on the many aspects of a substantial business undertaking.

IV. *Management improvements and commerical "spin-off":*
   The growth of FUNBEC from a $10,000 operation in 1960 to $400,000 in 1967 is certainly impressive. The fact that much of the original equipment has been allowed to deteriorate while new divisions with precision optical, electrical, and mechanical equipment have been added shows that the innovative frenzy of the group has outstripped its ability to manage the operation.

   I am quite sympathetic with his request that the Ford Foundation help him obtain the services of a consultant or consultants who would help him with the streamlining of his present operations (size of inventory, work routing and scheduling, quality and financial control), and counsel him on questions related to the direction which his organization should take. Is it conceivable that

40

specialists at the São Paulo School of Business and FAPESP can help him in this regard?

V. *Evaluation of FUNBEC materials:*

In evaluating the accomplishments to date of our grant PA 67-111, we have in our files here Isaias' narrative report of June 4, 1968, and memos by Dr. Morris Cogan and Miss Eva van Ditmar summarizing their impressions of the operations. Hopefully, Dr. Raw's second report, due in July 1969, would provide some evaluation and can be supplemented by an evaluation by outside consultants versed in the art and science of curriculum improvement. I believe we should have such an evaluation in hand prior to a serious consideration of the new proposals.[35]

This was not K. N. Rao's first attempt to call the attention of FUNBEC to the need to introduce an evaluation element into its program. Three years earlier, in fact, at the time of the award of the 1966 grant to IBECC, he had written:

Although there are indications that the "new" texts have been accepted and are being used in some states, I don't know if a systematic evaluation has been carried out of effectiveness of the new curriculum materials in the Brazilian classroom. Since these are translations of materials developed in the U.S., what are the special difficulties faced by Brazilian teachers and students in using these "new" texts? In the U.S., in some school districts, the introduction of the P.S.S.C. course discouraged many students from electing physics as one of the high school subjects. Is there a similar tendency in Brazil? What are the present rates of failures in the science courses in schools using the new materials and how do they compare with rates previously? Have college entrance examinations changed to accommodate the "new" materials? Put it another way, how do those who are brought up on the "new" texts fare in university entrance examinations? I am afraid that the number of Brazilians qualified to systematically evaluate the new materials is also very small.

The new university entrance tests that are being developed by the Chagas Foundation will shed some light on how effective instruction in the "new" math and sciences is at the secondary level. The teachers' manuals, whose translation and publication, which the present grant is expected to support, will provide one additional means to increase instructional effectiveness in the classroom. After these developments take hold one could plan for a systematic evaluation of the secondary science reform efforts in Brazil in the next couple of years.[36]

Isaias Raw took note of these suggestions made to him by the Ford foundation officers and within a relatively short time, after re-studying his original proposals for an expanded program, prepared a greatly modified grant request to the Foundation:

I would like, summing up our several discussions to reshape our request for a grant. We hope to accomplish the following objectives:

(a) develop a series of new original projects in Brazil, using mainly local manpower, although considering some limited consultantships. We expect to do so, with Latin Americans, hoping for a two-way flow of information, skills and educational results.

(b) improvement of our operating conditions, especially in the managerial and administrative capacity, with consequent improvement of our financial situation to cope with the growing activities we are reaching.

(c) evaluation of our impact in education.

For this program, we are now asking for a two year grant of $378,000 for production and publication equipment, personnel, training programs, and strengthening management capacity.[37]

On receiving this reformulated proposal, the Brazil office of the Foundation prepared a thorough review of the three chief components of the proposal namely, the development of four new curriculum projects, the strengthening of FUNBEC's managerial capacity, and the initiation of an evaluation of FUNBEC's products. On the development of four new curriculum projects, the field office commented as follows:

In our judgment the time is ripe for FUNBEC, as the most successful and innovative group in Latin America working on curriculum reform, to expand its activities to include new fields and levels of the educational process. Apart from the obvious benefits it will be able to accomplish directly, the proposed expansion of FUNBEC's programs may stimulate the efforts of other groups (as it did in the secondary sciences) and help focus the attention of government agencies. Moreover, new initiatives are the essence of FUNBEC's continuing development.

FUNBEC's present financial difficulties are principally the result of a rapid, disorderly growth (annual sales having risen over the past eight years form $10,000 to $400,000) coupled with poor internal management.

Dr. Raw has recently taken two measures to place FUNBEC's future development on a sounder financial and managerial basis. First, the distribution of FUNBEC's kits and laboratory equipment will shortly be contracted to a commercial firm, while FUNBEC will retain exclusive rights to production.

Second, FUNBEC has hired a new manager for its production division. To date, FUNBEC's growth and development has been guided (and sometimes misguided) by secondary shcool teachers and university professors.

These two measures, although of obvious significance for the development of the organization, will not help to alleviate FUNBEC of its immediate financial strains. To lessen these strains, the Foundation would provide assistance for the purchase of new production machinery (such as copying lathes, plastic devices, and packaging equipment) and for partial salary payments, declining over the two-year period, for the new manager.

We are budgeting a small amount of funds to enable FUN-BEC to initiate an analysis and evaluation of its past efforts and present directions. The principal objective of such an undertaking would be to measure the degree and extent to which FUNBEC's activities are changing the teaching and learning of science in Brazil.[38]

K. N. Rao of the New York office again raised the basic questions of FUNBEC's future development: the adequacy of its management capacity; the need to set priorities among its many lines of work; and the desirability of commencing a thorough evaluation of its products and their impact on Brazilian schools:

a) At the operating level, the appointment of a business manager who combines engineering background and teaching of business administration is a good beginning.

b) Although it would be imprudent to straitjacket an innovative individual or group, I believe it would be helpful to FUNBEC itself and to outside organizations interested in supporting this activity to be able to examine the total scope of this undertaking and the priorities assigned to the different aspects of development. Such an exercise might also lead to the identification of bottlenecks and plans for their removal.

I am pleased to see your consideration of support for a systematic evaluation of the activities to date of FUNBEC. We would also need to obtain more detailed plans for the systematic development of the experimental editions, their trial in selected schools and subsequent revision, and the preparation of "final editions" of the materials that are to result from the four new curriculum projects now proposed. Does the estimated budget include any funds for such field trials of the new materials?[39]

After much discussion of the plans put forward by Raw for an enlarged FUN-BEC operation, on May 1969, Foundation officers in Brazil and New York concurred in recommending a grant to FUNBEC in the amount of $378,000. But at that precise moment of agreement, a most tragic blow befell Isaias Raw.

The story is best told in his own words:

At seven o'clock at night I was informed by my wife what the official radio news had said. I was officially retired from the University and forbidden to teach or do research. My immediate reaction was one of relief. If you are wondering how I could feel this way about my different activities and colleagues, please do not judge me hastily. How long could you support an activity, in conditions where you had to try to guess between the lines of the newspaper, what would happen the next day?[40]

The attack on Raw represented the culmination of years of interpersonal strife and rivalry between himself and colleagues in and out of the university who were hostile to his crusading efforts. He fled the country within hours of the word of his dismissal and sought haven in the United States.

8.   *FUNBEC continues to advance under new leadership*
Although shocked by the sudden departure of Raw, staff members of FUN-

BEC quickly re-distributed his responsibilities among themselves to prevent a serious interruption in the on-going program of FUNBEC. In response to a request by the Ford Foundation to supply information on their new assignments of duties within FUNBEC, Myriam Krasilchik, who had assumed several of Raw's professional responsibilities, wrote:

> With the departure of Professor Isaias Raw, whose qualities and capabilities are hard to enumerate and describe, FUNBEC's leadership suffered a great loss which will be difficult to overcome.
>
> Some of Prof. Raw's responsibilities, however, were distributed among the members of FUNBEC's staff and directors. Thus, Prof. Manuel Jorge Filho now coordinates the FAPESP project and other new projects which are being developed at the workshops; Prof. Antonio de Souza Teixeira, Jr. coordinates the work of professors and the general work on existing projects; Prof. Myriam Krasilchik now coordinates the development of new projects, courses, and relations with other institutions for joint work purposes, and contacts while Prof. Ernesto Giesbrecht, of the Chemistry Department of the University of São Paulo, member of FUNBEC's Board and Coordinator of the Chemistry Sector, has become the scientific director.
>
> With this division of labor it is hoped that the activities of FUNBEC will continue without interruption in this period of transition.[41]

On October 2, 1969, the Ford Foundation awarded FUNBEC a two-year grant (70-28) of $194,000, a somewhat reduced sum over what Raw had earlier requested. That this did not imply any loss in confidence in FUNBEC's new leadership, however, is shown by an interoffice memorandum prepared by Rao at that time:

> Had Dr. Isaias Raw stayed in Brazil and FUNBEC's financial management steadily improved, the chances of making effective use of a larger grant would have been good. Isaias Raw's departure has possibly slowed down the rate of innovation, but, surprisingly, the foundation is held together by a group of dedicated scientists and collaborators of Raw.
>
> The present proposals, comprising a well structured group of projects in curriculum development, seem to be well within the scientific and management capacities of FUNBEC. From FUNBEC's and our own point of view, they are easy to monitor. The present emphasis on primary level curriculum improvement and leadership and teacher training is a logical development for FUNBEC, which concentrated until this time on secondary school curriculum improvement projects. The plan for trying out the new materials in the State of Bahia would provide the opportunities for linking this effort to the teacher training project that the Foundation is discussing with educators there.[42]

In awarding this two-year grant to FUNBEC, a grant which placed funds more in support of specific projects than on general support to FUNBEC itself, the Ford Foundation was acknowledging the relative maturity of FUNBEC as an institution; its basic organizational pattern, its policies and procedures. Its reputation and capability were all now relatively established. Its needs were for funds for accomplishing specific tasks and for new projects. Thus, Ford Foundation officers could write about that grant:

> The largest share of grant funds would be used to develop texts and kits for teaching sciences and mathematics in primary schools. These materials would be oriented toward practical subjects such as personal hygiene, public health, nutrition and agriculture. FUNBEC would offer ten internships for leaders in Brazil's regional science centers to participate in developing the materials and would train 90 science teachers to use the new materials. This follows FUNBEC's now standard pattern of involving teachers in developing new curricula and materials and then disseminating the new approaches into schools.
>
> The grant also would be used for projects at junior- (ginasio) and senior-high-school (colegio) levels. At the junior-high-school level, FUNBEC is developing a series of texts and experimental kits based on conservation (of matter, energy, life, species and environment). Two texts are to be completed in 1970, and grant funds would be used to involve five interns and train 60 teachers in the new series. At the senior-high-school level, FUNBEC plans to develop an integrated chemistry and physics curriculum, patterned after curricula developed at the Education Development Center.[43]

The grant also set aside small amounts for the initiation of systematic evaluation of FUNBEC materials.

Specific budget provisions were made for exploration of new areas for project development as a direct challenge to the new leadership of FUNBEC. The Foundation expressed its confidence in that leadership in this way:

> The dynamic, not to say fluid, situation of Brazil and of FUNBEC make predicting chancy. However, if FUNBEC continues to perform as successfully as it did under Dr. Raw's leadership and if it demonstrates need for further support, Foundation staff would by sympathetic.[44]

This confidence was well placed, for a year later, reporting on FUNBEC's performance under its new leadership, Peter Hakim was able to write:

> The narrative report provides a comprehensive description of the progress that FUNBEC has achieved over the past year toward meeting the objectives specified in the grant documents. . . .
>
> A comparison of the accomplishments noted in the report with the timetable established during the grant preparation stage indicates that FUNBEC has managed to keep pace (or close to it) on most of the projects with the preliminary projections made more than a year ago.

Explanation of New Lines of Project Activity

> The modest amount included in the grant to permit FUNBEC to explore potential new areas seems to have been espe-

cially productive. Numerous contacts and meetings with geography professors at the University of São Paulo have resulted in the formulation of a group of approximately five geographers who are enthusiastic about the prospect of developing competent teaching materials in both physical and human geography for secondary schools. Work on six to eight units should be initiated shortly. This prospective project in geography will be FUNBEC's first effort to move outside the area of science and mathematics, and will provide an entrance (through human geography) for FUNBEC to become involved in the social sciences, an area which has been under discussion for several years.

Evaluation

The principal effort at evaluation under the grant will make use of the results of Carlos Chagas Foundation's university admission examinations to help determine the effectiveness of the high school science curricula developed by FUNBEC. Each candidate for the examination is required to fill out a questionnaire, which this year includes questions concerning the textbooks and laboratory equipment available to the candidate. Scores on different portions of the examination will then be correlated with the texts and laboratory materials used by the candidate in his secondary science courses, after other relevant variables (e.g. socio-economic status) have been taken into account. . . .

Evaluation will (and should) consume a significantly larger portion of any new grant proposal. If there occurs a stringency in funds, however, we should not be willing to sacrifice evaluation efforts or improved pre-testing of curriculum to permit the initiation or continuation of a wider range of concrete projects. Indeed, we probably should encourage strongly FUNBEC to hire, contact, or train the staff necessary for more systematic evaluation and testing of their own materials and techniques.

Financial

The financial situation at FUNBEC hasn't changed measurably. Depending heavily, as it does, on purchases and payment from government agencies, FUNBEC will not be able to free itself (without a large injection of outside funds) from continued financial difficulties. No suitable purchaser for the production side of FUNBEC yet has been identified, but FUNBEC staff continue to regard the divestment of the production and distribution portion of its operation as a live possibility.

The business manager contracted about two years ago has left FUNBEC without making a significant impact. Apparently it was not possible to separate the managerial from the substantive aspects of FUNBEC's labors and the presence of an administrator who did not understand the functions and objectives of FUNBEC was the source of considerable tension.[45]

9. *FUNBEC develops capability in testing and evaluation*
In keeping with her new responsibilities as administrative and intellectual

leader of FUNBEC, Myriam Krasilchik recognized the desirability of establishing fresh contact with leaders of educational innovation in other countries. Under a travel grant provided by the Ford Foundation, she travelled to the U.S. for a series of visits to curriculum development centers and particularly to testing and evaluation centers, including the Educational Testing Service at Princeton and the Colorado headquarters of the Biological Sciences Curriculum Project (BSCS). Her visits deepened her grasp of sophisticated evaluation techniques and their applicability to curriculum development and impressed upon her the need to carry out evaluation of curriculum materials and methods developed at FUNBEC:

> In recent months, the FUNBEC leadership has become increasingly concerned with the lack of a more reliable basis for product development and evaluation. This concern may be traced particularly to the heavy emphasis being placed on development of the primary science materials and the junior high school conservation series. In both cases, even early feedback from informal testing has shown that the materials may be poorly designed and above the age levels for which they are aimed. Furthermore, FUNBEC's leaders are well aware of the difficulty in selling any radical new approach. In order to persuade the publisher to undertake commercial publication of the materials FUNBEC will require a more thorough and reliable process of product analysis than it has used in the past.[46]

Upon her return to Brazil, therefore, she at once set up programs for testing and evaluation of the primary level science materials and for evaluating the impact of FUNBEC's adaptation of BSCS materials.

The Ford Foundation officers in Brazil saw FUNBEC's needs for specially trained personnel to permit it to embark upon these evaluation programs in a satisfactory manner. Realizing that their earlier grants had made little provision for such staff development, Foundation officers recommended awarding a grant to FUNBEC for staff development in testing and evaluation:

> FUNBEC's Scientific Director, Ernesto Giesbrecht, and Training Director, Myriam Krasilchik, both have expressed their desire to strengthen that organization's capacity for sophisticated product development and evaluation.
> On the basis of discussions with Giesbrecht and Krasilchik, expertise in the following areas appears to be required:
> 1. *Tests and Measurements and Research Design.*
> 2. *Human Development Psychology and Instructional Design.*
> 3. *Product Design.*
> 4. *Analysis of Marketing and Diffusion Feasibility.*
> Special emphasis is required in the fourth area above, since it is particularly difficult to break into a traditional market with highly innovative materials.
>
> If FUNBEC wishes to have widespread national impact through its materials it must develop the capacity to test and evaluate them under a variety of educational conditions, not just the relatively privileged educational environment of urban São

Paulo. To do this, it would be necessary to build a permanent team with the skills in the areas described above, which would be available to FUNBEC for systematic product development and evaluation.

While on the one hand, strengthening FUNBEC's capacity for testing and evaluation, its leaders wish to continue development of new curricula and materials. Highest on the priority list of new materials is continued development of the geography series.[47]

Officers in the New York office welcomed this recommendation. K. N. Rao, in particular, expressed his enthusiasm as follows:

... The questions and concerns on the evaluation have been well summarized in the background memoranda. I am, however, concerned with the availability in the short run of the required expertise in Brazil for the evaluation. Hopefully the long-term fellowship program, for which some support is contemplated, will provide indigenous experts. In the short run, FUNBEC might have to depend heavily for professional help from outside. While Dick Tolman would be very helpful in the biology area and the BSCS-FUNBEC evaluation exercise may help train some Brazilians, it will probably be necessary to locate experts in other subject areas....[48]

He gave his full support to a grant to FUNBEC for this evaluation component in its program. But he also raised, for the first time, the question of the appropriate time to terminate aid to the FUNBEC program. His concern in doing this was to encourage his colleagues to evolve a satisfactory Foundation policy and procedure on termination of a grant to a successful grantee such as FUNBEC which for the most part depended upon non-government sources of support for its innovation activities. Thus, he first pointed out that the small exploration fund of $10,000 given to FUNBEC in the 1970 grant had, indeed, stimulated FUNBEC to open up a new area for development—the geography textbook development. He then asked his Foundation colleagues:

Should we confine our interest at FUNBEC to mathematics and the sciences only and encourage others to pick up the major development costs after we have funded the initial exploration? It is my view that the *modes of curriculum innovation had been demonstrated* in the science area and FUNBEC must now be encouraged to apply these techniques to other fields with funds from other sponsors.

After nearly ten years of work with FUNBEC and an investment of $450,000, the question of the future interest of the Foundation in FUNBEC will need to be raised at this time. After we have worked quite successfully with the organization through innovation-development-evaluation-commercialization cycle, what do we do next?

The question, then, of how close this grant is to a terminal action becomes extremely pertinent.[49]

Officers in the Brazil office of the Foundation accepted his challenge to reexamine their recommendation for an additional grant to FUNBEC and replied:

> When successive grants are requested and approved, they should be shaped in order to stimulate the development of the institution, when such a development is desired by both the grantee and the Foundation. This is the case for the present supplemental grant; FUNBEC leaders Ernesto Giesbrecht and Myriam Krasilchik are convinced that it is necessary to develop evaluation capacity; we have been working with the institution for nearly ten years and are also convinced that the time has come for FUNBEC to develop this capacity in order to become a more autonomous research and training center.[50]

The Foundation took further steps at that time to assist FUNBEC in building up its capability in evaluation. It provided the consulting assistance of Dr. Hulda Grobman, a specialist on educational evaluation. It also awarded a grant to the BSCS project headquarters in Colorado to facilitate collaboration between BSCS and FUNBEC in conducting a highly sophisticated evaluation study of one of the FUNBEC products, the adapted version of the BSCS (Green Version) textbook and laboratory units already in use among Brazilian biology classes. Under this grant, BSCS staff consultants Richard Tolman and James Robinson worked in Brazil with the FUNBEC team over a period of several years. The outcome of that evaluation with students and teachers in 300 Brazilian classrooms appears in a final report published by the BSCS, entitled "An Evaluation of Biologia." It summarizes the evaluation in these terms:

> 1. No significant differences were found between the experimental and control groups and no interaction effects occurred.

> 2. The use of the Class Activities Questionnaire, even though it was adapted to Brazilian classrooms, remains in question. Asking students to question a part of their culture that is usually not questioned seems to invalidate the cognitive aspects of the CAQ. The novelty of being in an experimental situation may also have led students to give what they thought would be the most valued responses.

> 3. The investigators feel that the multiple matrix sampling model was successful, as was the repeated measures technique, with some qualification. Although each student responded to only 15 test items, the results obtained were an estimate of the scores that would have been obtained had all students responded to all items. Thus a great deal of information was obtained with a minimum expenditure of student time.

> 4. A determination of the influence of the three-week in-service program for experimental group teachers was the final objective of the evaluation program. The greatest difference between experimental and control group teachers was in the ideal conditions they described for opportunities for student discussion. Teachers with in-service training indicated that an ideal biology class would provide much opportunity for student discus-

sion, but teachers without the special training program were inconclusive on opportunities for class discussion. Students confirmed this difference in their perception of the opportunity for discussion in the classroom. The investigators consider this single shift in teacher behavior a significant contribution for such a short in-service program.[51]

Hulda Grobman wrote after her visit to FUNBEC in 1972 where she worked for a month to assist the evaluation team to organize its program, as follows:

My first reaction to FUNBEC was one of amazement. I had heard and read about the work of the organization for some years, and had seen the high school biology volumes produced. However, I was not aware of the large scope of operations and the productivity of the staff. I found the organization and its staff impressive.

FUNBEC seems to be well on the way to solving a number of its problems. I believe that the new emphasis on evaluation encouraged by the Ford Foundation grant will be extremely useful in improving the curriculum produced and the manner of its production and dissemination.

In conclusion, I am highly optimistic of the future of the evaluation project and the staff as well as the directions being planned.[52]

The FUNBEC evaluation team is continuing to demonstrate experience and expertise in relatively sophisticated evaluation techniques, ensuring in FUNBEC a capability in formative evaluation for its future developmental work. That team is now bringing other FUNBEC products under study. For example concerning its recent work to evaluate primary school materials, one Ford Foundation officer observes:

Using a carefully planned research design and sophisticated data analysis (step-wise regression), the team evaluated the first set of primary science materials. The evaluation had two goals: (1) investigate the content of the materials in terms of adequacy of language, clarity of instructions and illustrations, and sufficiency and adequacy of the kit contents; and (2) evaluate the degree to which the materials develop in the students the abilities emphasized by the kits.

The researchers claim that the kits tested are effective. The kits explain twenty-one of the twenty-six percent explained variance between the experimental and control groups in gains between pre- and post-testing. All of the children tested liked the kits. Ninety-one percent had no difficulty with the vocabulary. Twenty-nine percent needed no help from the teacher. Group use was shown to be more effective than individual use. The level of a teacher's prior training apparently had no significant influence on the results.

The Specific research results are not as important as their impact on FUNBEC. There is a growing confidence in research-based, formative evaluation, which has been shared with others. . . .[53]

10.   *Rising school attendance in Brazil creates new challenges to FUNBEC's resourcefulness*

Two recent assignments taken on by FUNBEC witness to its growing capability as a creative center for curriculum development. First of all, in September 1971, Editora Abril, the largest publishing house in Latin America, invited FUNBEC to prepare a unique set of 50 kits of science experiments which Abril will sell to manufacture and distribute nationally on newsstands throughout Brazil. Each kit is to contain a biography of a great scientist as well as an experiment illustrating his work. It is also to include an easy instruction booklet and the simple materials required to perform the experiment. FUNBEC has agreed to design prototypes for the experiments and instruction booklets. The financial implications for FUNBEC of this relationship with Abril are significant, for at the average retail price per kit of Cr$8,00, a total sale of 150,000 kits (which Abril predicts), will yield about Cr$2 million to FUNBEC's account.

The President of Abril, Victor Civita, describes this unusual collaboration between FUNBEC and his company in these words:

> It is with great pleasure that we are presenting and airmailing to you, under separate cover, the first edition of our latest collection, "OS CIENTISTAS, A GRANDE AVENTURA DA DESCOBERTA CIENTIFICA" ("The Scientists, the Great Adventure of Scientific Discovery").
>
> This is a unique project, developed jointly by our company (ABRIL) and FUNBEC (a Brazilian nonprofit institution for the development of science teaching techniques) consisting of a part-work series presenting the biography of the most important scientists of all times, accompanied by a kit with materials and a manual which will allow the reader to perform the same experiments that led to some of the greatest discoveries....[54]

The second recent evaluation and advisory assignment taken on by FUNBEC originated with the Brazilian Ministry of Education and Culture in the wake of its effort to restructure the school system and to extend compulsory education from four to eight years. This new structure, an eight-year primary school (first level or *primero grau*) followed by a four-year secondary school (second level or *segundo grau*) replaces the previous arrangement in which primary schooling of four years was followed by a middle school (*ginasio*) and higher school (*colegio*).

In line with these changes, the Federal Council of Education of Brazil, in 1971, issued decree No. 6592, declaring that new forms of science courses must be available in the secondary schools:

> Diversified science offerings in a developing country such as Brazil are now considered desirable for future professionals during their middle and upper levels of secondary schooling. Two different groups of students are: those who do not go to university but leave school for employment; and those who do go to university but not to continue studies along technical or scientific lines. The time for science study for these students is one year, owing to course requirements in other areas.
>
> Science courses should contribute to general education. The student should have the option of taking a basic science—chem-

istry, physics, or biology—or an "integrated" science course. This integrated science course is the preferred option. Pedagogical, scientific, and citizenship points of view should be reflected in this integrated science course. Separate chemistry and physics courses for the general student are inferior to an integrated course which gives a better global view of science.

Integrated science should develop interest by presenting science as a story of human progress and by involving students in *solving problems* drawn from the surrounding community—pollution, for example. An integrated course should provide a base for the training of a future citizen in taking decisions on questions of community interest which involve a basic comprehension of science but not a specific knowledge of physics, chemistry, or biology.[55]

In its desperate need to have a suitable kind of offering in science, one that would fit the specifications given in this Law No. 6592, PREMEN,[56] the section of the Ministry of Education responsible for curriculum improvement in Brazil's schools, has requested CECISP to prepare an integrated science course for secondary schools. The PREMEN contract with CECISP, for an amount of Cr$600,000, specifies:

In the absence of an integrated science course, the Brazilian student obtains a deformed and mutilated vision of science. In an integrated course of one year, however, he should receive knowledge of basic concepts presented without the traditional division of science and including, if possible, new areas such as anthropology, psychology, theology, and social sciences. The goals for the integrated course shall be: "to present to students basic concepts of science and their implications in a modern world; to see to it that students understand the interaction of man and his environment; and to give students basic science information in order to comprehend the fundamental principles of this branch of knowledge."

The following topics are to be developed:
- The great steps of science.
- The materials used by man.
- Living species and man.
- The energy used by man.
- The human population.
- Modern man and science.[57]

The FUNBEC team, a group of highly experienced science educators, together with consultants drawn from psychology, linguistics, statistics, and other fields relevant to their task, have now taken up the challenge implicit in preparing a course with these specifications and goals. The team is already exploring many unconventional and untried learning procedures in an effort to translate the broad range of course objectives into a coherent and pedagogically meaningful program of study. Representative of their exploratory vigor and daring is their examination of the potential in children's games as devices for enabling the classroom student to experience problem-oriented thinking and decision-making in the framework of such a science course.

REFERENCES

1. January, 1970, *Personal Memoirs* of Isaias Raw (communicated privately to RHM).
2. Stefan Zweig, *Country of Tomorrow*, São Paulo.
3. Raw, *Memoirs*, p. 12.
4. *Ibid.*, p. 12.
5. *Ibid.*, p. 14.
6. *Ibid.*, pp. 16-17.
7. "An Effort to Improve Science Education in Brazil, 1950–1966," FUNBEC booklet.
8. Summary Report of the Activities on Science Education, IBECC-UNESCO, São Paulo, 1960, pp. 10-11.
9. Summary Report of the Activities on Science Education, IBECC-UNESCO, São Paulo, 1960, pp. 8-9.
10. 1960 Summary Report of the Activities on Science Education, IBECC-UNESCO, São Paulo, pp. 2-6.
11. 5 April 1960 interoffice memorandum, Alfred C. Wolf to F. F. Hill, Ford Foundation, New York.
12. 18 September 1960 report to the Ford Foundation, New York, by Dr. Arthur Roe, Dr. Karl Dittmer, and Prof. Paul Klinge.
13. 18 September 1960 report to the Ford Foundation, Drs. Roe, Dittmer, and Klinge.
14. 11 August 1960, Isaias Raw to Alfred C. Wolf, Ford Foundation, New York.
15. 28 September 1960 memorandum, Robert S. Wickham to Alfred C. Wolf.
16. 18 January 1961 Request for Grant Action (OD-781G).
17. 16 June 1966 memorandum, John F. Baxter to S. Widdicombe.
18. 12 September 1962 Request for Grant Action (OD-1083G).
19. 14 December 1964 IBECC-UNESCO report.
20. 19 May 1964 report by Isaias Raw to R. E. Carlson, Ford Foundation, New York.
21. 17 January 1962 UNESCO report, Raw to Alfred C. Wolf, the Ford Foundation, New York.
22. 4 May 1962 letter, R. E. Carlson, Ford Foundation, Rio de Janeiro, to J. L. Morrill, Ford Foundation, New York.
23. 30 April 1962 letter from Isaias Raw to Robert S. Wickham, Ford Foundation, New York.
24. 11 January 1966 "Proposal on Science Education Leadership," Isaias Raw.
25. 14 June 1966 memorandum, John F. Baxter to S. Widdicombe.
26. 17 June 1966 memorandum, S. Widdicombe to Harry E. Wilhelm, Ford Foundation, New York.
27. 12 September 1966 letter from Raw to S. Widdicome, Ford Foundation, Rio de Janeiro.
28. 9 November 1966 interoffice memorandum, K. N. Rao to Robert S. Wickham.
29. Fundacio Brasileira para o Densenvolvimento do Ensino de Ciencias.
30. FAPESP = Scientific Research Council of the State of São Paulo.
31. FUNBEC report, Isaias Raw.
32. 16 July 1968 memorandum, Morris L. Cogan to Peter D. Bell.
33. 10 November 1970 memorandum from Raw to Dr. William D. Carmichael.
34. 7 January 1968 letter to Julian Lauchner, Ford Foundation, São Paulo.
35. 5 March 1969 memorandum, K. N. Rao to William Carmichael, Rio.
36. 9 November 1966, K. N. Rao to R. S. Wickham.
37. 14 March 1969 letter from Isaias Raw to William D. Carmichael, Ford Foundation, Rio de Janeiro.
38. 18 March 1969 memorandum from William D. Carmichael, Brazil Office to K. N. Rao, Ford Foundation, New York.
39. 2 April 1969 memorandum from K. N. Rao to William D. Carmichael, Ford Foundation, Rio de Janeiro.
40. Isaias Raw, Personal Memoirs, p. 1.
41. 4 July 1969 Report by Myriam Krasilchik to Ford Foundation, Brazil.
42. 18 August 1969 interoffice memorandum, K. N. Rao to Harry E. Wilhelm.
43. 24 September 1969 Request for Grant Action (70-28, David E. Bell to McGeorge Bundy.
44. *Ibid.*
45. 28 January 1971 interoffice memorandum, Peter Hakim to William D. Carmichael.
46. 30 April 1971 report, Carmichael and Nicholson.
47. June 1971 memorandum from R. S. Sharpe and Alberto Carvalho da Silva to Carmichael.
48. 24 June 1971 memorandum, K. N. Rao to Carmichael.

49. 24 June 1971 memorandum, K. N. Rao to W. D. Carmichael.

50. 20 July 1971 memorandum, Alberto Carvalho da Silva to Stanley Nicholson.

51. An Evaluation of Biologia, Volume I, Brazilian Adaptation of the BSCS Green Version, June 1973.

52. 28 June 1972: Hulda Grobman's report of visit as consultant to FUNBEC, São Paulo.

53. 12 March 1973 interoffice memorandum, Stanley A. Nicholson to William D. Carmichael.

54. 7 July 1972 letter, Victor Civita to K. N. Rao, the Ford Foundation, New York.

55. Rough translation of the relevant portion of this by R. H. Maybury.

56. Programa de Esparsao de Melhoria de Ensino.

57. FUNBEC and CECISP (Centro de Treinamento para Profesores de Ciencias) are separate legal units. FUNBEC is a private, non-profit foundation; CECISP is financed by the Ministry of Education as a center for teacher in-service training). However, buildings, space, and staff members are common to both.

Premen was originally created in the Ministry of Education with assistance from the U.S. AID. In 1972–73 it has allocated $1 million to curriculum development and teacher education in science. To accomplish the actual writing and instruction called for in this massive program, PREMEN is inviting the participation of the CECI's and preparing contracts with each similar to the one with CECISP.

LEBANON AND OTHER ARAB COUNTRIES
OF THE MIDDLE EAST

1.   *The Middle East office decides to emphasize science education improvement*
Improving science teaching in schools of the Arab countries of the Middle East became a programme emphasis of the Beirut office of the Ford Foundation in the late 1950s in response to the thinking of two Foundation Officers, Harvey Hall and Hugh Walker. These officers saw the slow rates of progress in these countries as due in part to persisting pre-scientific modes of thought among the populace. Accordingly, they believed that better teaching of science in the schools of these countries could lead to a modernization of this self-limiting thought and thereby remove a major hindrance to progress.

Their first move was to invite Professor Milton Pella, a science educator from the University of Wisconsin, to come to the Middle East to study difficulties in science teaching in the schools of Lebanon and other Arab countries of that region. Professor Pella, who had previously carried out a similar mission for the Ford Foundation in Turkey, came to the Middle East early in 1962 for a period of several months. During that visit, he interviewed government authorities, educators and scientists. He went into school classrooms and laboratories. He also took part in a summer course for science teachers at the American University in Beirut where he worked closely with its sponsors, the National Council for Secondary Education,[1] in organizing the program and serving as one of the course instructors. Pella summarized his observations of science education in Lebanon in a report that he submitted to the Ford Foundation:

Teachers:
- very little attempt to achieve any objective other than a body of knowledge to be memorized.
- only a few use the laboratory.
- great deficiencies in the effective practice of teaching and no pedagogical basis for activities in the classroom.

Textbooks:
- generally modern, but followed without deviation.

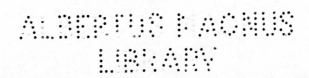

- most from England or translations of French textooks into English.
- regrettable that the sciences are not taught in the language of the land, Arabic.

Facilities:
- all schools visited had a room set aside for laboratory with facilities more usable than used.
- the laboratory is a separate room from that in which instruction is given. The teacher of the didactic portion does not conduct laboratory sessions. The laboratory thus becomes a course separate from the didactic course.
- a definite deficiency in chart and pictorial material.

Equipment:
- some deficiencies. However, that which is present is generally not being used.
- the real problem is lack of desire on part of teacher to use equipment.

Recommendations:
The most pressing problem is the teacher of science. He needs academic and professional preparation so that he may develop a sound and reasonable philosophy of science teaching.

In-service education aimed at improving science instruction emphasizing use of demonstrators and laboratory activities —activities as data gathering experiences so that generalizations or facts may be learned inductively.

Step I:
Instruction (of teachers) in use of equipment and in the function of self-experience in the teaching-learning process.

Step II:
Attention to use of audio-visual materials. Involve academic scientists to add modern knowledge and teach a unit using demonstrations, laboratory activities, and modern visual aids.

Step III:
1. Discuss and arrive at objectives for teaching science in secondary schools.
2. Plan a six-year program to include a developmental sequence in the problem-solving aspect of science.[2]

2.   *The University of Wisconsin takes on a "resource base" role*

After reviewing his report, Ford Foundation officers requested Pella to develop a long-term project for the improvement of science education in Arab countries of the Middle East. Pella accepted the assignment and once more visited the Middle East to prepare such a plan. One of the ideas that at first seemed attractive was to establish a regional science-education center.

However, after reviewing the difficulties inherent in such a course, primarily, the difficulty in finding an adequate number of trained specialists to staff such a center, Pella turned away from that idea. Instead, he recommended a radically different course for science-education improvement efforts by the Ford Foundation in that part of the world:

Professor Pella's work with science teachers and discussions with scientists and educational leaders in the Arab countries convinced him that it was premature to consider the establishment of a regional science center at this time. Considerable improvement in the teaching of science would be possible if closer contact were established between scientists and science educators in those countries and centers of creative work on the teaching of science in the United States. Specifically, Professor Pella proposed a program consisting of:

(1) the appointment of a program specialist in science education to work with teachers and educational institutions in the Arab countries.

(2) a program of research at the University of Wisconsin in problems of science education in underdeveloped countries.

(3) the graduate training of selected science educators from the Arab countries at Wisconsin.[3]

Upon completion of his fact-finding in the Middle East, Pella returned to the United States to persuade his colleagues at the University of Wisconsin to join him in sponsoring this project of assistance to the Arab countries. Representatives from the Ford Foundation office in New York also travelled to the University of Wisconsin campus to explain the Pella proposal to university officials. One Ford Foundation officer described his visit to Wisconsin in these words:

This trip to Wisconsin was a success, and I think we have everything squared away at this end. I talked to Milt Pella's dean, and both the academic and business vice presidents of the University. All were cordial to the idea of building up their competence in the field of science teaching in underdeveloped countries, since they recognize in it an important and relatively unexplored field of comparative education. It so happens that the "Pella Plan" also fits in rather neatly with a policy decision the University has recently taken regarding the objectives of their overseas educational activities.[4]

In negotiating with the Wisconsin officials over setting up a Ford Foundation program there for training Arab science educators, the Ford Foundation officers went beyond asking the University to provide certain services, and urged the University to see itself as more than a mere "bookkeeper" of its grant funds.

I express concern about Wisconsin acting only as bookkeeper, accepting our funds to train selected students and to add one man for three years, all with our money without really contributing to basic developments in this field. It seems we should find some way to strengthen science teaching research at Wisconsin as we go along.

As I recall, Pella was quite concerned about the need for some very basic research on the part of Western institutions regarding materials and techniques adaptable to developing countries, as well as the problem of training science teachers. This seems an extremely important aspect of the problem and maybe we can needle Wisconsin into accepting the challenge without it costing too much.[5]

The University of Wisconsin officers responded favorably both to the request to provide services and to the Foundation invitation to go further and develop a research program on Arab development:

> *Research.* It is the intent of the appropriate department of the University to foster research on the problems of science education in developing countries, with the ultimate objective of perfecting materials and techniques designed to cope with them. In particular, it is understood that the foreign graduate fellowship students referred to in paragraph 2 above will be encouraged to consider topics of peculiar relevance to their own countries, and following completion of their residence requirements to carry out field research in the geographical areas from which they came.[6]

The Ford Foundation officers stoutly affirmed their belief that the Foundation's funds should be used for building up the University of Wisconsin's capability to serve the program in the Middle East:

> Some may look upon this as a contract for services to be rendered, whereas we look upon it as a grant. If it were a contract it would be quite appropriate to measure our action by what the Foundation expects to get in return. This is not, however, the sole measure of a grant, where benefit to the grantee is a prime consideration. With respect to the present example, this means that the development of Wisconsin's interest and competence in the problems of science education in Arab countries is an integral part of our concern.
>
> Now I think a university contract may be an appropriate mechanism when we have, on the one hand, a clearly defined project which requires services that only a university can provide; and on the other, a university with the professional competence to provide them. But our experience has led us to believe that when such conditions are not present, the university contract is not the best solution.
>
> Opposed to the well-defined project is the type represented by the Wisconsin-Arab area science education undertaking. Here we don't have, so far, any clear picture of what kind of an institution should evolve, or even a very clear notion of what research problems need to be tackled, and certainly not how to go about them. The emphasis at this stage is entirely on developing competent people and exploring ideas. The project by its nature, therefore, needs to be left flexible—we define our ultimate objective but then rely on the competence, imagination, energy, and integrity of the people involved to move it ahead. . . . With a university contract, we tend to lose contact; with this kind of an arrangement we become working partners. Of course, we are counting heavily on the quality of the people, but if they weren't any good I doubt if we would get anything more out of them, in this type of a project, by binding them to a contract.
>
> [Some may] expect Wisconsin itself to produce the answers and develop the materials for improved science education in the

Arab countries. Actually, however, our objective is to develop Arabs with the competence to do this, and eventually to work with them in the establishment of some kind of a center through which they can be effective. An essential ingredient in attaining this objective is the strengthening of American competence, in terms of individuals at an American university, specifically Wisconsin. If, in the process of training, research, and consultation, Wisconsin develops some applicable techniques and materials it will be a welcome by-product, but this is neither the primary nor ultimate objective of our grant.[7]

Negotiations between the Foundation and University officers eventually culminated in an agreement, and on 30 April 1963, the Foundation awarded a grant of $141,000 to the University of Wisconsin, so that it could serve, over a five-year period, as a "resource base" for a program of cooperation in science education with the Arab countries of the Middle East. Included in that program were these provisions:

1. The Foundation will appoint, on the nomination of the University of Wisconsin, a program specialist in science education to be attached to the Beirut office for two years (approximately June 1963–June 1965). . . .

2. Following his two years in the field, the program specialist will return to the University of Wisconsin, where he will receive an appointment in the School of Education in science education, with special attention to training and research relevant to the Arab countries of the Middle East. The Foundation will continue to pay his salary for three years, after which the University will maintain him on the professional staff from its regular budget.

3. Over a period of five years (1963–1968), up to five science educators from the Arab countries will be brought to Wisconsin for graduate study. . . .

4. Following the return of the program specialist to the University of Wisconsin, and coincident with the departure of the first graduate students for their field research (i.e., in 1965 or 1966), it is expected that the professor of science education at Wisconsin (i.e., Pella) will supervise the research of the graduate students, and to discuss with local scientists and educators, in cooperation with the Foundation representative in Beirut, the development of national institutions, or possibly a regional center, for training and research in science education. It is also understood that Professor Pella will have general responsibility for the administration of the grant, and will maintain close contact with the program specialist during the latter's tour overseas.[8]

As soon as the grant was awarded, Pella began to search for a suitable candidate for the position of science educator as provided by the grant. He soon identified James Busch, a science supervisor for the State of Wisconsin, as his first choice for this position. Pella then wrote to several science teachers in the Middle East whom he had identified during his 1962 visit inviting them to apply for admission to graduate study to serve as the Ford Foundation consultant in science education. Much of Busch's subsequent activity in that position, which lasted over a four-year period, was carried on through the National Council. He assisted the Council in organizing and conducting in-service courses for Lebanese science teachers. He collaborated with the Council's own staff specialist in publishing and distributing a newsletter for science teachers. He visited many schools and worked closely with the teachers in promoting better teaching practices in their classrooms and laboratories.

Pella and Busch also worked closely with the science committee of the National Council for Secondary Education in formulating objectives for science teaching in secondary schools in Lebanon and in drawing up lists of materials required for satisfactory teaching in those schools.

Pella returned to Wisconsin in June 1963, leaving Busch in Beirut as planned at the University of Wisconsin. Yacub Namek, a science teacher at Beirut's International College (secondary school) was the first to enter Wisconsin under this program (September 1963). Attempts to enroll a Syrian teacher whom Pella had identified were unsuccessful at that time.

3.   *A five-year period of the Wisconsin program lays the foundation for the future Middle East science education program*

One by one, as Pella succeeded in identifying them, young Arab science educators arrived at Wisconsin to take up their studies leading to doctoral degrees in science education under his direction. To identify these talented individuals, Pella travelled to the Middle East at least once each year in that early period. In the spring of 1963, for example, he and Busch went to Lebanon where they assisted the National Council on Secondary Education in planning another summer course for science teachers. Pella worked assiduously in drawing scientists into cooperation with the educators in staffing the course and in persuading the American University in Beirut (AUB) to organize special degree programs for science teachers. Pella and Busch also worked closely with the science committee of the National Council for Secondary Education in formulating objectives for science teaching in secondary schools in Lebanon and in drawing up lists of materials required for satisfactory teaching in those schools.

In 1964, Pella returned once again to the Middle East as a consultant to the Foundation's Beirut office. This time, in addition to counselling with the National Council on its on-going program for science education in Lebanon, he enlarged his search for science teachers for the Wisconsin program in science education. It was on this visit that he chose Wadih Haddad from Lebanon and Asaad Loutfi from Syria, both of whom entered Wisconsin in September 1964 to take up their graduate study in science education.

Pella's 1965 consultant travel to the Middle East took him to Jordan, at the invitation of the government, to participate in the planning and development of a Science Faculty at the University of Jordan, a project given large assistance by the

United Nations Development Programme with UNESCO as the executing agency. During his three months at the University, he advised on building plans, on purchase of furniture and fixtures for laboratories and classrooms, on development of course outlines for first year chemistry, biology, physics, and mathematics, on ordering of laboratory equipment and supplies, and on other matters.

Pella returned to Wisconsin from that 1965 Middle East visit to welcome a fourth science teacher, Omar Hassan, from Jordan into the special graduate program in science education. At that time, also, the first science teacher to enter the Wisconsin program, Yacoub Namek, completed the required course work, minor and preliminary doctorate examinations, and returned to Beirut to assume a teaching position at AUB.[9] As called for by the plan of the special training program, Namek then initiated a research project on an aspect of education in the Middle East.

To provide financial support to Namek and the other teachers who would soon follow him to the Middle East in carrying on this research phase of their training programs, Pella turned to the Ford Foundation with a request for additional funds. He provided this rationale for the request:

> The students' return to the respective home countries upon completion of two or three years of study to teach and carry on appropriate science education research. The first research project should require one to two years since the student will be devoting about half time to teaching. Financial support for 1/3 to 1/2 of the salary of the student in his home country is to be paid from the grant to the appropriate agency by the University of Wisconsin ... Upon completion of the data gathering aspect of the individual research projects, the student shall come to the U.S. to prepare a final report. The time required in the U.S. is to be about three months ... Each research project shall be outlined with the student prior to his departure from the U.S. and shall be guided to completion by the faculty of this university.[10]

The insistence that the science teachers return to their *own* countries to carry out a research study on topics related to those countries was a cardinal feature of Pella's request, one that greatly pleased the Ford Foundation officers:

> The plan would, in effect, extend the training of these men, reaching out to include field work in their own countries which would have direct relevance to the needs of their home area.
>
> Pella states that each program would be designed and approved through himself and the university before it starts. We were pleased that Pella's plan to bring the students back to the campus at the end of the research would not simply be to meet degree granting legalities but would be a genuine continuation of their training through summer courses and seminars.[11]

Pella also included funds in his request to bring George Za'rour, then Assistant Professor of Science Education at the AUB, into this research phase of the project. Za'rour had previously received a Ph.D. degree in science education at Wisconsin under Pella (1959) prior to the creation of this special program. Pella considered him to be a capable and experienced educator who, through the additional research support from this grant, would not only contribute to science education research in the Middle

East but would also provide leadership and assistance to the program of the five additional junior science teachers.

The Request for Grant Action prepared by Ford Foundation officers at that time (4 August 1966) lists these items to be met by the proposed sum of $57,000:

1. financial support for released time; up to one-half of full salary for two years, for each teacher.

2. the cost of equipment, supplies, travel, secretarial help, etc., necessary to the conduct of the research.

3. international travel, tuition, maintenance costs for the teachers for the time they would spend at Wisconsin to finish their doctoral programs.

In August 1966, the Ford Foundation awarded the grant supplement of $57,000 to the University of Wisconsin, allowing Pella to maintain the momentum of his program.

Pella again travelled to the Middle East as a Ford Foundation consultant in mid-1966, this time to meet officials of agencies or universities that could employ the Arab science educators upon their completion of the initial phase of their training at Wisconsin (the AUB and Ministries of Education in Jordan and Syria). In every case, the officials agreed to enter into arrangements that would permit these returning educators to carry out research in some aspect of science education related to local conditions.

While in Syria, Pella obtained the agreement of the Minister of Education to Asaad Loutfi's remaining at Wisconsin for a third year of graduate study made necessary by the difficulties he had experienced with the English language in his first year at Wisconsin. Also while in Syria, Pella served as a consultant to a committee from the Faculties of Agriculture and Engineering of the University of Aleppo to a Faculty of Science at the University, submitting a report to the Ford Foundation office in Beirut for their use in making a grant to the University of Aleppo.

Pella then went to Jordan to meet a scholarship committee of the Ministry of Education to select the fifth candidate for the special program at Wisconsin. The candidate selected was Victor Billah, who held a B.S. degree in biology from the AUB. While in Jordan, Pella also conferred with the acting Dean and the faculty of the Faculty of Science of the University of Jordan concerning the curriculum for year two and the progress and experience of year one.

On his return to Wisconsin from that 1966 visit to the Middle East, Pella welcomed the fifth Arab science educator, Victor Billah, from Jordan, into the special Wisconsin program, while Haddad returned to Beirut to join Namek at the AUB, and begin his on-the-spot research. In addition to carrying on their research Namek and Haddad began teaching at various schools and universities in Lebanon on a half-time basis. Throughout the 1966-67 academic year, James Busch assisted Namek and Haddad as thesis adviser in the conduct of their research.

June 1967 brought war between Israel and the Arab nations of the Middle East, disrupting the unbroken flow of developments in the science education program up to that time. Busch returned to Wisconsin to join Pella at the School of Education[12] while Pella had to cancel his annual visit to the Middle East. Fortunately for the program, however, the Arab science teachers in Wisconsin were able to continue their studies without interruption. Moreover, Namek and Haddad were able to leave Lebanon and rejoin their colleagues at the Wisconsin campus to complete the final stage of

62

their programs. When they completed their degree work a few months later, Pella wrote proudly:

> The first two students [Namek and Haddad] in the Arab Science Teachers Program have received the Ph.D. and are back in Lebanon. The pace was rapid and the task interesting. I will send you the three volumes that represented the two Ph.D. Theses in case you are interested. If the quality of the project and performance in a university are indications of future benefits to a country these men should be of great value to the Arab world.
>
> You may also be interested to know that the man who returned to Syria has been given permission to carry on his research in that country despite the political situation.[13]

Table 1 indicates the titles of doctoral dissertations completed by these Pella protégés.

Table 1
Doctoral Dissertations of Arab Science Educators
in the University of Wisconsin Program

Dr. Asaad Loutfi "A Comparison of the Relative Effectiveness of Inductive and Deductive Methods of Teaching Selected Concepts Related to Geometrical Optics." Completed this research project with our financial support and guidance in Syria. Presently half-time teaching Science Education courses, University of Damascus; and half-time conducting research and development in the Syrian Ministry of Education.

Dr. Omar Hassan "A Test Related to the Particle Nature of Matter with a Minimal Verbal Component." This project was completed in the U.S. due to political difficulties in Jordan at the time. Presently teaching and developing materials in Ministry of Education-Teacher Education phase, Jordan.

Dr. Victor Billah "Cultural Bias in the Attainment of Concepts of the Biological Cell by Elementary School Children." The research was completed in Jordan with financial and professional support from here. Presently employed—Assistant Professor, Biology Department, American University of Beirut.

Dr. Yacoub Namek "The Effect of Integrated Laboratory Work on Achievement in Secondary School Chemistry." This research was completed in Lebanon with financial and professional support from here. Presently employed half-time Assistant Professor of Science Education, American University of Beirut, and half-time Lecturer, Lebanese University.

Dr. Wadih Haddad "Relationship Between Mental Maturity and the Level of Understanding of Concepts of Relativity in Grades 4-8." This research was completed in Lebanon with financial and professional support from here. Presently Assistant Professor of Science Education and Director of the Science Education Center, American University of Beirut.[14]

The Middle East crisis forced Omar Hassan, the Jordanian, to remain on the Wisconsin campus throughout 1967, an extension to his original timetable. Although Jordanian authorities agreed to this extension, they were unable to provide him a salary. Pella came to his rescue, however, and provided him with living expenses for that period.

4.   *The Ministry of Education in Lebanon*
        creates the science advisory committee

On receiving their doctorates at Wisconsin in late 1967, Namek and Haddad returned to Lebanon to teaching positions at the School of Education of AUB. Upon their arrival at AUB, Habib Khourani, then Chairman of the Department of Education, opened informal discussions with the Beirut office of the Ford Foundation concerning ways to utilize the talents of these science educators. Despite Pella's success in getting the scientists and educators of AUB to participate in the National Council summer courses for teachers, he was unable to convince those university departments to join forces in establishing a science education program within AUB's Department of Education. This lack of interest in such a program at AUB threatened to force Pella's protégés to look elsewhere, for positions of useful service.

At this point, the Ford Foundation office in Beirut, eager to save its investment in these Arab science educators, decided to promote their employment with the Ministry of Education of Lebanon. The Beirut office indicated to the Lebanese Director-General of Education, Joseph Zarour, that the Foundation would support a Ministry-directed activity for science education improvement.

The government response was immediate. In the summer of 1968, Joseph Zarour set up a scienceadvisory committee to study problems of science education in Lebanon. The committee comprised two physicists, two chemists, two mathematicians, and a biologist, representing three of Lebanon's four universities. In support of this government initiative, the Ford Foundation provided a grant of $5,000 from discretionary funds available to the representative of the Beirut office. An additional grant provided to support Wadih Haddad as a consultant to the committee in the capacity of its coordinator and executive secretary.

The high-level scientists and university officers of that committee then made an unprecedented display of concern for improving schools. They actually visited schoolrooms throughout Lebanon to sample the problems of education and to prepare a report for Zarour. They made a particular effort to determine teacher reaction to a recently revised curriculum, that the Ministry planned to put into effect in 1969, and soon discovered that Lebanon's science and mathematics teachers were unprepared to handle this proposed program. This led them to formulate plans for in-service courses for teachers and to urge the Ministry to seek Ford Foundation support for these courses.

In addition to his nation-wide service with this Science Advisory Committee, Wadih Haddad and his AUB colleagues George Za'rour, Namek, and others, prepared a proposal for a science education program in the Department of Education of AUB:

> The American University of Beirut is in a position to make a
> real contribution to the improvement of science and mathematics
> education in the area. This is because of its unique position and
> the presence on its staff of a team of professors especially trained
> in the modern approaches in the fields of science and mathe-
> matics education. Such a contribution can be facilitated by the
> establishment at the University of a Science and Mathematics

Teaching and Research Center which will constitute an integral part of the Department of Education. Its tasks would be:

A. The training of prospective teachers for a degree in the fields of science or mathematics.

B. The training of in-service teachers.

C. Field service on two levels:

    1. *School level.* The center personnel will advise schools on textbooks, curriculum designs, equipment, setting up of laboratories, and improved methods of evaluation.

    2. *Country level.* Middle East governments will be encouraged to consult the center about revision of the science and mathematics curricula or training of their teachers.

D. Research and development.

    Some areas of research and development which may be undertaken by the center are:

    1. Developmental research.

    2. Methods research.

    3. Curriculum research which involves the evaluation of proposed curriculum improvements.

    4. Field research.

    5. Writing of elementary and secondary science and mathematics textbooks.

    6. Development of equipment.[15]

Their proposal outlined facilities and personnel (professors and assistants) and described the course offerings to be provided. Haddad and his colleagues tried valiantly to interest the other departments of AUB in their proposed center:

The proposed center will try to cooperate with the science and mathematics departments according to the following possibilities:

1. The formation of a Science and Mathematics Education Committee composed of the staff of the center and one representative from each of the mathematics and science (physical and natural) departments. The functions of this committee will be:

    a. To discuss general policies and requirements for the preparation of teachers of science and mathematics.

    b. To coordinate activities involving the Center and one or more of the science and mathematics departments.

    c. To recommend projects in research and development that should be undertaken by the center.

2. The utilization of the facilities of the science departments by the Center and vice versa.[16]

In their proposal, they described support which they expected from the AUB administration: provisions of space, facilities, and payment for half of the academic personnel concerned with teaching and research in the centre.

One Ford Foundation consultant, Clinton Cook, who was in Beirut at that time, commented on this proposal by Haddad and his AUB colleagues as follows:

Several factors have led to the belief that Lebanon might be ripe for reform of science education:

(1) The adoption of a somewhat reformed curriculum and the creation of an advisory committee to the Director General for Education (Joseph Zarour) to implement the reforms.·

(2) The desire for reform on the part of scientists at American University of Beirut and the Lebanese University.

(3) The presence of several bright young science educators (particularly Wadi Haddad and George Za'rour) on the staff of the Education Department at A.U.B. Particular importance has been attached to the fact that they seem to have the respect and support of their colleagues in science. They propose to establish a Science Training Center at A.U.B. to provide a means for demonstrating modern laboratory teaching and have requested support from Ford Foundation for this project.[17]

In spite of these favourable comments and the good will built up by Haddad, he and his colleagues in the Department of Education could stir up no response during the first half of 1969 from the AUB administration to the proposal for a science education center. In the meanwhile, however, Haddad's efforts at the national level as a consultant to the government brought him more satisfying results. The Science Advisory Committee on which he served submitted a report to the Ford Foundation on Science education in Lebanon that soon led to a grant of $59,000 for summer institutes with Lebanese science and mathematics teachers:

The present grant would provide for two in-service institutes of six weeks each, to be held in the summers of 1969 and 1970. The institutes would be able to handle 120 teachers in the first session and 160 in the second, drawn from both the Government and private schools systems. In order to meet the projected time schedule for the introduction of curricular reforms, the 1969 institute would cover physics, chemistry and mathematics for teachers of the fifth and sixth secondary; the 1970 institute would continue these same subjects, plus biology, for the seventh secondary. (These comprise the last three years of secondary education in Lebanon.) Training would be in both French and English, to sections of about 20 teachers each. In order to simulate actual teaching conditions, the institutes would be held in one of the Ministry's own secondary schools; the instructors, however, would be drawn from the best qualified professors in the several universities, including members of the advisory committee itself.

The objective of the planned institutes would be to update the subject matter knowledge of the secondary school teachers and to develop in discussion with them new ideas on how science and mathematics can best be taught, given current limitations imposed by curriculum, examinations, and facilities. This dual approach should both improve the quality of teaching and point up obstacles to further improvement which would be of value to the advisory committee in its subsequent deliberations.

Although the Ministry of Education will provide space and laboratory equipment for the 1969 and 1970 institutes, it cannot, for budgetary reasons, provide funds to meet the operational costs of a special, short-term project such as this. It has therefore requested support from the Foundation as summarized in the attached budget estimate. The Middle East regional office expects to continue its interest in the Ministry's efforts to build its capacity for educational planning and development, and in the work of the advisory committee. While future considerations may be given to possible support for the long-range plans of the Ministry and the committee, it is understood that the Ministry will undertake responsibility for the full operating costs of continuing programs of in-service training for teachers.[18]

This request set off policy discussions within the Foundation on the problem of support to teacher training. In defense of such a grant, the program officer for the Middle East wrote:

Two different kinds of activity are required to support the Ministry's goals and one is, indeed, teacher education. In this area, there is a first attempt to introduce a somewhat revised curriculum in science that requires the immediate training of the teachers, and there is a long-range requirement for a mechanism to provide continuous in-service training so the teachers can keep pace with further modernization and change.

This part of the overall program would not usually be the piece that the Foundation would pick up, and we are only picking up the short-range portion. It had become apparent—and very lately so—that the teachers are not now equipped to handle even the first curriculum revision which is already scheduled for introduction, part next year and part in the following year. This is an emergency need and one which our Beirut office has recommended supporting.

It is the sense that the future of the overall program will be damaged by a failure at this stage, that has pulled us into teacher education. However, as the grant action notes, the Ministry is to be responsible for all operating costs of any future in-service training of teachers. After this one shot, we are out of the teacher education business.

The other kind of activity and the long-range phase in which the Beirut office is interested, is the strengthening of the educational system itself through the Ministry and through the science commission. The Ministry wants to take effective leadership in educational planning, to undertake a developmental role in its relationships to the schools, and to take the lead in developing and introducing new curriculum and methodology. The future interest of the Foundation would thus not be in the teachers, but in strengthening the Ministry's capacity to carry out these purposes. I would envisage this interest as being expressed through the provision of advisory services, possible training opportunities for ministerial staff, and further support for the work of the science commission itself.[19]

6.   *The Ford Foundation awards a grant to establish AUB/SMEC*

Despite these favourable developments for Haddad on the teacher training front, financial crises at AUB in mid-1969 threatened to eliminate any further possibility of his establishing the proposed science education center there with his Wisconsin-trained colleagues:

> Matters came to a head in 1969, when AUB informed Haddad that because of its serious financial problems it could only give him a further one-year appointment, and that there was serious doubt whether the Department could look forward to expanding the number of staff members specializing in science education. Faced with this uncertainty as to his future, Haddad was strongly tempted to return to the U.S. and seek his professional fortune outside the Arab countries.
>
> Thus was presented a further danger lurking in the background of the Wisconsin project: that the Ph. D. fellows might be overtrained and therefore attracted to more rewarding jobs in some developed country or with an international agency. Pella and the Beirut office were willing to let the fellows struggle for a time with the problem of reentry, but the Beirut office in particular, resisted the prospect of their drifting out of the Arab world completely.[20]

Determined that their investment in Haddad and the other Arab science educators should not be lost to the region, Ford Foundation officers worked feverishly with AUB administrators and with Haddad and his colleagues to prepare a revised proposal for a science education center that the university could submit to the Foundation. Out of these efforts finally came an AUB request for a grant of $167,000 over a three-year period for such a center. The request set forth a rationale for establishing a science education center at AUB, an outline of its functions, and principal budget lines:

> The American University of Beirut has a fairly strong Department of Education that is both research and service oriented. It has a nucleus of three Ph.D.'s in science education who have been able to build sound working relations with the science and mathematics departments.
>
> The proposed grant would strengthen AUB's capacity to contribute to three specific objectives: (1) the pre-service and in-service training of science and mathematics teachers and those responsible for the administration of teaching programs; (2) research in the improvement of science curricula, materials, and teaching methods; and (3) consultation on problems of science education throughout the region. The proposed program would be managed by an interdepartmental committee on which the several science departments would be represented.
>
> 1. The training of prospective science and mathematics teachers would include special attention to the creative use of laboratories and equipment. The center would undertake a continuous evaluation of its teacher training programs, keeping them compatible with modern trends and practices.

2. Likewise, the in-service training courses would acquaint teachers with recent developments in science and mathematics teaching and assist them to adapt some of these developments to their classrooms. Included, as well, would be efforts to improve their own mastery of the subject matter. Among the activities for in-service teachers would be graduate degree courses, summer institutes, as well as conferences and workshops.

3. The equipment and materials portion of the grant is intended to make it possible for the center to develop the design and local manufacture of laboratory equipment.

4. The field consulting services of the center, which could be extended to both individual schools or to national ministries, is the most speculative aspect of the program. AUB already receives requests from time to time for expert consultation. The present expectation is that the reputation of the center will grow and induce requests for training, consultation, and research.

5. The center proposes to carry a reasonable load of research directly related to, or suggested by, its training and consultation activities. Areas of research would include curriculum evaluation, methods testing, materials development—both text and equipment—and field research to relate science teaching to the cultural setting, develop science policy and design resources for special situations and problems.

It should be emphasized that the chief function of a science education center at AUB would be to serve as a resource base for experimentation and research. Although, as described above, the center would do some training of teachers, it would not try to meet the quantitative teacher training demands of a national program. The center at AUB would complement these national efforts by providing the guidance, research, and evaluation that they would need to improve the training process and keep teaching methods and materials up to date.

Estimated Budget:

Personnel (4.5 man-years)	$ 81,700
Equipment and books	14,875
Travel, conferences and research costs	13,400
Supplies and materials	29,225
	$139,200
University overhead (20%)	27,800
Total	$167,000 [21]

The Ford Foundation promptly awarded the grant of $167,000 to the AUB in April 1969, enabling the center to begin operating in October of that same year. The university appointed Haddad as director, and George Za'rour and Namek as faculty members of the center. Formal by-laws adopted on 20 February 1970 named the center "American University of Beirut Science and Mathematics Education Center" (AUB/SMEC), and listed its functions, organization, the advisory committee, research and development projects, and amendment procedures:

1. *AUB/SMEC functions*
   a. The preparation of prospective science and mathematics teachers on both the undergraduate and graduate levels, in cooperation with the science and mathematics departments.
   b. The training of teachers in service by means of institutes, conferences, workshops and evening classes.
   c. A consultation service to schools and governments regarding textbooks, curriculum planning, equipment, laboratories and methods of evaluation.
   d. Research and development in the fields of science and mathematics education.
   e. The production of textbooks, experimental curricula and instructional materials for science and mathematics education.
   f. The development of a library of sources and instructional materials for science and mathematics education.

2. *Organizational pattern for SMEC in AUB*
   a. The Center shall function as part of the Department of Education.
   b. The faculty of the Center shall be the science and mathematics education professors of the Department of Education. The Chairman of the Department shall be an ex-officio member of the faculty of the Center.
   c. The Center shall have a director who will be responsible to the Chairman of the Department of Education. He shall be appointed by the Chairman of the Education Department after consultation with the faculty of the Center and other members of the Center's Advisory Committee, normally for a term of two years.

3. *An advisory committee to SMEC comprised as follows:*
   The Center shall have an advisory committee composed of the Chairman of the Department of Education (as Chairman), three faculty members from the Center who have full-time university appointment and one of whom is the director, and one representative from each of the Physics, Chemistry, Biology, and Mathematics departments. The committee shall meet at least once every semester.

By providing funds for establishment of AUB/SMEC, the Ford Foundation made possible an institutional base for the creative energies of the three Pella protégés, Namek, Haddad and Za'rour. Only one of the original five Arab science educators identified by Pella remained in the training program at this point (Victor Billah). On completing his doctoral studies at Wisconsin in June 1969, Billah prepared to return to Jordan. At that point, Pella wrote to the Jordanian authorities, asking them to assign Billah to a suitably challenging post.

In actual fact, Billah did not go to Jordan. A controversy arose between him and the Ministry over his obligation to repay his training through service to the country. He resolved this by paying an amount required to free himself from the obligation and then joined the biology department of AUB in Lebanon. From there, in 1970,

Billah subsequently joined the staff of AUB/SMEC, raising to four the number of Pella-trained science educators on the AUB/SMEC staff.

7. *The Ford Foundation extends its grant to Pella*

Although Pella continued to visit the Middle East during each of the years 1968, 69, 70 and 71 to confer with SMEC and AUB faculty and administrators relative to the organization, operation and research and development conducted by the center, Billah's departure from Wisconsin marked the close of the special Ford Foundation-financed program there. On reviewing his funds, however, Pella found that a balance of $80,000 still remained on hand, owing to his stringent operational economies through the years. He explained these as follows:

> The goal of a Center for Science Education in the Middle East has been realized; however, it is not quite as envisioned. Lacking is the interplay between professional personnel of Syria, Jordan, Iraq, etc., and the center in Beirut. The desire was to stimulate research and development in science education in the Middle East. This is a big order for five people generally of the same generation.
>
> This situation has not been the result of inadequate planning for the program but rather consequences of the times. Records will show that I was involved with a number of projects in the Arab world during this period of the program at the University of Wisconsin, University of Jordan, University of Alleppo, AUB, etc. These additional duties made it possible for me to perform some of the tasks in the Arab countries anticipated in planning at no extra expense. Because of excessive involvement with other duties and programs, I was unable to be relieved when the Arab program was developed. [22]

Pella then submitted a proposal to the Foundation, outlining additional training and research opportunities for science educators in the Middle East:

> The University of Wisconsin will accept for graduate training one qualified individual in mathematics education and one qualified individual in science education (earth science, biology, or chemistry) from the Arab countries and will provide and administer fellowships for these students for about three years each. Selection of the candidates will be the joint responsibility of the University and the Foundation in consultation with the appropriate institutions in the Arab countries.
>
> The University will purchase such books and materials as may be required to carry out the program.
>
> It is the intent of the Department of Curriculum and Instruction (Science Education) of the University to foster research on problems of science education in developing countries, with the ultimate objective of perfecting materials and techniques designed for improved instruction. The foreign graduate student who comes to the U.S. for study will conduct the research required for an advanced degree in his home country.
>
> The University of Wisconsin representative will cooperate

71

with the science educators in the Arab countries in the conduct of relevant research. The institution of emphasis is to be the Science Education Center at the American University of Beirut.

The appointed University of Wisconsin faculty member will spend approximately 30 days per year working with science educators and graduate students in the Arab countries on the establishment and/or conduct of research and development activities and in identifying students who could accept the noted fellowships. It is presently envisioned that this activity would extend from the Science Teaching Center at the American University of Beirut. Cooperation with the personnel in the Science Teaching Center at the AUB has been assured.

The research activities envisioned would relate primarily to the teaching of science in the individual Arab countries—curriculum development, concept attainment, evaluation, elementary school science, general levels of scientific literacy, et. In some cases there would be studies involving the replication of studies in the U.S. [and] in the Arab countries and vice versa.[23]

In response to these proposals, the Foundation extended the special training program at Wisconsin for an additional six years. At the present time (1974) Murad Jurdak, a Lebanese mathematics teacher from the AUB/SMEC staff, is completing his doctoral program at Wisconsin. A team of six science educators from the United Arab Republic is also there pursuing their study of science education under Pella's general guidance.

8.   *AUB/SMEC begins its service to Lebanon and the other*
       Arab Countries of the Middle East.

From 1969 to the present, AUB/SMEC staff have been contributing to science education improvement along four major lines of endeavour:

Teacher education:

Curriculum development;

Research in education; and

Service to the community—Lebanon and the other Arab countries of the Middle East.

In 1971, Wadih Haddad and his colleague, Victor Billah, went to Jordan as Consultants of the Ford Foundation to study the technical aspects and quality of a large in-service training programme there under the auspices of the Jordanian Ministry of Education. That program was being conducted by the Ministry with financial help from UNICEF and was based at the "Certification and In-Service Teacher Training Institute" (CITTI) in Amman. It was attempting to upgrade over 4,000 certified teachers (80 percent of the entire corps of 6,000 teachers in Jordan). The CITTI program is based on a model that had first been developed by the UNRWA/UNESCO Institute of Education in Beirut for teachers in the Palestinian refugee settlements in the Middle East. In that model, supervised self study among teachers allows them to remain on the job in their classrooms while tutors help them to master the in-service course material.

72

Following their consultant mission in Jordan, Haddad and Billah prepared a report to the Ford Foundation in which they recommended that CITTI tutors themselves be upgraded through appropriate graduate-level study. They also recommended that the CITTI Curriculum be revised and that a unit be organized in CITTI that could carry on continuous evaluation of the work being done with teachers.

On the basis of these recommendations, the Ford Foundation then awarded a grant of $172,000 to the Jordanian government for improvements to the CITTI program. The grant specified SMEC and the English Language Institute of the American University of Cairo (ELI of AUC) as principal sources of assistance to CITTI:

> The grant is designed to improve the quality of the science and mathematics and the English language elements of a comprehensive in-service teacher training program now underway in Jordan with major UNICEF support. The funds requested would be used to finance service agreements between the Ministry of Eduction in Jordan and two Foundation-supported education centers in Lebanon and Egypt which specialize respectively in science and mathematics education and in English teaching. The grant would enable these centers to provide technical assistance services to the government, and would also be used to cover the costs of three specialized institutes and seminars to be operated by the centers plus equipment necessary for these special programs.
>
> The in-service model which is being introduced was pioneered by UNESCO/UNWRA in Palestinian refugee schools and shows promise of meeting the needs of many Middle Eastern countries for improving the quality of elementary and intermediate education. The model is attractive because it enables large numbers of under-qualified teachers to be retrained in little more than two years without having to replace them on the job.
>
> In addition to making an important contribution to the quality of this program, a major Foundation objective is to strengthen the two specialized centers; the Science and Mathematics Education Center (SMEC) at the American University of Beirut and the English Language Institute (ELI) at the American University in Cairo, in order to increase their ability to serve.
>
> A program of assistance was worked out by both organizations and approved by the government. Under these arrangements, SMEC would provide extensive consulting and technical assistance services in science and mathematics, both to the in-service program and to CITTI itself, supervise staff training programs, and help plan and install a model science laboratory and workshop at CITTI and train the professional and technical staff in its use. The laboratory concept grew out of the SMEC evaluation and had thus not been included in the government's established budget for the program. Agreeing with SMEC as to the importance of this component, the Middle East office proposes to include the necessary equipment in this grant action.
>
> AUB and AUC recognize the need to become more service-oriented: this project offers both institutions an opportunity to

build a reputation of concern for, and of competence to deal with, educational problems faced by the countries of the Middle East. It encourages a regional approach to problem-solving, and a major interest of the Middle East office in recommending this grant lies in its potential for regional applicatation. The quality of teacher training is a general concern of governments in the area and is a longstanding program interest of the Middle East office. In addition to its Jordan project, UNICEF has already had enquiries or has begun preliminary work on teacher training projects in Syria, the Sudan, and both Yemens. Hence the experience gained by UNICEF, SMEC and ELI in Jordan can be expected to have early application elsewhere in the region.[28]

This first extra-Lebanon service rendered by SMEC alerted the Beirut office of the Ford Foundation to needs within SMEC that would have to be met if it were to take on additional assignments of this kind in other countries of the region. Accordingly, in 1972, as the first three-year grant to SMEC was approaching its termination point, the Beirut office supported SMEC's application for a new grant, writing to the New York office of the Foundation as follows:

The proposed supplement would finance the continued expansion of the work of the Science and Mathematics Education Center (SMEC) at the American University of Beirut. Financed almost entirely by the Foundation when it was established three years ago, SMEC has already built a reputation and developed its services to the point that the proposed Foundation contribution for the next year would amount to less than one-half of SMEC's operating costs.

SMEC has already begun to serve as an important regional resource for the education program of the Foundation's Middle East field office. Two members of its staff served as local consultants to the Foundation in developing an in-service teacher training project in Jordan (720-0348, approved July 13, 1972, for $172,000). $36,283 of this grant will support training of Ministry science and mathematics trainers and supervisors by SMEC staff in Jordan and at AUB, and one man-year of technical assistance from SMEC to the Ministry.

When awarded, this new grant supported additional SMEC service to the region, giving to SMEC an increasing "resource base" character on which science educators in the Middle East could draw. For example, in March 1973, George Za'rour and Victor Billah took on a Ford Foundation consultant mission to the Sudan where they examined the problems and prospects in science education at the request of the Sudanese Ministry of Education. In their report to the Ford Foundation, Za'rour and Billah proposed a long-term program of collaboration between SMEC and the science educators of the Sudan aimed at acquainting the Sudanese leaders with contemporary ideas and practices in curriculum development in the sciences. At the time of this writing (1974), that proposed program has been launched and the first group of science educators from the Sudan have arrived at AUB/SMEC to begin work with its staff in curriculum development tasks.

9.   *The Lebanese Ministry of Education establishes the*
        Centre for Educational Research and Development (CERD)

Not long after he assumed the leadership of SMEC, Waddih Haddad began to show concern for the wider tasks of promoting educational reform in schoolrooms throughout Lebanon. He realized clearly that although AUB/SMEC could serve as a strong and creative center for developing science curriculum materials for schools, it was unable to shoulder the responsibility for disseminating those innovations to Lebanon's 60 secondary schools and 1200 primary schools. Only a program centered in the Ministry of Education itself could achieve that large-scale task. Through his consultant position in the Ministry, Haddad took up the search for appropriate ways to develop such a wider program. Meanwhile, however, SMEC organized and conducted summer institutes in 1970 and 1971, supported in large part by the 1969 Ford Foundation grant of $129,000. Altogether 136 science teachers participated in 1970 and about 2,000 in 1971. But even these achievements fell far short of the goal Haddad had in mind. He began to contemplate a full-scale reorganization of the Lebanese Ministry of Education. Historically, education in Lebanon had been privately financed and operated, mostly by religious communities prominent in the nation's affairs. Even as late as 1960, less than half of the secondary school students attended public schools. Primary education was almost entirely a privately operated service. A change in this situation was gradually occurring, however, as shifts in the Lebanese population structure were bringing more and more pupils into public education. Finally, in 1971, government leaders recognized that public educational structures of the country would have to be reshaped in order to meet the heavy social responsibilities being demanded of them. The newly appointed Minister of Education, Dr. Nejib Abu Haydar, requested Wadih Haddad to head up a task force, responsible only to the Minister, and to prepare recommendations for a reorganization of the Ministry as well as complete overhaul of the entire school curriculum. This request stemmed from work SMEC had done on the intermediate science and mathematics curriculum, and from SMEC efforts to conduct in-service institutes for secondary school teachers in Lebanon. Haddad set up this task force as requested and received minor supporting costs for staff work, supplies, and secretaries from the Ford Foundation in Beirut.

The task force recognized that a major weakness in the structure of the Ministry was its inability to carry on effective, sustained effort in educational research and development. With the concurrence of the Minister, the task force recommended establishment of a Center for Educational Research and Development under the sponsorship of, and financed by, the Ministry, but autonomous in its operation. The Center's responsibilities were to include all matters relating to the Ministry's instructional program, including supervision of both preparatory and in-service training of teachers. Other areas of concern were to be research and planning; curriculum; evaluation of instruction; publications, including textbooks; documentation and statistics; design of educational facilities; and development of educational aids.

On 13 May 1972, Dr. Nejib Abu Haydar appointed Wadih Haddad President of the Center for Educational Research and Development (CERD) which had been established earlier by Presidential Decree No. 2356. The decree gave this public agency, operating directly under the Ministry of National Education, vast and sweeping responsibilities in the educational system: research, educational planning, and recommending the patterns of examinations, teacher training, degree criteria, and textbooks and other teaching materials.

To help launch its research and documentation program, the Ford Foundation awarded CERD a small grant and justified its action as follows:

Haddad is organizing the new Center into three basic sections:

1. A Research Office dealing with educational planning, research, curriculum development, statistics, and the evaluation of examinations.

2. A Facilities and Instructional Materials Office to study and supervise the specifications for school buildings and to develop textbooks, audio-visual aids, and uses of media.

3. A Teacher Training Office to supervise the work of the ten teachers colleges, and to carry on in-service training of teachers, supervisors and school administrators.

Among the first tasks of the Center will be the collection of studies which have been done of aspects of the Lebanese education system, and to analyze the status of the system. The analysis is expected to serve as a basis for educational planning, provide a basic document for researchers in special fields of education, and identify aspects of the system which require deeper study or immediate corrective action.

The study is expected to take a year and to be carried out by the staff of the Center aided by a number of specialized consultants, most of whom can be found in Lebanon. All major elements of the formal education system will be considered, including public and private, pre-school through university, and general, vocational and technical. Educational aims and priorities will be examined, and then the structure, curriculum, teaching methodology, examinations, facilities and management of the system will be described. Estimates of the costs and outputs of various elements of the system will be calculated.

While the Center has had transferred to it the normal budget of the teacher training colleges and a small research section of the Ministry, these funds are inadequate to permit it to undertake a major study this year. The Center has therefore requested one year of assistance from the Foundation to enable it to begin its work in timely fashion. Funds will be more abundantly available to the Center in the next fiscal year which begins in January 1973.[30]

With the creation of CERD, the educational system in Lebanon now possesses a mechanism for channeling the research results and development products from a creative center such as SMEC to all sectors of the nation's educational system—to its schools, teacher training institutions, examination and degree-certifying boards, etc. Haddad hopes that CERD may play a sufficiently comprehensive role in Lebanese education to give that educational system a continuously self-renewing quality, keeping it ever alive to growing and changing learning needs among the Lebanese people.

10. *SMEC stands before a new threshold*

Today, AUB/SMEC itself faces increasingly heavy demands upon its creative capabilities. The Government organization in Lebanon now headed by Wadih Haddad, CERD, through contracts with SMEC, are assigning it a heavy curriculum development load. At the same time, because its its reputation as a center of creative work in science education is spreading throughout the Arab countries of the Middle East, SMEC is constantly under demand to provide consultant services and traineeship opportunities at SMEC and at the AUB Faculty of Education where SMEC staff also serve as instructors.

SMEC's director, George Za'rour, a proven and highly productive reasearch scholar, ponders the consequences, for him and his colleagues, of these rapidly mounting demands upon their time and talent. Realistically, however, he must solve two critical issues before SMEC can effectively serve as a true regional center as first visualized by Milton Pella at the time of his visit to Beirut in 1962. Za'rour must find a secure base of funding for SMEC and its enterprises and he must add other Arabic language speaking specialists in science education to its staff.

REFERENCES

1. Organized in 1960 with Ford Foundation assistance, the National Council for Secondary Educaion brought together educators from the various religious and language groups of Lebanon in programs of benefit to Lebanese schools. The Council actually devoted almost all of its program resources, derived from a $200,000 Ford Foundation grant, to improving science in Lebanese private schools. In addition to organizing summer courses for science teachers, the Council provided science books, audiovisual materials, and laboratory apparatus to private (excluding Maronite) schools throughout Lebanon, and awarded prizes and scholarships to students to encourage the study of science.
2. 1962 Report submitted by Milton Pella to Ford Foundation at close of visit to Middle East under consultant contract 61-371 approved 29 September 1961.
3. Request for Grant Action, dated 26 March 1963 (Ford Foundation, New York).
4. 25 February 1963 letter, Harvey Hall, Ford Foundation, New York, to Hugh Walker, Ford Foundation, Beirut.
5. 11 March 1963 letter, Hugh Walker to Harvey Hall.
6. 19 March 1963 letter quoting the Wisconson request, Harvey Hall to Hugh Walker.
7. 10 April 1963 letter, Harvey Hall to Clark Bloom, the Ford Foundation, Beirut.
8. Request for Grant Action of 26 March 1963.
9. AUB = American University of Beirut.
10. 28 March 1966 letter, Pella to J.M. McDaniel, The Ford Foundation, New York.
11. 8 April 1966 letter, Thomas D. Scott to Clark Bloom, Beirut.
12. Busch remained at Wisconsin with Pella for only one year and then transferred to the Green Bay campus of the University of Wisconsin. Pella has continued to be the only Foundation-supported Wisconsin science educator associated with the special teacher training program.
13. 10 November 1967 letter, Pella to Scott.
14. 19 January 1970 letter, Pella to William T. Irelan, the Ford Foundation, New York.
15. 27 November 1968 draft, "Proposal for the Improvement of Science & Mathematics Teaching."
16. 27 November 1968 draft, "Proposal for the Improvement of Science & Mathematics Teaching."
17. 7 November 1968 Report on Consulting Visit by Clinton D. Cook to Ford Foundation, Beirut.
18. 6 June 1969 Request for Grant out of Appropriation (#ID-424) Ford Foundation, New York.
19. 20 May 1969 Inter-Office Memorandum, Thomas D. Scott to David Bell, Ford Foundation, New York.
20. 1973 Interim Evaluation of "The Regents of the University of Wisconsin, Science Education in Arab countries of the Middle East," by Harvey Hall, Ford Foundation, New York.
21. 15 April 1969, Request for grant out of Appropriation (#ID-393), Ford Foundation, New York.
22. 19 January 1970 report, Milton Pella to William T. Irelan, Ford Foundation, New York.
23. 19 January 1970 report, Milton Pella to William T. Irelan, Ford Foundation, New York.
24. Concise annual reports of AUB/SMEC accomplishments, prepared by its Director are available from AUB/SMEC in Beirut.
25. 8 August 1973 letter, Samir Makzoume of SMEC to Robert H. Maybury.
26. UNRWA - United Nations Relief and Works Agency
27. "Better Teachers", UNESCO Paris (1970)
28. 6 July 1972, Request for Grant out of Appropriation, Ford Foundation, Beirut, to Ford Foundation, New York.
29. 5 September 1972 Request for Grant Action No. ID-1462, Ford Foundation Beirut to Ford Foundation, New York.
30. 4 December 1972 grant letter in response to 20 October 1972 Request for Grant Action No. ID-1525.

THE PHILIPPINES

1.　*Philippine leaders identify needs in science education*

Not long after assuming responsibility for the system of education they had inherited from the former colonial era, Philippine government authorities declared that teaching of science and mathematics should be compulsory in all elementary and secondary schools. That decision, taken in 1957 out of a need to increase the pool of technical manpower in the country, plunged Philippine educators into a morass of difficulties:

> Thousands of unqualified teachers were pressed into service without benefit of pre-training and guidelines for teaching. They taught unprepared students in makeshift rooms and ill-equipped laboratories using sparse and odd collections of instructional materials and facilities. Inevitably, there was confusion, hapless endeavors and tragic errors. But the precipitate enforcement of the program did serve to focus attention on major problems and needs, provoke interest in new ideas, foster the development of favorable attitudes, and promote aggressive action. Since 1957, many activities have been undertaken by public and private agencies for the improvement of the program. Very much, of course, remains to be done.[1]

The gravity of these conditions in the schools drew Philippine educators and scientists into collaboration on projects aimed at improving matters. In 1958, in one of the earliest actions taken, the Secretary of Education set up a National Committee on Science Education to formulate objectives for the teaching of science at all instructional levels and to recommend appropriate remedial steps to upgrade science teaching. The report prepared by that Committee identified the following areas in which improvement efforts were needed:

(a) *Integration of Science with Classroom Instruction.*

(b) *Acquisition of More Science Equipment and Tools.*

(c) *Coordination of Efforts with Other Agencies.*

(d) *Negotiations for a Science Institute for Teachers.*

(e) *National Science Talent Search and Fellowships.*

(f) *Higher Salaries of Science and Mathematics Teachers.*

(g) *Raising the Quality and Contents of Science Textbooks.*

(h) *Promotion of Science Teachers' Competence.*

79

The report recommended two remedial actions:

(1) *Plan for Creation of New Positions for Teachers in Science, Mathematics, and Guidance and Counseling, at Higher Salaries.* To increase the number of teachers qualified to teach science, mathematics, and guidance and counseling, the Department of Education has recommended creation of additional items for such teachers with increase in salary as an inducement. It is more difficult and more expensive for students to major in these subjects.

(2) *Joint Program with National Science Development Board.* Offering in cooperation with the National Science Development Board, vacation refresher and advanced courses in science, physics, and mathematics for secondary school teachers at the University of the Philippines and for elementary school teachers at the Philippine Normal College, to update and upgrade their knowledge and competence.[2]

Supplementing these actions by the Secretary of Education were those taken by the major governmental body for science policy and research, the National Science Development Board (NSDB) to upgrade subject-matter competence of teachers of science and to improve curriculum materials, laboratory equipment and science facilities in schools. The Division of Development Assistance (now the Division of Education and Training) of the NSDB, organized its action along these lines:

(1) Science education surveys.
(2) Science teacher-training programs.
(3) Summer institutes for science teachers.
(4) Upgrading the science teaching in teacher-training institutes.
(5) Regional conferences to orient.
(6) Curriculum development programs.
(7) Training of science and mathematics aides.
(8) Manufacture of school science equipment through the Don Bosco Instrumentation Center.
(9) A TV classroom project.
(10) Science teaching aids for teachers.[3]

In that same year, the UNESCO National Commission of the Philippines, the Asia Foundation, the NSDB, and private commercial groups joined forces in initiating an annual national conference of science teachers of the Philippines, while UNESCO, U.S.A.I.D., and the National Economic Council sponsored a five-year physics teacher-education program at the University of the Philippines. This program brought teachers to the university for a period of advanced study while trainees drawn from graduates of the engineering and science departments of the university took over their classrooms. In the next few years, this program prepared 54 trainees and 118 teachers.

To these initiatives must be added several others that also occurred in that period of ferment. In 1960, the Asia Foundation, the Philippine Steel Manufacturers' Association and the Shell Corporation gave support to a training course at the University that upgraded dozens of chemistry teachers from Philippine schools. The year 1961 marked the formation of the Philippine Association of Science Teachers. Also in that same year the Chairman of NSDB, Dr. Paulino J. Garcia, created an Educational

Mission Committee, which conducted a survey of the status of science teaching in Philippine schools and universities and then toured U.S. classrooms to observe innovative practices there. Through its survey of Philippine schools, this Committee found that: "All the levels of science instruction in the elementary, secondary, and higher education reveal the common lack of the following:

1. Adequate equipment and facilities in the laboratories.
2. Up-to-date and adequate textbooks, publications, and reference materials.
3. Qualified and imaginative teachers.
4. Provision for a systematic upgrading of teachers."[4]

Finally, in 1963, a special committee of the Philippine Senate issued a report on the state of science in the Philippines. Like so many statements by government committees or councils of scientists or educators in developing countries in the 1950's and early 1960's, this report alleged that scientific progress in the country lagged decades behind the U.S., the usual benchmark in the comparisons of that era. The Senate committee report went on to indict the Philippine educational system with its deficiencies as responsible for the lag:

> Our educational system is ineffective as a steady source of competent scientific and technological manpower. Most science teachers lack competence. There is a dearth of qualified teachers in science and mathematics. Science teachers are poorly paid. Laboratory facilities are inadequate. Supply of science textbooks and references is deficient. Private school officials say our educational system is regimented. Only a few universities are doing scientific researches.[5]

2. *Delores Hernandez establishes the Philippine BSCS Adaptation Project*

Into this general scene of activity in science education came a young Philippine science educator, Delores Hernandez, fresh from her doctoral studies in the United States (Indiana University). She at once decided to organize a program for the biology teachers in the Philippines. She obtained a small grant from NSDB and organized the BSCS[6] Adaptation Project at the College of Education of the University of the Philippines, with these aims:

a. To develop science interest and awareness among the people so that they can appreciate its value in their daily lives and in the economic progress of the country.
b. To imbue the average citizen with the basic knowledge and attitudes on science so that he can think and act in accordance with the principles of science.
c. To produce sufficient manpower resources from which to draw future science educators, scientific researchers, and technicians.[7]

The Dean of the College of Education, Dr. Alfredo Morales, supported her request to the Bureau of Public Schools (a division of the Ministry of Education) to draw biology teachers from ten schools into active participation in the project. School principals responded with dramatic enthusiasm to the Bureau's invitation. They not only designated biology teachers to participate, but set aside space in their schools to serve as laboratories for their teachers.

Soon after the project began, the national director of the BSCS in the USA, Dr. Arnold Grobman, visited the Philippines to observe the work being carried out by Delores Hernandez and these ten teachers in adapting the BSCS materials. A measure of his high opinion of the group is the fact that shortly after his visit, he sent a complete set of the BSCS materials to the group and invited two of its members, Delores Hernandez and Luz Sangalang of the Bureau of Public Schools, to come to BSCS headquarters in Colorado where they could observe adaptation procedures as practiced there.

This BSCS Adaptation Project worked throughout 1962 and 1963 in adapting the Green Version of the BSCS laboratory manual and teacher's guide to Philippine specifications. One member of the BSCS staff in Colorado, Dr. Victor Larsen, then came to Manila in 1963, under an Asia Foundation grant, to assist the group for a six months period. The BSCS headquarters also donated 1,600 copies of the BSCS Green Version textbook to the group to enable them to begin experimental teaching in pilot schools. Following this trial use of the materials in the schools, the Adaptation Project completed a Philippine version of BSCS in 1964.

3.   *The Ford Foundation awards a grant to support science*
      education improvement in the Philippines

The first representative of the Ford Foundation in the Philippines, Dr. Harry Case, took up his residence there in 1964. One of the first problem areas to which he turned was that of Philippine education. Its grave needs convinced him to direct an important part of the Ford Foundation program to meeting them. To formulate a suitable program of educational assistance to meeting those needs, he retained the services of Dr. John C. Warner, President of Carnegie Institute of Technology in Pittsburgh (USA) as a consultant. After many months of interviewing educators, scientists, and government officials, and observing schools and universities, Dr. Warner prepared a report for the Ford Foundation, entitled: "The Teaching of Science and Mathematics in the Elementary and Secondary Schools of the Philippines." He listed recommendations for a program of assistance under these headings:

I.   Curriculum and Course Development
II-A.   Introduction of the new courses into the schools
II-B.   Upgrading the present teachers so they are competent to teach the new courses
II-C.   Preparation of the TV Version
II-D.   Modernization of curricula for training elementary school teachers and for training science and mathematics teachers for the high schools[8]

Warner's visits to schools and universities had familiarized him well with the many ongoing projects for improving science education in the Philippines. Consequently, he was able to counsel that:

> Study groups would not need to start from scratch. Indeed, we should expect study groups to take full advantage of everything which has already been done in the Philippines and in other countries. For example, in designing math and science for the elementary schools, full advantage should be taken of the work already done by the Philippine Normal College and by the Textbook Project for which US-AID had provided paper. In courses for the high schools full advantage should be taken of the extensive work

on mathematics, biology, chemistry and physics courses done in the United States, on the work already done on some of these courses in the Philippines, and on the materials for high school science included in the Textbook Project. My best suggestion at present is that the elementary school curriculum and course development job should be done by the Philippine Normal College.... In my opinion, the high school curriculum and course development job should be done by the University of the Philippines. I believe their idea of doing it by setting up a "Curriculum Development Center" is a good one from the standpoint of getting people from various area or disciplines to join in the project.[9]

The "Curriculum Development Center" to which he referred was an idea that had only recently been submitted to the Ford Foundation by the University of the Philippines in a paper entitled, "Proposal to Establish a Science Teaching Project."

That proposal referred to the many institutes, seminars, and conferences already in progress, but went on to say that:

The present efforts are very modest and proceed for the most part as assisted projects designed for specific or special purposes, or as isolated activities of different units, particularly the Graduate College of Education and the Division of the Natural Sciences. The University now considers it important and urgent to devote more vigorous effort to the improvement of the science teaching program of the country, and proposes to expand and enlarge the present activities.[10]

The proposal differentiated sharply between attempts to solve large, quantity needs in the educational system and the responsibility (largely the University's) to ensure quality in education by training leadership and developing suitable instructional materials for schools:

In the improvement and reform of science teaching of the country, the University does not propose to undertake the training of large numbers of student teachers and teachers in the field, or to conduct studies on the administration of the program. Rather, the University can best meet its obligation and produce significant results with maximum impact [by] producing graduates who can provide leadership and furnishing the educational authorities, teachers, teacher's schools, and other entities with suitable instructional materials, tools, models and examples of good teaching practice.[11]

It set forth objectives of the proposed Center, limiting them carefully to efforts to improve the quality dimension in science education:

1. the need for responsible definitions of the subject matter to be taught to science teachers and of the contents of science courses at various levels; and
2. the need to put instruction on a sound basis suited to local conditions and resources by providing materials and tools prepared from local materials as much as possible, in sufficient quantity at moderate cost, and of acceptable standards

to guarantee the quality of the teaching and learning processes.[12]

Finally, the proposal outlined the part to be played by the University in improving quality in science education:

1. Preparation of guidelines and handbooks for science teachers.
2. Development of textbooks, experimental manuals, and other teaching aids.
3. Design and construction of apparatus, equipment and other facilities and teaching aids, and the preparation of blueprints or instruction manuals so the items can be fabricated or improvised by schools or industrial shops.
4. Strengthening of the science teacher training program of the Graduate College of Education at the undergraduate and graduate levels.
5. Conduct of germane research and development work directed to the improvement of the science curricula for all grades, the formulation of more precise evaluation methods, the conduct of experimental programs, and the demonstration of pedagogical devices, methods and practices.[13]

In August 1965, the President of the University of the Philippines, Carlos P. Romulo, submitted a formal request for a grant to the Ford Foundation, outlining the items for which support was desired:

Specifically, our request is for operational and staffing costs of the Center; for provision of one foreign advisor for a two-year period and for consultants in the specialized scientific fields; for fellowships for the advanced training of science teachers and supervisors; and for essential equipment and books for the Center.[14]

The Ford Foundation office in Manila then prepared the customary formal Foundation document, the Request for Grant Action (RGA), which describes the proposed project and justifies the Foundation aid to the Philippines, and on the materials for high school science included in the Textbook Project.

In the Request for Grant Action pertaining to the Philippine Science Teaching Center, Harry Case wrote:

The University proposes to create a science teaching center with a full-time administrative and technical staff which would be empowered to organize work groups composed of educational and scientific personnel within the University, Department of Education, Philippine Normal College, resource persons from other agencies and selected teachers from public and private schools to carry out curriculum development and materials preparation projects.

Foundation assistance at this time would be a critical factor in enabling the University to bring together quickly the necessary resource personnel and in making possible the flexibility required in the collaboration and coordination among the various participating governmental and private educational bodies. The available talent will have to be assembled and organized into working teams in each of the major project areas: elementary science, physics, chemistry, biology and mathematics. This would be the responsibility of the center's small staff, composed of a director at the level of professor and two associates at assistant professor or instructor level.[15]

Case commended the Philippine leaders for the remarkable degree of cooperation he observed among the many groups playing a part in the establishment of the Science Teaching Center:

In my earlier communication with you, I suggested that this proposal would be an interagency one. This is true in part in that it will call for collaboration among a number of agencies and for enlisting the services of personnel from various sources to collaborate on the project. However, the grant, as you will see, is directed to the UP only. We have been very gratified to find a very good spirit of cooperation among the educational agencies here who would be participating in this program. I should add that the programs in educational television and science teaching should be mutually helpful.

We have also been impressed with the quality of the people who have been working on this proposal and who will be involved in its execution. Dr. Hernandez, who will head up this Center, is very impressive as is Dr. Augusto Tenmatay, the head of the Division of Natural Sciences at the UP. Dean Morales of the College of Education, who is also deeply involved in the project, is a very strong person.[16]

The Ford Foundation awarded the grant to the University of the Philippines on 25 September 1964, providing $310,000 over a two-year period for the Science Teaching Center. The principal provisions of the grant were the following:

Adviser (2 man-years)	$60,000
Consultants (8 man-months)	28,000
Compensation of participants and staff	80,000
Operating expenses (including leasing and leasehold improvements, clerical help, supplies and internal travel)	23,000
Books, journals, working materials	30,000
Equipment and apparatus	25,000
Publication	20,000
Fellowships abroad (4 man-years)	24,000
Regional workshops (honoraria, travel and per diem)	10,000
Travel abroad (professional staff)	10,000
	$310,000

4. *Organization of the Science Education Center*

Upon receipt of the grant from the Ford Foundation, University of the Philippines President, Carlos Romulo, took the following steps to create the Science Teaching Center:

(a) He appointed Delores Hernandez as Director, following the recommendation of Alfredo Morales, Dean of the College of Education and Augusto Tenmatay, Acting Director, Office of Institutional Research;

(b) He allocated space to the Center: several offices and a small room for a library located in the College of Education;

(c) He left open the question of whether it would be a permanent independent agency, or ultimately be absorbed more directly into the regular university structure. Later, however, in 1966 when he again applied to the Ford Foundation for a second grant for the Science Teaching Center, he unhesitatingly assigned the Center a permanent place in the University:

> The establishment of the Center as a permanent unit of the University has been my intention since the inception of the project. This view has been strengthened by my experience as Secretary of Education.[17]

On assuming her position as Director of the Science Teaching Center, Delores Hernandez set about at once to organize[18] a staff and create advisory, administrative, and working groups. These included the following:

(a) *Curriculum Committee:*

Five faculty members from the Faculty of Arts and Sciences and the College of Education. Within six months these individuals became the full-time chairmen of the Work Groups (see below).

(b) *Steering Committee:*

Organized primarily to assist the Director in the administration of the Center, committee membership included: Alfredo Morales, Dean of the College of Education; Dr. Liseria B. Soriano, Bureau of Public Schools; Dr. Augusto Tenmatay, Head of the Division of Natural Sciences; and Dr. Enrique T. Virata, Vice President of the University of the Philippines.

(c) *Advisory Board:*

Representing a wide range of institutions in the country interested in improving science education, the Board included representatives of the University, the Bureau of Public Schools, NSDB, Bureau of Private Schools, and religious educational organizations.

(d) *Work Groups:*

With the major function to produce curriculum materials in science and mathematics for primary and secondary schools, the Work Groups drew together individuals from a large and varied number of institutions: experienced teachers and subject specialists of schools, colleges and universities—both public and private. As Work Group chairmen, five University of the Philippines faculty members were responsible for organizing the groups, supervising and aiding development of curriculum material and building consultant links to the specialists in their own departments. These five were:

Biology .... Professor Consuelo V. Asis
Chemistry .... Professor Pilar Da Silva
Physics .... Professor Segundo V. Roxas
Mathematics .... Professor Josefina C. Fonacier
General Science .... Professor Porfirio P. Jesuitas

One of the first activities of the Curriculum and Steering committees was to familiarize themselves with science curriculum materials from major centers abroad.

After a period of study focused on these outside materials, these committees prepared guidelines and schedules for the curriculum materials that were to be written by the Philippine Work Groups. The Steering Committee also served as a review committee of the output from the Work Groups, formulating the following overall directives to guide their writing:

(1) The tentative outlines of the chairmen of the Work Groups [should] tie up with the Bureau of Public Schools curricula.

(2) The course content of proposed materials [should] stress the spirit of inquiry while at the same time give essential information a citizen needed to know.

(3) Conservation of resources [should] be stressed throughout from grade one to fourth year high school.

(4) The materials [should] consider the needs of students for whom a particular grade becomes terminal.

(5) The applied parts of mathematics and the science courses [should] not constitute separate courses.

(6) Applications [should] not follow mechanically.[19]

To enable the Work Groups to turn out a large volume of writing on a tight schedule, the Steering Committee assigned a large number of individuals to the Work Groups. By June 1965, over 100 writers from 21 different schools and other organizations were actively writing manuscript under the guidance of the Work Group chairmen. Contracts signed between the writers and the Center specified writing guidelines, set firm deadlines, and fixed terms of compensation.

The Advisory Board, a widely representative group of Filipino scientists, educators, and public figures, convened for the first time in May, 1965. It gave an overall review to manuscripts previously approved by the Steering Committee. Its eleven members represented a wide range of agencies, including:

The Department of Education (Bureau of Public Schools)
The Department of Education (Bureau of Private Schools)
The Association of Christian Schools and Colleges
The National Science Development Board
The Catholic Education Association of the Philippines
State Normal Colleges
Philippine Association of Colleges and Universities

By involving many different agencies this way, the Advisory Board brought a broad spectrum of ideas to the Center's work on improving the teaching of science. It also ensured wide acceptance and use of the curriculum materials to be produced.

An important provision of the Ford Foundation grant to the University was for a science education adviser to the Center. Accordingly, upon award of the grant, the New York office of the Ford Foundation began a search for a suitable individual to serve in this capacity. Robert Ward, a professor of physics at Williams College in Massachusetts and a consultant to the AAAS[20] primary science curriculum project, accepted the Foundation's invitation to serve as this adviser to the Philippine Center. Before going to Manila, he visited many science curriculum projects in the United States in order to establish working links between them and the Philippine project.

5.   *The UPSEC prepares its first innovations*

With the appointment of permanent staff, Work Group writers and committee members, the Science Teaching Center entered on its first full year of operations. At the end of that first year, (1965), Delores Hernandez reported the chief accomplishments of the Center under the headings: Organization and Administration, Production, Physical Plant, Library and Teaching Aids, and Extension Work and Participation Outside U.P.

Under the first heading, Organization and Administration, she wrote:

> The Science Teaching Center was organized to develop and produce curriculum materials in science and mathematics for elementary and secondary schools. This constitutes the major goal for the first two years of the project.
>
> An interdisciplinary approach has been adopted in the organization of the three committees who have overall responsibility for the production of curriculum materials: Advisory Board, Steering Committee and Work Groups.[21]

Under the heading, Production, she reported in detail on the output to date from the Work Groups:

> Twenty-three detailed outlines have been developed for elementary and secondary courses in Science and Mathematics, as follows:
>
> Elementary Science . . . . 6 outlines
> General Science . . . . 2 outlines
> Elementary Mathematics . . . . . . 6 outlines
> High School Mathematics . . . . . . 4 outlines
> Biology . . . . 3 outlines
> Physics . . . . 1 outline
> Chemistry . . . . 1 outline
>
> Development of the foregoing outlines into manuscripts for textbooks, laboratory manuals, and teacher's guides will be accomplished by the writers of each Work Group. Success of the project depends primarily on the quality of manuscripts produced. The Work Groups are the most important members of the organization. This is the reason for the rigorous care exercised in their selection.
>
> It is anticipated that about 40 volumes comprising textbooks, teacher's guides and laboratory manuals will be developed out of the outlines. To date about a fourth of the total number of manuscripts expected have been received. Before being accepted, all manuscripts undergo no less than two, three, or even more revisions to insure quality. It is a difficult task involving searching analysis to determine adequate coverage and unity, accuracy, and pedagogical soundness.
>
> To secure a wider and more significant range of judgment, a meeting was held with 27 elementary school teachers from 5 nearby provinces (besides those from Manila and Quezon City) selected to represent different types of schools according to size: large central (regional) schools, city schools, rural schools (big

town, smaller towns, and barrios), and according to type: complete primary schools (I-IV), complete elementary schools (I-VI). They read all the sample manuscripts, and were asked to respond to a questionnaire prepared by Dr. Ward.

It was felt that the reaction of teachers from different types of schools and different provinces would provide the Science Teaching Center staff with useful information and fresh insights which could be passed on to the writers.[22]

By policy, the Science Teaching Center limited itself, during its first two years of existence, almost exclusively to work on curriculum development and adaptation of selected U.S. science curriculum materials. Hence the second annual report submitted by Delores Hernandez also showed this concentration of effort:

During the period under review major efforts of the Science Teaching Center staff have been directed towards the achievement of the immediate objectives of the project—production of curriculum materials in science and mathematics for secondary and elementary schools.

Production of the manuscripts. About 50% of the materials for elementary mathematics, grades 2 to 6, and about 60% of the materials for geometry and third year algebra have been organized.

In chemistry, most of the materials (textbook and laboratory guide are combined) have undergone revision—out of a total of 20 chapters, 17 have been revised.

In physics, 20 chapters of a total of 24 have been mimeographed or are being mimeographed for the feasibility classes. The other 4 chapters have been received and are undergoing revision. The teacher's guide lags a bit behind the text. Fourteen chapters are ready for mimeographing, 5 chapters are being revised, and 5 chapters have not yet been submitted. The Physics Work Group contemplates having a total of 22 experiments in the Laboratory Manual. Of these, 12 have been completed, 8 are being revised, and 2 have still to be written.

In biology, the volume *The Gene Concept* has undergone final editing by the consultant-editor, Dr. C. Lawson, and awaits final planning of format and layout before it undergoes typing for offset printing. The volume *Common Plants of the Philippines* is being prepared for final editing by Dr. J. Beaman of Michigan State University.

The outlines for Elementary School Science, grades I to VI, have undergone revision to incorporate suggestions of Dr. C. Lawson (for the biological science part) and of Dr. J. DeRose (for the physical science part). The resulting outlines emphasize the conceptual schemes involved and suggest a better balance of physical and biological science activities. Further work on the outlines has also made it possible to indicate clearly the science processes involved which are to be developed in particular sections.

The outlines for High School Science I and II were similarly revised. Production of manuscripts based on the new outlines is now proceeding. A few manuscripts have been received and revised.[23]

Consultants from abroad made important contributions to the project in that first two-year period. The Foundation officers in Manila and New York assisted Robert Ward to identify consultants who could meet the precise requirements suggested by the writers in the Work Groups. Those who came to Manila in 1966 included the following:

Dr. J. Arthur Campbell: June 13 to July 2
Consultant in high school chemistry, CHEM Study[24]
(Harvey Mudd College, Claremont, California)

Dr. Charles Brumfiel: July 10 to August 6
Consultant in mathematics, SMSG[24]
(University of Michigan)

Dr. J. Chalmer Roy: July 23 to August 27
Consultant in earth science, ESCP[24]
(Iowa State University)

Dr. Chester Lawson: 4 weeks in September
Consultant in biology and elementary science, SCIS[24]
(Michigan State University)

Dr. James De Rose: October 3 to November 4
Consultant in elementary science
(Marple-Newtown Joint Schools, Newtown Square, Penna.)[25]

Some idea of the significant contribution that these consultants had made to the work of the Science Teaching Center can be gained from the following extract of a report by one of them:

It was possible to visit several schools and talk to many teachers in my weeks here. In addition, I presented two lectures to teacher groups on two of the Saturdays of my stay. Philippine elementary teachers have generally from 40 to 50 students in a class. Children are attentive and docile. Every teacher is a teacher of English, and sometimes more attention is put upon pronunciation and sentence structure than upon concepts. Some teachers are very good, but most have weak preparation by States' standards.

During the period of my stay here, I was able to read and write detailed comments upon all materials in high school mathematics prepared by the Science Teaching Center.

These high school materials are patterned after the study group textbooks (particularly S.M.S.G.). The material in geometry parallels quite closely one of our better new geometry texts in the States. It is well-written, uniform material, and it should be possible to complete this geometry text with very little consultant help.

The materials in algebra are a little uneven—reflecting the fact that several writers have participated in the writing of algebra material. Some of the algebra material is quite good, but some falls into several of the standard errors found in all of our traditional texts in the States, and a few superficially "modern" texts. It would be well if someone competent could make a final reading of the algebra chapters.

The arithmetic of H.S. I and II can probably be satisfactorily revised on the basis of my criticisms. I feel that Professor Josefina Fonacier is thoroughly competent to supervise the changes that should be made here.

In general these high school texts represent a considerable forward step in curriculum development in the Philippines.[26]

Brumfiel was particularly observant of learning difficulties exhibited among Filipino children:

One basic weakness, and one impossible to remedy, is that many of the new ideas that have been introduced into School Mathematics in recent years are only superficially treated. What stands out, and what will certainly be emphasized by teachers, is the new *terminology* rather than the new *concepts*. There often occurs in the writing an introduction of powerful ideas, but then these ideas are not treated in such a way that their ability to unify mathematics is made clear. There will still be much emphasis upon rote memorization as these texts are used. Students will pass through this material and will obtain little understanding of the concept that *proofs* can be organized in arithmetic and algebra as well as in geometry.

But the more sophisticated approach necessary to give students a deep understanding of the structure of mathematics does not seem to be suitable for Philippine schools at this time. These texts will serve well their intended purpose and will begin to move mathematics teaching in the proper direction.

I understand that the task of arranging for these texts to be used in a wide variety of schools may be difficult. The Ford Foundation should stand ready to encourage the use of these materials. Writing the books has been good training for the staff. But the books deserve to be used. Indeed, it is most unfortunate that arrangements have not been made for these materials to be taught under conditions controlled by the Science Teaching Center. Perhaps the allocation of some funds to facilitate experimental teaching of these texts is in order. I see many rough spots in the texts that can only be ironed out by teaching the material and carefully observing this teaching.[27]

A most important date for the Science Teaching Center was July 1966, when a series of "feasibility studies" with materials ready for tryout in school classes began. Participating in the program were the U.P. Elementary School, U.P. High School, San Francisco High School, and Manuel L. Quezon High School. These small-scale tryouts enabled the work groups to prepare manuscripts for the future experimental editions. The tryouts allowed the groups to perfect format presentation, workability of certain lessons, etc. The tryouts were not an attempt to evaluate the materials in an organized manner, although they did give the Center staff an opportunity to reach informal judgments on the pedagogical promise of the materials.

6.   *UPSEC seeks an extension of the Ford Foundation grant*

In mid-1966, with the first two-year period of Ford Foundation support drawing to a close, the Steering Committee opened negotiations with the Ford Foundation on the subject of extending the grant for an additional period of three years. The resident consultant, Robert Ward, assisted the Steering Committee during these negotiations in many useful ways. For example, he was able to explain to them the Foundation's policies on grants. During those negotiations, Delores Hernandez took the occasion to outline to the Foundation two new areas, in addition to curriculum development, for which she sought support; first, staff development through short-term and long-term training; and second, a thoroughgoing evaluation of the work and products of the Science Teaching Center.

To promote staff development at the center, she requested funds for two kinds of travel and residence abroad: short-duration trips by staff members seeking some specific information or wishing to acquire a particular skill; and year-long (or longer) study grants for staff desiring to earn advanced degrees in fields related to the work of the Center.

Her request for these funds reflected the great weight that Delores Hernandez consistently placed on staff development for these project across the years. Thus she could write in mid-1966:

> During the year under review the Center continued its policy of a strong development faculty program for its staff. Among the accomplishments in this area are:
>
> A. Degree program completed
>   1 M.A.
> B. Ongoing programs
>   3 PH.D.s
>   1 apprenticeship in art and publication
> C. Scheduled for early AY 1972
>   2 short term on Ford Foundation
>   3 short term on UNESCO-UNDP
> D. Requested for the near future
>   5 degree and short term fellowships —
>   Australian government
>   9 degree and short term fellowships — UNDP[28]

The second new activity introduced by Delores Hernandez into those 1966 negotiations with the Ford Foundation, was evaluation of the Center's educational materials. She described this as follows:

> A small scale trial run of those materials which are ready will be made this school year, starting July 1966. This will involve only 1 or 2 teachers per course and one class per teacher. The purposes of this small-scale tryout (feasibility study) are: to determine the workability of the materials in actual classroom situation, to help get them in shape for printing (experimental editions), and to give the S.T.C. staff ideas and some experience which will be valuable in planning the forthcoming two-year evaluation program.
>
> The evaluation program will run for two years. To help the Center plan and run its evaluation program, the services of a chairman for evaluation and a full-time assistant will be secured.

The evaluation program will mainly involve securing teacher reactions to the materials, observing the experimental classes, and testing the students. The latter procedure may include both testing children's achievement through teacher made tests, and testing children's growth in the development of objectives through evaluative measures prepared by the evaluation committee.

About ten teachers (from public and private schools in different parts of the country) will be selected to try out the physics and chemistry books, each teacher teaching two experimental classes. The other courses will be tried by four or five teachers (per course). Summer institutes, supported locally, will be organized to orient these teachers and to acquaint them with the new materials.

During the evaluation period some rewriting will be done on the basis of feedback received from the evaluation. During this period and, perhaps during the third year, a number of consultants will be invited to do some editorial work as well as to suggest ways of improving both presentation and content of the materials.

A total of about 100 teachers and 10,000 students will be involved in trying out the materials throughout the two-year evaluation period.

The teachers will have to be oriented before they use the materials; this can be accomplished through summer institutes which it is hoped will be partially supported by the N.S.D.B. In addition, there will be frequent meetings between the S.T.C. staff and the experimental teachers. Regional conferences with experimental teachers in a particular region will have to be organized. To be able to do all these, the S.T.C. staff will do more traveling than has been the case in the first two years of the project.[29]

These negotiations eventually reached a point of general agreement between the Ford Foundation office in Manila and the Science Teaching Center. At that moment, a draft proposal or request for an extension to the grant was drawn up and submitted to the Foundation under a covering letter from Carlos P. Romulo, President of the University of the Philippines. That letter is remarkable in its reference to the long range hope felt by the staff of the Center and Romulo himself that "the Center should continue as a permanent unit after the Ford Foundation grant now being requested is terminated."

The Ford Foundation office in Manila again prepared a Request for Grant Action, describing the additional program components suggested by Delores Hernandez and justifying Ford Foundation support over an additional three-year period:

Training
In the two years that the center has been in operation, two candidates for training to the Ph. D. level have been identified and several candidates for training to the masters are available for the two positions to be filled. In addition, funds are requested

for special training for three writers and travel and observation abroad by the directing staff.

Evaluation Program

The experimental editions of the students' textbooks and teachers' guides will for the most part be ready for production by the end of 1966 and for testing in July 1967. Funds are requested to cover the cost of publishing experimental editions of texts and teachers' guides for 20 courses which would each be tested by about five teachers with 100 students, thus involving 100 teachers and 10,000 students in the total trial program.

Throughout the evaluation and at its conclusion, the results would be used to provide guidelines for the revision of the materials. As these results come in, additional consultants would be invited to assist with the rewriting, and to suggest ways of improving the presentation and content of the materials.

The full-time adviser to the project is requested for two years of the three-year period. In the final year outside assistance would be limited to the use of consultants.[30]

This Request for Grant Action triggered exchange of views among the Foundation officers on the subject of the Foundation's policy regarding short-term and long-term support to projects. In particular, New York officers asked Harry Case in Manila to clarify his position on long-term support to the Center:

We understand that the proposed three-year extension would complete the original objectives of the grant and of the Center, and in that sense support for this would be terminal. Do you mean to indicate, however, that there is no possibility that the Science Teaching Center would look to the Foundation for any kind of assistance in the future, especially of the "institutionalizing" type? Perhaps it would be wise to leave the door ajar considering the interest in science education in the Philippines.[31]

In replying to his colleagues, Case reassured them that he would indeed keep the door open on longer-term assistance to the Center:

This supplement is intended to provide support during the final phase of materials production. As President Romulo noted in his letter, a continuing role for the Science Teaching Center is being actively considered by the University of the Philippines. The question is not whether there will be a Science Teaching Center, but rather what form it would take and what functions it would perform. We certainly do wish to keep the door ajar, and do desire to stand ready to assist worthwhile new undertakings of the Center. The form and functions must be designed by responsible Filipino educational leaders, and we continue to work in close contact with them directly and through the director and advisor, Robert Ward, at the Center.[32]

On 30 September 1966, the Ford Foundation sent a grant notification letter to President Romulo, awarding a sum of $265,000 to the University of the Philippines to continue assistance to the Science Teaching Center for an additional three-year period.

With that grant in hand, the Science Teaching Center initiated the evaluation program almost at once.

7.　　*UPSEC sets up a long-term evaluation program*

To give leadership to the evaluation program, UPSEC appointed an educational psychologist, Dr. Aurora Minoza, as Chairman of its Evaluation Committee. In that capacity, she conducted a series of weekly meetings to orient the Work Group chairmen to evaluation procedures. Following this orientation they then prepared behavioral objectives and test items for evaluation in each discipline. Finally, the group laid out a plan for the evaluation program that would start in July 1967 as follows:

(1)　observations and visitation of experimental classes by STC staff;

(2)　secure feedback, both written and oral from the teachers;

(3)　secure reaction of the children in experimental classes;

(4)　test achievement of the students.

Central to the evaluation plan were the experimental classes in selected public and private schools. The teachers in these classes received orientation to the new materials and to the evaluation program through summer institutes conducted in 1967 and 1968 under the auspices of the NSDB.

The outcome of the first stage of the evaluation program with the curriculum materials in the trial schools was unfortunately less conclusive than had been expected:

> To the subject chairmen, therefore, who are responsible for curriculum development, the most important and useful parts of evaluation were the feedback and the analysis of student performance on achievement tests which were analyzed in terms of their implications to development and improvement of the materials.
>
> How efficacious are the SEC curricular materials for instructional purposes? This general problem has been resolved through finding answers to the following specific questions:
>
> 1. Do the SEC curricular materials enable pupils to gain significant growth in attaining such objectives as acquisition of concepts and development of skills in thinking processes?
>
> 2. What is the consumers' attitude toward these materials? Consumers refer to the administrators, supervisors, teachers and pupils who are to directly or indirectly use the materials.
>
> 3. What area(s) and aspect(s) of the curricular materials need revision in terms of (a) level of language used, (b) concept presentation, (c) application of principles, (d) use of visual aids, and (e) manipulative activities and exercises and evaluation techniques used to determine pupils' subject achievement?
>
> 4. What is the quality of the SEC-developed tests?
>
> 5. How do the SEC participating teachers measure in personality traits considered important for teacher effectiveness?

While the research hypothesis (that the experimental classes in which SEC materials and methods were used would show better learning results in terms of processes and concepts than the control classes) *couldn't be definitely held as established*, nevertheless, the trend in which the pupils' gains within the experimental classes were generally higher than those of the control classes allows for a tentative statement that the SEC materials and methods are effective in meeting the Center's objectives.[33]

These initial difficulties failed to discourage the Evaluation Committee, however, for two years later it repeated its attempts to evaluate the materials, using improved and modified tests and questionnaires. But again it was unable to demonstrate that the Science Teaching Center's materials were more successful than traditional materials. Nevertheless its report declared that the evaluation effort had at least benefitted the writing groups by alerting them to weaknesses in the materials:

Since this year's evaluation is the second tryout of SEC materials in specific subject areas, reconsideration of findings, especially the teacher recommendations, will help in revision of materials before final printing. Reassessment of these materials may for instance, give further explanations of the tendency for scores to cluster around 50%, instead of their being raised to 75% or above after another year of using the materials. Likewise, the tendency for scores to be lower with the second and third achievement tests may be corrected so that better results may be expected in the later use of these materials.

Feedback from the field(verbal) suggests strongly that UPSEC books, especially those on the high school level, are too abstract/too difficult/remote from current technology/have too high a vocabulary level. While there may be much truth in these criticisms, such feedback gives no specific information for action. Hence, it is recommended that staff and graduate students be encouraged to undertake studies which will provide specific information about the UPSEC materials.[34]

8. *The Philippine government places the Science Teaching Center on a firm statutory foundation*

The Science Teaching Center (STC) moved nearer to becoming an established component of the Philippine educational system after receiving the second Ford Foundation grant. One evidence of its stronger position was the increasing number of calls upon the Center to supply educational services: the NSDB called upon it to conduct conferences and seminars for science teachers; The University of the Philippines asked it to carry on the Physics teacher training program and the Shell Chemistry teacher program, and the Bureau of Public Schools requested it to prepare teachers' guides in mathematics for the public schools.

In keeping with this growing stature, the STC Steering Committee recognized a need to put the institutional and financial positions of the Center on a longer-term footing. Accordingly, in late 1966, that Committee opened a series of deliberations on these issues:

In the seventy-eighth meeting, 9 November 1966, the Director (D.H.) first informed the Steering Committee about a planned financial aid for STC as a permanent unit of the University of the Philippines. Attorney Perfecto Fernandez was to draft a bill to secure Congressional assistance for the STC.

In preparing the draft, the functions of STC in the future have to be laid out. The attorney suggested that if STC could demonstrate a wider impact on the country as a whole, it would be easier to secure financial aid. He also suggested a program of scholarships for teachers from different provinces as well as for undergraduate students.

Dr. Tenmatay commented that the function of STC would be mainly research and extension work. In the future STC hoped to collaborate with the College of Education and the College of Arts and Sciences in revising courses of these colleges in connection with teacher preparation.

Dr. Tenmatay suggested that at least P 100,000 ($15,000) should be requested in the bill. Prof. Nemenzo inquired if the word *Teaching* in "Science Teaching Center" was appropriate. Congress might get the impression STC teaches and is a degree-granting institution. The Director remarked that it may be better to change the name to "Science Education Center."[35]

Discussions at the 81st Meeting of the Steering Committee (10 January 1967), centered on conditions to be met in establishing STC as an autonomous and permanent unit:

a. funds for its operation;
b. a set of functions;
c. staff to carry out its functions:
    i. to prepare curriculum materials;
    ii. to prepare materials for teacher education in collaboration with the College of Education;
    iii. to serve as a resource center.[36]

At its 84th meeting (22 February 1967), the Steering Committee then discussed the draft of a legislative bill, "An Act to Define the Functions of the Science Teaching Center, Provide for its Support, and for Other Purposes."

In this and several subsequent meetings, the Steering Committee examined details of the organizational structure of STC as well as the implications of institutionalizing it within the University. Delores Hernandez' paramount concern was to ensure autonomy of the center even while placing it into good contact with all those capable of assisting it. These meetings finally attained their goal when in June 1969, the Philippine President, Ferdinand Marcos, signed into law the Republic Act 5506, establishing the Science Education Center (UPSEC) as a permanent unit of the University of the Philippines.[37] That act earmarked 250,000 pesos ($50,000) annually from the national Special Science Fund for support of the Center. It also provided for adoption of the products of the Center as officially approved textbooks for all public schools upon the certification of the Secretary of Education and reserved all royalties from the books exclusively for the support of the Center.

9.   *The Philippine Science Education Project becomes*
        a network of dissemination centers for UPSEC innovations

A n event of the highest significance for Philippine science education occurred in 1969 with signing of an agreement between the Philippine Government and two United Nations agencies, UNICEF and UNESCO, to form the Philippine Science Education Project. This brought into existence a nationwide network of centers for disseminating the new science curriculum materials and methods being developed by the Science Education Center (UPSEC) to schools throughout the Philippines.

Discussions among Philippine educators and outside aid-giving agencies on the need for such a network had begun in 1968 at the time a UNESCO science education consultant, Dr. Edward Crunden, first took up his duties in Manila. Crunden had recognized that UP/SEC could not shoulder the *quantitative* burden of providing in-service training to the thousands of teachers in the Philippines and at the same time fulfill its *qualitative* responsibility — to create highly innovative curriculum materials. At the same time, he saw the excellent work being done by several of the teacher training colleges and universities in the Philippines in providing in-service training for teachers. He recognized that proper coordination of these institutions could effect a satisfactory dissemination of the SEC materials.

He saw one program as a prototype of the kind of center that could be replicated throughout the country to form a dissemination network. That program embraced a group of Catholic schools and colleges in the provinces of Cotabate and Sulu, known as the Notre Dame Educational Association. These were providing a host of services to member schools and colleges, including in-service courses for the teachers of science and mathematics and, under a Ford Foundation grant, the services of a resident adviser, Dr. Merritt Kimball, a science educator from the United States.

Through Crunden's initiative, representatives from a wide variety of educational and scientific organizations joined in a study to determine the most suitable type of collaborating center on which to base a disseminating network. Participating in that study on the Philippine side were: UPSEC, the Bureau of Public Schools and the Bureau of Private Schools, the NSDB, the Notre Dame Educational Association, and various colleges and universities. On the side of aid-giving agencies were: the United Nations agencies (UNESCO and UNICEF), the Ford Foundation, and the U.S. Peace Corps. The study led to drafting a plan of operation[38] for a major national project having the following objectives:

   a. improvement of pre-service education of science/mathematics teachers.

   b. modernization of in-service and upgrading programs for science/mathematics teachers.

   c. local development and production of science texts and equipment and other teaching materials for science/mathematics courses in secondary and elementary schools.

   d. evaluation of locally produced science materials.

   e. research studies on teaching-learning processes related to science/mathematics subjects.[39]

In order to attain these objectives, the plan called upon contributors to the Project to take the following steps:

   1. Establishment of Regional Science Teaching Centers located

in five strategic points of the country to serve the following purposes:

    a. Centers for Summer Science Institutes for elementary and secondary school science/math teachers.

    b. Conduct experimental programs for pre-service education for science/math teachers.

    c. Science curriculum and resource materials center for the region; and

    d. Regional base for science education improvement programs.

2. Faculty development for Teacher Educational Institutions through fellowships in U.P. for M.A. in Science/Math Teaching.

3. Science Laboratory Improvement of selected educational institutions through the grant of UNICEF science/math kits.

4. Promotion and encouragement of local production and manufacture of science teaching equipment by selected technical and vocational schools and private groups.[40]

The plan proposed a National Coordinating Committee to oversee the entire Project operation. Its membership was to be as follows:

Chairman .... NSDB Chairman
Members .... Department of Education
U.P. Science Education Center
U.P. College of Education
Notre Dame Educational Association
Notre Dame of Marbel College
International Agencies (UNICEF & UNESCO)
Ford Foundation
Other bilateral and local agencies
Secretary .... Mauro L. Gonzales, Chief, DET, NSDB[41]

The NSDB was designated to serve as the executing agency for the project.

The plan outlined three major activities of the Project, all of them linked directly to SEC. First was a *graduate programme at the Science Education Centre* itself; second, the establishment of five Regional Science Teaching Centres; and third, activities in the schools. The first phase of the programme called for scholarships for a small number of selected educators from a limited number of carefully screened teacher-training institutions, geographically distributed throughout the country. A national survey of over 500 teacher education institutions identified 25 institutions as possible regional teaching centers for science education.[42] Site visits by the survey teams drawn from the University of the Philippines, Department of Education and the National Science Development Board led to a reduction of the list to 11 institutions, with 3 alternates. From these 14 institutions were drawn the scholars for the first special 18-month course at the Science Education Center. This course provided training to these teacher educators in the new science courses under development to enable them to return to their home institutions and conduct pre-service and in-service courses for elementary and secondary school teachers of science and mathematics. These scholars could satisfy the University of the Philippines requirements for the award of the degree of Master of Arts in Teaching. At present there are 25 cooperating institutions receiving equipment from a UNICEF grant to the project.

In 1970, four regional science teaching centers additional to that at Notre Dame were established, all drawn from the 14 institutions identified in 1969, bringing to a total of 5 the regional science teaching centers making up the dissemination network. These four new centers were: Ateneo de Davao College, Silliman University, St. Louis University and Aquinas University.

These centers assumed the following functions:

(a) provision of high quality programmes for school science teachers, making use of modern science curriculum materials, teaching aids, and equipment.

(b) organization of in-service training programmes for science teachers, including summer institutes of about 6 weeks duration.

(c) supervision and visits to science teacher-training programmes in other colleges and schools within its region.

(d) visits to selected classes in schools for evaluation, advice and guidance.

(e) conduct of meetings on science teaching improvement for science teachers.

(f) organization of regional conferences for school administrators.

(g) provision of professional advice and information concerned with setting up libraries, development and use of new equipment and teaching aids, etc., to colleges and schools as requested.

Starting in 1971, teachers from 25 schools in the area of each Regional Science Teaching Center assembled at the Regional Center to follow a 6 week course. After the course, staff from the Centers paid visits to the teachers in their schools. In 1974 the number of schools involved in the programme was 250, the number of teachers was 625. The National Science Development Board provides each teacher tuition, travel expenses, a book allowance and a living allowance, while UNICEF provides equipment to the colleges and schools as follows:

(a) sets of equipment for institutions sending college teachers to the 18 month graduate course at the Science Education Centre. There is a separate set for each subject area, i.e., physics, chemistry, biology, general science, high school mathematics, elementary school science, elementary school mathematics. The Science Education Centre at the University of the Philippines receives one of each set.

(b) sets for schools sending teachers to the 6-week summer institutes at the Regional Science Teaching Centre. There are only two different sets, i.e., the high school set and the elementary school set.

In each case the content of the sets was decided upon in 1969 by the Science

Education Center with the assistance of Unesco and Ford Foundation science education specialists. The lists were carefully drawn up to provide equipment so that the experimental work in the courses under development at the Science Education Center could be carried out.

A feature of the project that has proved most successful is the decentralization of the administration. Thus each Regional Science Teaching Centre is autonomous, being responsible for selection of schools and teachers. The bimonthly meetings establish common guidelines; thus the project has uniformity without a heavy burden of bureaucracy.

The United States Peace Corps participated in the project throughout the period 1969 to 1972. The main help was to send volunteers to the participating colleges to take the place of teachers attending the Science Education Centre graduate programme. They also assisted with the field work in high schools to extend the work of the 6-week summer institutes.

In 1972, the three parties to the original plan signed an addendum extending their support to the end of the five-year period, 1969-1974. The accompanying table summarized the contributions by the participating agencies:

TABLE I

Contributions to the Philippine
Science Education Project

Government	*1969-1974*
NSDB	4,291,957 Pesos
SEC	431,400 Pesos
Department of Education	388,432 Pesos
UNICEF	469,000 Pesos
UNESCO	(One science education adviser)
Ford Foundation	1969 and 1971 grants to SEC
	1971 grant to Notre Dame Educational Association
U.S. Peace Corps	597,770 Pesos
	(54 volunteers)

The preceding description of the Philippine Science Education Project is adapted from a personal communication to the author from Dr. Cecil T. Crellin, UNESCO Science Education Advisor, who is now in Indonesia.

10. *UPSEC continues to develop and expand its program of educational innovation*

The accomplishments of UPSEC over the six year period 1965 to 1971 have been summarized in a comprehensive report prepared by Delores Hernandez. Generous excerpts from this report follow in an attempt to present an overview of the level of UPSEC activity in this period.

Curriculum development achievements between 1965 and 1972 are the following:

Texts

Completed and available to the general public:

The Gene. Vibal Press (P4.35)

Plants of the Philippines. University of the Philippines Press (P55.00)

Fundamentals of Physics. National Book Store (P15.00)

Practical Chemistry for Philippine Schools. Alemar Phoenix (P16.90)

Completed and being prepared for the press:

Elementary School ScienceI—Teachers Guide
Elementary School Science II—Teachers Guide
Elementary School Mathematics I   Workbook
Elementary School Mathematics I—Workbook
Elementary School Mathematics II—Workbook and Teachers Guide
High School Mathematics I—Text and Teachers Guide
High School Geometry—Text and Teachers Guide

Experimental editions completed and still being tried out/refined:

Elementary School Science III
Elementary School Science IV
Elementary School Science V
Elementary School Science VI
Environmental Science I (2nd ed.)
Environmental Science II (1st ed.)
Integrated Science I (1st ed.)
Elementary School Math III
Elementary School Math IV
Elementary School Math V
Elementary School Math VI
High School Math II
High School Math III

Equipment

Prototype equipment has been produced to accompany the UPSEC textbooks. This activity has been most thorough in the area of physics owing to an earlier project, "Physics Equipment Project," funded by the NSDB and cooperatively carried out by the Bureau of Public Schools, Bureau of Vocational Education and the UPSEC.

A complete set of physics equipment to go with *Fundamentals of Physics.*

A few pieces of equipment to go with Practical Chemistry for Secondary Schools.

A complete set of prototype equipment for *Integrated Science I* (I.S.I.)

A few pieces of equipment for
    Environmental Science I
    Elementary Sciences

Teacher Education:

1.21 Special summer institutes: These have been held each summer starting 1967 for experimental teachers in most courses.

The courses for special summer institutes are innovative in that they are built about the content of the new curriculum materials and the skills and techniques the teacher needs in teaching the new materials.

1.22 Regular summer courses: These are courses which may be credited towards a Master of Arts in Teaching (M.A.T.) degree.

1.23 Department of Science Teaching: The senior staff of the UPSEC serve the College of Education as its Department of Science Teaching. Activities in this connection include teaching mainly on the graduate level, advising student research, revising and improving programs and courses, and work on improving the undergraduate program.

1.24 Teacher-educator's graduate program, funded by UNICEF-NSDB is part of the national program of the Philippines.

From 1969 to the present a full complement of subject area majors in sciences and mathematics (leading to the M.A.T. degree) has been offered; each program lasts for 18 months (mid-June to mid-December of the year following). To date, the programs (have enrolled 109 participants).

1.25 Follow-up program: The participants are visited and observed by UPSEC staff as they conduct their first summer institutes particularly in the Regional Science Teaching Centers. Consultant services are provided in these visits and feedback are secured which help the staff improve their own courses.[43]

To provide UPSEC with a secure financial base, has been one of Delores Hernandez' concerns for many years. In a 1971 report to the Ford Foundation, she described a plan for a special fund that would provide UPSEC with this secure base:

Republic Act 5506 (Appendix E) provides for the maintenance (partial) of the Center at the rate of P250,000 per year. This amount to be allocated from the science tax fund. The science tax is a 5-year tax (now in its 3rd year).

At present, the university contributes the balance of the SEC's local budget which is not covered by the P250,000 grant from the special science tax fund. This amount represents about P75,000 - P80,000 yearly.

The royalties accruing from SEC publications, as indicated by RA 5506, is in a special account reserved only for the use of the Center. This increases the amount available for the contribution of the various projects of the Center. The royalties are used mainly for salaries of short-term personnel on specific projects, materials and sundry expenses for projects, and honoraria of writers and local consultants. The yearly amount forthcoming from this source averages P100,000 starting about three years from this date (when more books become available to the public).

Attempts are being made to raise counterpart funds for the U.S. $10,000 portion of the terminal grant of the Ford Foundation which is intended mainly for local chairs to be used by local consultants. There are hopeful indications that a separate foundation can be set up. As of this date a U.P. alumnus has given a pledge for P10-P20,000 for the foundation.[44]

In November of that year, she then set up the Foundation for the Advancement of Science Education, Inc. By registering it as a non-profit, non-stock, private corporation with the Securities and Exchange Commission, she has enabled it to accept donations on a tax-deductible basis. A brochure describing the Foundation is available from UPSEC.

12.   *UPSEC advances toward the future*

A visitor to the UPSEC today would find a marked shift in the preoccupation of its Work Groups from what it was in the early 1960's. Except for work by primary science Work Groups, the earliest course development centered on improving science instruction related to Philippine manpower needs in scientific and technical fields—largely on secondary school science courses. Swift demographic changes of the last decade have been filling Philippine schools with pupils having goals other than to enter the scientific and technical professions. As a result the schools are demanding science curriculum material that can help these new pupils to comprehend such problems as population growth, health, nutrition, and environment.

In response to this demand, UPSEC has prepared two different integrated science courses: The Integrated Science Program (a Philippine adaptation of the Intermediate Science Curriculum Study (ISCS), Florida, USA) and the Environmental Science Course. Both aim at the seventh and eighth years of Philippines schools; both include a wide spectrum of objectives. UPSEC is intentionally offering schools a choice between two courses of a similar nature but with different topical interests.

One course employs the scientific themes of energy and matter as keys for opening up understanding of everyday areas: the environment, human nutrition, hygiene, and drug abuse; the other course incorporates study of the physical aspects of the earth and atmosphere and the relationships between living organisms and their environments (ecology).

The two courses also offer schools low unit costs of classroom materials. UPSEC, conscious of the economic limits in Philippine education, is attempting to help schools meet those limits in a realistic way. The Philippine adaptation of ISCS is built around a kit of equipment costing 1000 pesos (about US $200); one kit is to be used by 150 students. The cost of a textbook (7 pesos or about US$1.50) brings the unit cost (per student cost) of this course to approximately U.S.$2.00. The Environmental Science course requires a school to purchase a few simple pieces of apparatus totalling 200 pesos per class of 40 students and a textbook costing eight pesos, so the unit cost is also about U.S. $2.00. The ISCS course places a well-stocked kit in the classroom while the Environmental Science course expects the teacher and students to find suitable materials for the experimental work in the course at home or in the market. In choosing between these courses, the school authorities would need to weigh equipment costs against the willingness of teachers and students to do the additional work of "scrounging" for materials required by the Environmental Science course.

The demographic changes affecting Philippine schools have had other consequences as well for UPSEC's curriculum development program. For example, UPSEC is beginning to pay much greater attention to language and other socio-cultural factors in the preparation of classroom materials. Primary schools in rural areas require materials written in the local Philippine language (Tagalog). They also need materials that are compatible with the rural environment of their pupils. In response to these needs, UPSEC is taking the following measures:

1. A special panel of teachers drawn from various language-group areas in the Philippines are working with linguists in developing a uniform and manageable (by students) glossary of science terms for UP/SEC writers;

2. UPSEC Work Groups are meeting primary and secondary school science educators drawn from provincial areas in developing curriculum materials adapted to rural circumstances;

3. UPSEC staff are holding discussions with anthropologists on the ethnic and linguistic determinants of cognitive development among Filipino children and the relation of this development to science learning; and

4. UPSEC staff are redirecting their fundamental research projects to problems of child learning behavior in the Philippine culture and society.

Matching these moves by UPSEC are moves by the Philippine government to render its educational system more responsive to the learning needs of its burgeoning population. In 1970, President Marcos created a Presidential Commission to carry out a survey of Philippine education. That survey was followed in 1971, by setting up an Educational Task Force. The Task Force is currently preparing plans for major new education projects which may be financed largely by the International Bank for Reconstruction and Development (IBRD). One program on the Task Force drawing board is a Curriculum Coordinating Unit to be located in the Philippine Department of Education. This unit would guide educational improvement in all subjects fields and at all school levels. This "total" curriculum project would mobilize intellectual resources from throughout the Philippines and guide the development of curriculum materials for Philippine schools pupils and teachers. Most importantly, the plan calls for UPSEC to shoulder the tasks of maintaining a watch on quality and insisting upon relevance in the materials produced and distributed to Philippine schools.

REFERENCES

1. 1964 program statement of the "Proposal to Establish a Science Teaching Project," University of the Philippines.
2. 15 May 1959 Report by Hon. Manuel Tim, Secretary of Education, entitled "Shortcomings of the Philippine Educational System."
3. 1965 Report of DDA to the Governing Board of the NSDB.
4. 1 November 1961 Report on the Status of Science Education in the Philippines, by the Educational Mission Committee.
5. 1963 Report of Philippine Senate, entitled "On the Problems of Science in the Philippines."
6. Biological Sciences Curriculum Study, a U.S. curriculum project supported by the National Science Foundation.
7. 1962 First Progress Report NSDB Project No. 2.61, by Delores Hernandez.
8. 1964 memorandum, "Projects for the Improvement of the Teaching of Science and Mathematics in the Elementary and Secondary Schools of the Philippines," J.C. Warner to Harry Case, Ford Foundation, Manila.
9. Ibid, p. 6.
10. 1964 program statement on the "Proposal to Establish a Science Teaching Project," University of the Philippines.
11. Ibid.
12. Ibid.
13. 1964 program statement on the "Proposal to Establish a Science Teaching Project," University of the Philippines.
14. 5 August 1964 letter, Carlos P. Romulo to Harry Case, Ford Foundation, Manila.
15. 13 August 1964 Request for Grant Action (OD-1548).
16. 4 August 1964 memorandum, Harry Case to George Gant, Ford Foundation, New York.
17. 15 July 1966 letter, Carlos Romulo to Harry Case, Ford Foundation, Manila.
18. In (January 1974) a letter from Delores Hernandez to the author, she states: I did not appoint the various committees, mentioned on this page. Dr. Enrique T. Virata, chairman of the *Ad Hoc* Committee for the Science Teaching Project (in consultation with Dr. Tenmatay, Dr. Morales and myself) recommended all the initial appointments to the University President.
19. Pages 12 and 13, Andres Bolinas, "The Structure and Functions of UPSEC, A Historical Study," M.A. Thesis, College of Education, University of the Philippines (April 1971).
20. American Association for the Advancement of Science.
21. Annual Report, Science Teaching Center, (November 1965).
22. Annual Report, Science Teaching Center, October (1965).
23. Annual Report, Science Teaching Center, (1966).
24. CHEM Study: Chemical Education Materials Study (California)
    SMSG: School Mathematics Study Group (California)
    ESCP: Earth Science Curriculum Project (Colorado)
    SCIS: Science Curriculum Improvement Study (California)
25. P. 6, Draft Proposal from Science Teaching Center to Ford Foundation, Manila, dated July 19, 1966.
26. 6 August 1966 report, Charles Brumfiel to Harry Case.
27. Ibid.
28. 19 July 1966 Draft Proposal, STC to the Ford Foundation, Manila.
29. 19 July 1966 Draft Proposal.
30. 30 August 1966 Request for Grant Action, F.C. Ward to McGeorge Bundy (OD-1851).
31. 10 August 1966 Memorandum, Pfanner (Ford Foundation, New York) to Harry Case (Ford Foundation, Manila).
32. 23 August 1966 Memorandum from Harry L. Case to David E. Pfanner.
33. Fourth Annual Report, Science Teaching Center, 1967-68.
34. Eighth Annual Report, Science Education Center, 1972.
35. Summary of 78th meeting of Steering Committee on 9 November 1966; taken from MAT thesis, Andres L.B. Bolinas, College of Education, University of Philippines, Manila, April 1971: "Structure and Functions of the University of the Philippines Science Education Center, a Historical Study."
36. Bolinas, Summary of 81st meeting.
38. 28 October 1971 Plan of Operation, Science Education Project in the Philippines (FEP/800) UNICEF, Manila.
39. December 1971 NSDB Report on the Science Education Project of the Philippines (1969-1971).
40. Ibid, p. 2.
41. December 1971 NSDB Report on the Science Education Project of the Philippines (1969-1971).
42. The Manila office of the Ford Foundation met the costs of this survey out of its discretionary funds.
43. Delores Hernandez, "Summary of Faculty Development Plans, Five-Year Program for UPSEC staff."

44. July 1971 Narrative Report to the Ford Foundation for the period 1969 to 1971, SEC.

TURKEY

1. *Introduction*

On 1 September 1963 the only visible sign of Turkey's Science Lycée was a pile of clay roof-tiles on a quiet hilltop outside of Ankara with a magnificent view of the city. The cornerstone was laid on 18 September 1963.

Less than thirteen months later, on 12 October 1964, the date of the opening ceremonies, an administration building, a library, a four-story classroom building, and three two-story laboratories — one each for biology, chemistry, and physics — had been completed and furnished.

The contractor needed just about another month to finish the two dormitories and the cafeteria. And for a short time student lockers and double-decker bunks had to be set up in classrooms, the library became a temporary dining room, and a make-do kitchen was set up outside.

But nobody seemed to mind, least of all the 100 students who turned up on Saturday the 11th to settle in over the weekend. These were the survivors of over 5,000 who took the first stage of the competitive examinations, and of 1,000 who qualified for the second stage. Their faces were something to see as they wandered around classrooms and laboratories, literally drooling with excitement and expectation.

Monday the 12th was clear and warm as a crowd of several hundred people representing governments, universities, teachers, parents, and students gathered for the ceremony, serenaded by the Presidential Band. There were three speakers: İbrahim Öktem, Minister for Education; Kemal Kurdaş, President of METU,[1] without whose energy and devotion the Lycée simply would have not opened this fall; and Dr. E. P. Northrop, for the Ford Foundation. A Vice President of McGraw-Hill took a look, and said flatly it was the best school science facility in the world. Nice as it will be to be admired, everyone concerned is hoping for no visitors during the next few months. By next spring, things ought really to be in shape to be seen.[2]

In these words, Eugene Northrop, the Ford Foundation consultant-representative in Turkey, recorded his keen sense of accomplishment on seeing the Science Lycée finally open its doors to its first group of Turkish students. He had worked for that day during almost four years, beginning in April 1960, when he had come to Turkey as the Foundation representative. Over those long years, he had labored with diligence, patience and singular vision in guiding the Foundation's contribution of technical assistance to those Turkish scientists, educators and government authorities who stood behind the Science Lycée idea. The story of the cooperation between then and the Ford Foundation in establishing the Science Lycée unfolds in the pages that follow.

2.   *Appointment of Eugene Northrop as Ford Foundation Consultant-Representative in Turkey*

Throughout the 1950's, the Ford Foundation program of technical assistance to Turkey centered on the education sector. By 1959, that aid had climbed to the million-dollar mark, with grants going to teacher education, a pilot program on the comprehensive school, and a study of the entire educational system by a National Commission on Education. Against this record of cooperation as background, then, in 1959 the Minister of Education in Turkey, Celâl Yardimci, made known to the Foundation his interest in having them place a representative in Turkey to guide the Foundation program of assistance and to act as his advisor:

> We would like to have one of your experts to be a represen-
> tative of the Foundation and also to be our counsellor. We are
> very much interested to have someone in the area of curriculum
> in secondary field. His major field would be prefereably mathe-
> matics and science.[3]

To fill this position, the Foundation turned to Eugene Northrop, then William Raney Harper Professor of Mathematics at the University of Chicago and an active leader in national programs for improving the teaching of mathematics at secondary school level in the United States. In accepting the invitation to serve in Turkey, Northrop saw a unique opportunity to direct the Foundation's technical assistance on the improvement of science education in that country's schools:

> It was most gratifying to learn from Mr. Hill of your interest
> in receiving me as a person who, while serving as the Ford
> Foundation's representative in Turkey, can at the same time be
> of service as a consultant in educational matters, especially in the
> areas of mathematics and science.[4]

A few months before Northrop was due to arrive in Turkey, Celâl Yardimci was removed from his post as Minister of Education, a victim of protests that had broken out among university professors in Turkey against government interference in university affairs. This event was a harbinger of the uncertainties at the Ministry level in the government of Turkey that would continue to plague Northrop's relations with the government throughout the ensuing decade of his tenure there. In fact, soon after Northrop did arrive in Turkey, in May, 1960, a military coup toppled the government in power (Menderes), and ushered in an era of great political uncertainty. Over the next several years, one Minister of Education after another succeeded to that post as cabinets came and went.

However, in 1959 when Northrop was preparing to go to Turkey, aside from the sudden dismissal of Celâl Yardimci, the grounds for a favorable government-

Foundation cooperation appeared good. Thus, in a welcoming letter to Northrop just before he set out for Turkey, the new Minister of Education, Atíf Benderlioğlu made a sincere effort to assure Northrop that there would be direct and open relations between them:

> I have been emphasizing cultural relations that could strengthen and develop our educational system ever since I took office. On this occasion (of your coming), I would like to express my thanks and pleasure over the cooperation between the Foundation and the Ministry.
>
> I have already been told a great deal about you and your interest in our educational system. When you come in April, I shall be very pleased to have you as the ex-officio member of the Educational Planning Committee of the Ministry. In addition, it will be a pleasure for me to cooperate with you on certain projects.
>
> I would like you to communicate with me directly. Any information you would like to have will be through my channel. I make this point clear at this time in order to clarify to you the methods we are going to follow during our work and mutual relations. I hope this way of direct contact will please you, and prove to be a short-cut for you.
>
> I am looking forward to seeing you in Ankara. Our best wishes. [5]

3.   *The idea of a special high school for science takes root*

Upon his arrival in Turkey, Northrop set out at once on a round of interviews and discussions with leaders in scientific, educational, governmental and business circles "to find out what Turkey's chief problems are in the area of science and mathematics—with the ultimate aim, of course, of discovering whether and in what way the Ford Foundation might be of help."[6] This period of intensive "diagnosis" lasted throughout the balance of that first year of Northrop's term in Turkey. It reached its culmination on 25 January 1961 at a highly significant meeting that brought Northrop face to face with three top government officials: Turhan Feyzioğlu, Minister of Education; Mukbil Gökdoğan, Minister of Public Works; and Şahap Kocatopçu, Minister of Industry. At this meeting, Northrop summarized his eight- to nine-month study of Turkey's needs in science, and presented to the three ministers a one-page memorandum he had prepared, entitled: *Memorandum on Promoting Scientific Progress in Turkey*. The memorandum identified a basic shortcoming in Turkey, the absence of a "central scientific organization that can speak for science in the government and in the nation at large." It went on to prescribe as a "suggested remedy," the "establishment of a National Advisory Committee on Science."

During this meeting, Northrop also introduced the subject of needs in Turkish science education as he had come to see them during his initial fact-finding period. He "sounded out" the three ministers on the idea of a special high school for gifted science students as one way of doing something bold and constructive about the country's need for future scientists. This idea of a special school for science had grown upon Northrop in his talks with Turkish scientists and educators during the period of his fact-finding. Northrop went from that meeting to prepare a second one-page memorandum, this one describing the special high school for science.

Just how significant was this meeting as a turning point for Northrop's efforts to plan a program of technical assistance can be sensed from the following excerpt from a letter he wrote to one of his closest advisors at the close of the meeting:

> Lively interest in both of the ideas was expressed by all of the Ministers. In particular, Feyzioğlu phoned the next day to request additional copies of the National Advisory Committee memorandum, and said he would be willing to push the idea in the Prime Minister's Office. Şahap-Bey[7] seized the occasion of an appointment with General Gürsel[8] on Wednesday afternoon to describe the idea to him, and reported a very favourable reaction. Feyzioğlu appears to be interested also in getting the Science Lycée talked about in his ministry. So perhaps things are gaining momentum on both fronts. [9]

To these two interests, a national scientific research agency and a special science school, Northrop soon added a third: support to graduate studies in basic science and mathematics at Turkey's newest university, the Middle East Technical University. He had come to this interest after finding that:

> The conditions and climate for research and communication between scientists are so bad that there is no steady output of research work, scientific publication is sporadic and sparse, and good foreign scientists—who are needed to bolster research and teaching—are discouraged from accepting any visiting appointments. Career opportunities in university science teaching are so unattractive that the best science talent entering the universities chooses *applied fields like medicine or engineering*. [10]

Turkish scientists and government authorities immediately pressed ahead on implementing two of the three ideas — establishment of the research council, and introduction of basic sciences in the METU curriculum. As a result, within a year, the Ford Foundation was able to award a grant in support of the program at METU, while the scientists proceeded to organize the research council. The third idea did not fare so well, however. Although the scientists pressed for its implementation, the government authorities failed to take decisive action in behalf of the Lycée idea; this delayed the award of a Foundation grant for almost two years.

Behind that government faltering was an internal debate among the educators on the relative urgency of meeting growing mass demands for educational opportunities and building an essentially "elite" project, as they saw the special science lycée. Stirring that debate were changes and developments that, beginning with the revolution of 1923, had touched every sphere of Turkish national life: social, economic and political. Education was not exempted, and secondary education was especially affected. Thus, whereas at the time of forming the Republic (1923) there had been only 95 high schools in Turkey with a total of 7,000 sutdents, by 1960, these numbers had risen to 700 high schools with a total of 229,000 students. [11]

This debate came to the surface at one point in that long period of hesitation and delay when the Ministry of Education requested Northrop to grant funds for a program that would help the Ministry to meet the severe shortage of science teachers in the schools. It reported a need for 15 such teachers for teacher training institutions, 480 for lycees and 1732 for the Middle or orta schools. In turning the request aside, Northrop explained that the Ford Foundation was unable to help with such large-scale needs but that it would consider contributing to the qualitative improvement of the educational system through providing fellowships for advanced training of a selected number of teachers.

These different positions taken by the Ministry and Northrop required many months of patient negotiations between the two in a search for a compromise as a base for continuing Foundation assistance to education in Turkey. To make matters worse, another change in government occurred at just that time, interrupting these vital negotiations through a shift of Feyzioğlu from his position as Minister of Education to that of Deputy Prime Minister and putting in Ahmet Tahtakílíç as Minister of Education.

In his first meeting with this new minister, in April, 1961, Northrop reviewed the earlier discussions on the science lycée and outlined those contributions that the Ford Foundation would make to such a special school: advisors on curriculum development; dollar costs of equipment not obtainable in Turkey; and training for teachers selected to be staff members of the Lycée. Northrop then stated his expectations of government commitments: buildings, teacher salaries, and scholarships for students. The Minister's response was enthusiastic, in fact, much to Northrop's surprise—and increasingly to his dismay—Tahtakílíç expressed a determination to open it at once. He wanted to take over an existing school building and bring in English-speaking instructors from abroad as staff members.

This conception of the special science lycée distressed Northrop deeply. Such a plan only demonstrated to Northrop that the Minister had failed to grasp the central purpose of such a special school. In Northrop's view, only *new* buildings and long-term training of *Turkish* teachers as staff members could give to the school that identity that would enable it to raise Turkish students' respect for study of basic science. Northrop rejected Tahtakílíç's proposal, therefore, and countered it with a proposal of his own. In this, Northrop outlined the following time schedule for developing the science lycée:

Stage 1: Appoint a steering committee of *scientists* and Ministry of Education people to oversee the project.

Stage 2: Simultaneously work on: (a) the design of buildings and (b) the selection of teachers by a competitive examination.

Stage 3: Simultaneously work on: (a) building of school; (b) training of staff and development curriculum; (c) examinations for selection of students.

Stage 4: Simultaneously work on: (a) purchase and install equipment; (b) select students.[12]

On receiving this counterproposal, Tahtakílíç informed Northrop that government funds could not be found for a new school building and once again insisted that Northrop should look at the existing school sites proposed by the Ministry.[13] These sharp differences between the two men brought further planning for the science lycée to a standstill for almost a full year.

Northrop now turned to the group that had been supporting the science lycée idea, seeking their advice on how to resolve the impasse with the Minister of Education. Particularly helpful to Northrop at that period was Kadri Yürükoğlu, Chairman of the Board of Education. Yürükoğlu believed that the best solution was to place the special lycée under the direction of a body of scientists rather than under the jurisdiction of the Ministry of Education. He hoped the newly formed Science and Technical Research Council of Turkey (TÜBITAK) would sponsor the lycée and supported the

111

idea of special legislation that would set the lycée apart from other secondary schools. As a further step in support of the science lycée idea, Yürükğlu used his influence to place the subject of the special high school of science on the agenda of Seventh National Education Congress (Şûra) that convened in February, 1962, a move that helped to keep the lycée plan alive as an option before Turkish educators. At that Congress, the Minister of Education referred to the science lycée in these words:

> As for our country, I find it suitable to found a High School of Science where students with high ability could be boarded without charge or to modify one of our present high schools into such a High School of Science. This High School should train the staff for our future scientific program and the graduates of such a high school should further their education in the fields where they are most gifted. The High School of Science will be mainly interested in the teaching of mathematics, physics, chemistry and biology, social sciences and Turkish. I don't think that this school for the gifted who seem to be apart from the mass or the country would be anti-democratic in any respect, because one of the ideals of our Constitution and of our democracy is to provide fields of development to everyone's ability. [14]

It was not until July, 1961, however, that the long impasse finally came to an end. In that month, a national referendum brought in a new government that once more led to a change of Ministers. In particular, Hilmi İncesulu replaced Ahmet Tahtakılıç as Minister of Education. Following that change, a sharp up-turn in the tide of events soon became noticeable. On 20 March 1962, İncesulu convened a meeting at the Ministry of Education to review the stalled plans for a science lycée. Northrop described that meeting as follows:

> FLASH! SCIENCE LYCÉE THREATENS TO GET OFF GROUND! Found self Turhan Feyzioğlu's office other day, talking role science in Turkey in general, his progress legislation Scientific and Technical Research Council in particular. Some progress reported. He noted Minister of Education (İncesulu) talked Science Lycée at Council of Ministers that morning. What I know? Answer: Nothing. Suggested we do something. Picked up phone, got Minister. Forty-five minutes later we together with Minister, Kadri Bey, Ferid Saner. Forty-five minutes still later had committee to draw up specifications. Members: Cahit Arf and Erdal İnönü, Nurettin Baç, Osman Ülkümen, Remzi Öncül, Eugene Northrop. Northrop asked draft frame of reference for Committee; has done, is talking Kadri Bey tomorrow, 10 a.m. [15]

4.   *The Ministry of Education gives its agreement*
      to the Science Lycée Project

The formation of this committee gave immediate forward momentum to planning for the Science Lycée Project. The committee set about at once to formulate the specifications for such a special school. To assist them in that task, Northrop invited Professor Milton Pella to come to Turkey to work at their side. Pella, Professor of Science Education from the University of Wisconsin, was in the Middle East at that time serving as a consultant on science education to the Ford Foundation.

112

In a very short time, the committee completed its work, producing a major statement of specifications entitled: "Report of a Committee Studying the Subject of Establishing a Science Lycée in Turkey." This important document continued to serve as the basic conceptual framework for the Science Lycée Project through all of its subsequent phases.[16]

In its body, the report set forth the following:

1. Reasons for the establishment of a science lycée.
2. The general characteristics of the science lycée.
3. Selection of students.
4. The Educational Program of the Lycée.
5. Teachers and other personnel.
6. Buildings and installations.
7. Administration.

Under (1) "Reasons for Establishing the Lycée," the report justified the idea of special attention to the highly gifted science student as a valuable human resource by arguing that "those nations that know how to utilize this resource have developed and progressed. Humanity is indebted for many things in every field to such highly gifted people. In our country, the group most neglected is the group of highly gifted children." It also justified giving special attention to gifted children in a nation where egalitarian principles were supposed to prevail:

> We perceive no conflict whatsoever between having every child developed and educated to the degree of his aptitude, and the equality principle of democracy. We believe that the utilization of highly gifted human resources for the progress and betterment of society does not conflict with democracy and justice.

Under (2) "General Characteristics of the Science Lycée," the report listed these specifications:

1. A co-educational boarding school for three years; without cost through granting of scholarships.
2. A student enrollment of 300.
3. Housed in a new building designed and constructed for this purpose.
4. Carefully selected teachers.
5. High educational aims;
   a) science courses as principal part of curriculum;
   b) general educational aims not basically different from those of other schools;
   c) distinctive emphasis on development of scientific talent, individual creativeness, critical thought, and social orientation and responsibility.
6. Administratively attached to General Directorate of Secondary Education of the Ministry of Education, but afforded sufficient freedom in work and administration to allow it to develop as required.
7. "An Administrative and Advisory Board" to be established to assist Ministry in development and administration of the school.

113

Appendix 2 of the Report set forth procedures for establishing the Lycée:

Stage 1: (*Spring 1962 to Spring 1963*)

a) A U.S. consultant as co-director comes to Turkey to develop basic concept of the lycée in cooperation with Turkish scientists and educators;

b) A Turkish scientist or educator also selected as co-director;

c) The co-directors identify scientist and teachers for training as teacher-trainers and staff of lycée;

d) A U.S. school-building specialist and architect comes to Turkey to advise on construction of lycée plant. Construction gets underway.

Stage 2: (*Summer 1963*)

Turkish scientists who will be teacher-trainers visit U.S. curriculum projects.

Stage 3: (*Academic year 1963-64*)

a) Turkish science teachers to be trained as staff for lycée by above-described Turkish scientist after first being brought to site of lycée (Istanbul and Ankara) and assigned to existing lycées on part-time basis while also attending in-service courses.

b) Nation-wide screening of students to select 100 for first year of science lycées.

Stage 4: (*Summer 1964*)

Turkish science teachers visit U.S. for special in-service course and to write course materials for first year of science lycée.

Stage 5: (*Academic year 1964-65*)

a) Science Lycée opens doors to 100 selected students.

b) Teachers, now as staff of Lycée, continue writing course materials along with instructing students.

c) Selected U.S. secondary school science teachers come to Turkey to work alongside Turkish teachers as consultants on new curricula.

Throughout the report, the committee took special care to emphasize that the project was one that would not only set up a special school for gifted science students but would also eventually promote improvement in science teaching in all of Turkey's lycées. Thus, the introduction to the report stated:

> ...this school will serve for the betterment of science courses in our existing lycées through the spreading of results obtained to other such schools, and for the augmentation of interest and prestige for science and the training of teachers.[17]

Then Appendix 2 to the report, under the section dealing with procedure, stated:

> ...teachers not assigned to the Science Lycée would work with others on the preparation of course materials with a view to trying part of them out with regular lycées. In this way, the

suggestion that the Science Lycée serve as an experimental center for the preparation of materials and the training of teachers would begin to be realized.

> Hopefully, at the end of two or three years there will have been developed a science program for the Science Lycée, with adaptations of it for other lycées and for teacher training institutions. These materials would then be for use in summer institutes for additional lycée teachers who . . . carry on the work of spreading the new program throughout the *entire school system*.[18]

Northrop underscored this intention of the committee to give the Project a two-fold character when, some months later, he wrote in the formal Ford Foundation document (the Request for Grant Action, or RGA):

> . . . the program is designed to accomplish two things: to provide a staff and curriculum for the new Science Lycée, and at the same time to provide a vehicle for upgrading staffs and curricula of regular lycées.[19]

Upon completing the report, the committee submitted it to İncesulu, the Minister of Education. Northrop describes the Minister's highly positive reception of the report as follows:

> Yesterday we had a meeting with the Minister of Education who pleased us all by his acclaim of our work and who astonished us all by his approval of the time schedule, the "Administrative and Advisory Board" (in which, please note, the scientists outnumber the Ministry of Education personnel) and everything else we had to say.
>
> The Minister agreed to appoint at once the 'Interim Administrative and Advisory Board' and to set it to work drawing up a formal agreement between the Minister, METU, and the Foundation, and when the time comes, AID. In the meantime, the Minister will get to work on the Ministry of Finance in discussions about the approximately million dollars in counterpart funds needed for the building.[20]

İncesulu lost no time in setting up the Interim Administrative and Advisory Committee with members as follows:

Selâhattin Okay . . . . Prof. of Zoology, Ankara University
Saim Saraçoğlu . . . . Prof. of Chemistry, Ankara University
Erdal İnönü . . . . Prof. of Physics, METU
Tuğrul Taner . . . . Prof. of Mathematics, METU
Remzi Öncül . . . . Ministry of Education
Osman Ülkümen . . . . Director General of Secondary Education

But once again, governmental uncertainty and instability interrupted this forward movement in the science lycée planning. Even before he could convene the committee, İncesulu became the victim of another government change. In that change, Şevket Hatipoğlu replaced him as Minister of Education. It was Hatipoğlu, then, who first convened the Interim Committee in July of that year, assigning it the task of preparing a document entitled "Project in Connection with Allocating Funds to the

115

Lycée."[21] In this Project Document, the Committee outlined responsibilities of the various parties who would cooperate in bringing into being the proposed science lycée: the Ministry of Education, the METU, the U.S.A.I.D.. and the Ford Foundation.

At this juncture in the planning, the necessary government promise of funds for the lycée buildings — classrooms, student hostels, etc., — became a critical but troublesome issue. Osman Ülkümen took on himself the responsibility of getting that promise from the government. So that he would have a stronger case in his appeal to the government, Ülkümen asked Northrop to provide him as tangible an evidence as possible of the intention of the Ford Foundation to support the lycée.

Northrop was able to supply this tangible evidence to Ülkümen shortly thereafter. On 22 August 1962, Northrop received a letter from the Foundation's New York headquarters addressed to the Minister of Education in Ankara and earmarking a sum of $1,100,000 for the Science Lycée Project.

On the strength of this assurance from his headquarters, Northrop now drew up the basic document through which a field representative of the Ford Foundation lays the case before his New York colleagues in behalf of a prospective grantee. In this document, called the "Request for Grant Action," Northrop set forth his reasoning as to the importance of the Science Lycée and then described the needs for Foundation funding as he and the planning committee had calculated them. On 22 October 1962, the Ford Foundation announced the award of its grant of $1,100,000 to the Ministry of Education in support of the Science Lycée Project.

But even this rapid succession of positive steps on the Foundation's part in behalf of the Science Lycée failed to elicit the hoped-for indication of funds from the government side. Moreover, a favourable move then made by Kemal Kurdas, President of METU, the lease of a tract of land from the METU campus to serve as a site for the Science Lycée, also failed to draw a Ministry response. As the end of that year (1962) approached with still no indication of government willingness to supply funds for buildings, Northrop lost all patience. He addressed a strong and admonitory note to Hatipoğlu, the Minister of Education:

> The Ford Foundation accepted its responsibility;
> The Middle East Technical University accepted its responsibility;
> The U.S. Agency for International Development accepted its responsibility;
> Yet the Ministry of Education and Ministry of Finance seem not to have acted with comparable decisiveness.
> This letter is an earnest request for prompt and firm assurances that the Ministry of Education and Ministry of Finance are in fact ready to accept the responsibilities assigned to them in the document "Project in Connection with Opening a Science Lycée.[22]

The Minister's reply to this letter reached Northrop on Christmas Day. It contained a promise that the 1963 budget of the Education Ministry would include 5 million Turkish lira toward the building of the Lycée.

That promise brought Northrop a joy fittingly matched to the day:

> On Christmas Eve Osman Ülkümen phoned me at home to wish me a very Merry Christmas and to announce that he was putting the Minister's letter in the mail. Enclosed are copies of

116

the letter and of my acknowledgement. The Minister's letter arrived on Christmas Day, and no one ever had a finer Christmas
present.[23]

5.   *The Ford Foundation appoints Stanley Marshall*
      principal consultant to the Science Lycée Project
      The stage was now set for collaboration between the Foundation and Turkish
scientists, educators and government authorities in establishing the Science Lycée.
The Request for Grant Action, which Northrop had prepared in support of the grant to
the Ministry for the Science Lycée Project (see above) described fiscal arrangements in
behalf of the project as follows:

> The Ministry of Education is including an item of $1,667,000
> for the Lycée plant in its budget request for the Fiscal Year 1963
> (beginning March 1, 1963) and is now negotiating with the Minis-
> try of Finance and U.S.A.I.D. for some $1,111,000 to $1,333,000
> of this amount in counterpart funds. In addition the Ministry will,
> of course, be paying salaries of Turkish teachers and most other
> local operating costs. Middle East Technical University has of-
> fered to provide land for the Lycée from its campus holdings and
> the services of its Campus Development Office in construction of
> the Lycée. This land is to be so located that the Lycée will have
> an identity of its own apart from the University. The Ford Foun-
> dation is asked to provide foreign exchange for equipment and
> furnishings, and to assume such costs of the three-year science
> teacher training program as the Ministry of Education cannot
> reasonably be expected to meet from its own funds. Mr. North-
> rop strongly recommends that the Foundation provide funds for
> these purposes in the amount of $1,100,000. Payment will be
> made contingent on the provision of land and funds as described
> above by the other parties concerned.[24]

The RGA document then went on to itemize in detail the sums allocated for
teacher training purposes and for purchase of foreign exchange materials. The teacher
training items alone totalled over $300,000 and, taken together with the foreign ex-
change items, represented a sizeable amount to be administered by the Ford Foundation. This led Northrop to request the services of a consultant who could come to
Turkey and handle this entire portion of the grant for the Foundation. A search for a
suitable consultant who could take on this assignment soon led to Professor Stanley
Marshall, Head of the Science Education Department of the Florida State University
in Tallahassee, Florida.
      Northrop submitted Marshall's name to the Interim Administrative and Ad-
visory Committee and requested their approval to an arrangement whereby Marshall
would be appointed to a dual position as consultant-administrator of the teacher training component of the Ford Foundation grant and as American Co-Director of the
Science Lycée. At its 24 November 1962 meeting, the Interim Committee gave its
assent to this proposition. That led to the drawing up and signing of a tripartite
agreement by the Ministry of Education of Turkey, the Ford Foundation, and Florida
State University which placed Professor Marshall officially and legally in the dual
administrative position referred to above.

117

Once it had struck these legal agreements, the Ford Foundation turned to the task of outlining specific guidelines for the administration of its grant by Marshall and his university department. Northrop expressed his pleasure over these arrangements with Marshall in these terms:

> On Saturday, I received an eight-page letter from Marshall about two topics—the 1963 summer program, and those items on the FSU budget that you asked him to write to me about (Stateside administrative assistant, research support, and American consultants). I wonder if he sent you a copy. It was a masterpiece of good sense, organization, and clarity, made the more impressive by the fact that it was transcribed from the dictaphone and sent off in his absence. There was not a single detail with which I would wish to quarrel. I think we are lucky indeed to have him.[25]

6. *Initial preparatory steps taken by Marshall and Florida State University*

The tripartite agreement took on a central importance at this point by distributing the many heavy responsibilities of the preparatory period among the principal parties involved. Thus, to Florida State University, it assigned the responsibility for selecting four U.S. Secondary School teachers of science who were to reside in Turkey for a two-year period beginning in September 1964, to work alongside the Turkish teachers serving as staff members of the Science Lycée. It also required Florida State University to select and purchase all of the furniture and equipment for the Lycée and the hostel as well as for the laboratories and workshops. Finally, it laid on Florida State University a responsibility to organize a set of orienting experiences in the U.S. both for the Turkish university scientists who would train the Lycée staff as well as for the Turkish secondary school teachers who would become that staff.

On the Administrative and Advisory Committee, the Tripartite Agreement laid the following obligations: to select a project administrator on the Turkish side; to identify and bring together a group of Turkish secondary school science teachers who would receive training as potential Lycée staff members; to conduct nation-wide screening of students in search of those who would make up the successive Science Lycée entering classes; and finally, to oversee the actual construction and furnishing of the Lycée buildings.

Stanley Marshall saw that these extensive and heavy burdens expected of him would require him to be away from his university more than he considered wise. Consequently, he decided to share those burdens with one of his colleagues, Dr. Ernest Burkman. Together they worked out a calendar of visits to Ankara over the preparatory period (1963-64), so that each would spend part of the year in Turkey and part in Florida.

Under this calendar, Marshall went at once to Turkey (February, 1963) where he remained for three months to acquaint himself with the overall organization and philosophy of the project and to become acquainted with Turkish leaders in science education and government and with educational conditions in schools. At the end of that first period, Burkman then went to Turkey for two months to orient himself to the project.

During his initial visit to Turkey, Marshall worked closely with Northrop and the Interim Administrative and Advisory Committee in selecting the nine Turkish university scientists who were to serve as instructors in the in-service training of the Turkish secondary school teachers. They were:

118

Professor Selhattin Okay . . . . Department of Zoology
Science Faculty, Ankara University
Dr. Kâmil Karamanoğlu . . . . Department of Botany
Science Faculty, Ankara University
Professor Ali Nazima Ergún . . . . . Department of Mathematics
Science Faculty, Ankara University
Dr. Tuğrul Taner . . . . Department of Mathematics
Middle East Technical University
Dr. Adnan Şaplakoğlu . . . . Department of Physics
Middle East Technical University
Professor Bahattin Baysal . . . . Department of Chemistry
Middle East Technical University
Professor Rauf Nasuhoğlu . . . . Department of Physics
Science Faculty, Ankara University
Professor Vedat Enüstün . . . . Department of Chemistry
Science Faculty, Ankara University
Dr. Cemil Şenvar . . . . Department of Chemistry
Science Faculty, Ankara University

After appointing one of their number, Dr. Cemil Şenvar, as the Turkish
Co-Director of the Science Lycée Project, the entire group then travelled to the
U.S.A. for the summer of 1963. At Florida State University, they participated in a
two-week workshop on science curriculum materials. Several scientists and science
educators from some of the major national science curriculum projects in the U.S.
served as consultants in that workshop to orient the Turkish scientists to those curricula.

As the close of that workshop, the Turkish scientists then travelled in the
U.S. for a five-week period, visiting the following science curriculum projects:

Biological Sciences Curriculum Study (BSCS), Boulder,
Colorado
American Association for the Advancement of Science (AAAS),
elementary science project, Palo Alto, California
Chemical Education Materials Study (CHEMS), Berkeley,
California
Oregon State University Science Education Center
University of Illinois Mathematics Program, Champaign,
Illinois
Physical Science Study Committee (PSSC), Watertown,
Massachusetts
Illinois Astronomy Project
Bronx High School of Science, New York
Junior High School Project, Princeton, New Jersey
Summer Institutes in Washington, D.C. area

Also visiting the U.S.A. at that time in connection with the science lycée was
Behruz Çinici, an architect from the Middle East Technical University, who had accepted responsibility for designing the Lycée buildings. Understandably he included
selected school laboratories and classrooms in his tour.

119

7.   *Preparatory steps taken in Ankara*

Paralleling these preparatory efforts by Marshall and his Florida State University colleagues were steps taken by the Interim Administrative and Advisory Committee. First of all, that Committee called upon the Research and Measurements Bureau of the Ministry of Education to develop a suitable screening procedure for selecting the teachers who would eventually become the staff members of the Science Lycée. In that task the Bureau sought the assistance of a consultant, Dr. George Angell, made available by the U.S.A.I.D. program in Turkey.

With his help, the Bureau prepared a battery of general aptitude, science achievement, and science aptitude tests and administered these to the teachers who applied as candidates for the Lycée teaching posts. The fifteen highest scoring teachers in each field (physics, chemistry, biology, and mathematics) then submitted to a second phase of testing that included first, interviews before a panel of university scientists and then completion of questionnaires on attitudes to teaching and new ideas in science. This second phase of testing led to selection of thirty teachers for participation in the first year of the Lycée teacher-training program.

These thirty specially-selected teachers were brought to Ankara where, during the summer of 1963, they underwent intensive training in the English language in a course conducted by the Georgetown University of Washington, D.C. As supplementary contributions to the Science Lycée project, the U.S.A.I.D. program in Turkey underwrote the cost of this English language training for these teachers.

At the end of that summer, the nine Turkish scientists returned to Ankara from their U.S.A. visit to organize a series of in-service courses for the thirty science teachers. Throughout the winter and spring, these teachers devoted half their time to these in-service courses while in the other half of their time they served as instructors in lycées in the Ankara area. The text-books used in these in-service courses were specially translated versions of certain U.S. science curriculum materials.

Stanley Marshall had negotiated agreements with the U.S. curriculum projects permitting the Turkish Ministry of Education to translate these textbooks into Turkish for use in the in-service courses. In each instance, these agreements rested on an understanding that the translation would be but a first step to a more thoroughgoing adaptation to Turkish educational situations. For example, in the case of the BSCS project materials, Marshall had written:

> I have just talked with Arnold Grobman about the copyright
> problem in connection with the BSCS materials. They are reluc-
> tant to have the materials translated to any other language for
> unrestricted use ... that is, the BSCS people believe that the
> materials must be *adapted* for use in other countries and not just
> translated. Their position is that differences in language, culture,
> religious beliefs, and other things may make single translation
> ineffective for the purposes of good education, and I think their
> position is well taken. They are, however, willing to let us trans-
> late and reproduce a limited number of copies if we guarantee
> them that adequate attention will be given later to adapting the
> materials to the needs of science education in Turkey. I have
> assured Dr. Grobman that this will be done.[26]

As another U.S. contribution to the Science Lycée project, the U.S. Information Service in Turkey provided a sum of 50,000 T.L. to meet the cost of translating these U.S. materials.

8.   *Administrative difficulties afflict the preparatory period*
The autumn of 1963 in that preparatory period saw ground-breaking at the building site of the lycée. That auspicious event ushered in a rapidly increasing load of administrative details connected with the physical development of the lycée plan: equipment ordering, customs clearance problems, etc. To improve the capability of the Interim Administrative and Advisory Committee to cope with this load, the Ministry of Education re-organized the Committee, giving it a permanent status and assigning to it the following members:

President	Osman Ülkümen, Director General of Secondary Education
Vice President	Remzi Öncül, Member of Board of Education
Secretary	Namík Tunalí, Professor of Chemistry, METU
Additional Members	Erdal İnönü, Professor of Physics, METU
	Sami Solu, Professor of Medicine, METU
	Hüseyin Demir, Instructor of Mining, METU
	Ferid Saner, Director General, External Relations Dept., Ministry of Education
	Hecati Girgin, Vice Director General, Higher Education, Ministry of Education

To improve its administrative position, that newly-constituted Committee then took the further step of setting up a separate administrative office to look after the Lycée project. Osman Ülkümen then matched these moves of the Committee by designating one of his Ministry of Education officers to serve as principal liaison officer between the Ministry and the project. Furthermore, Stanley Marshall took certain steps to bolster his team at Florida State University, appointing Garwood Braun as administrative assistant with special responsibility for arranging the visits of the Turkish Science Teachers to the U.S.A. in the summer of 1964.

But in spite of these various steps taken on all sides to strengthen the administrative machinery for conducting the ever-expanding preparatory phase of the Science Lycée project, severe administrative problems set in to plague the program. Northrop and Marshall found especially galling the unexpected obstructionist tactics adopted by the one person on whom all had counted to be a help, the Ministry of Education officer who had been appointed to provide liaison with the Lycée project.

Also plaguing the project at that time was a difficulty encountered by the Ministry of Education in meeting its pledge to provide supplementary salaries to the 30 Turkish science teachers. The Ministry had originally agreed to assign the teachers to half-time loads in the 1963-64 academic year (6-8 hours per week), and to allow them to devote the other half of their time to in-service training in preparation for responsibilities as staff members of the Science Lycée beginning in September, 1964. To provide incentives to the teachers to carry the heavy loads of in-service preparation in the earlier period and then of curriculum development later on, the Ministry had agreed to supplement the salaries of the teachers. The Ministry then found that the last provision ran afoul of the Turkish legal code governing teachers (Article 18 of Law No. 3656 and Article 3 of Law No. 1702) which prohibited payment by the Ministry of any salary supplements to teachers.

Therefore to preserve this vital monetary incentive, the Ford Foundation, with the concurrence of the Administrative and Advisory Committee, decided to revise its original grant provisions and to pay 600 Turkish lira per month to each of the 30 teachers from June 1963 until August 1964. While doing this, the Foundation also expressed a hope that, after August 1964, the Ministry would find a way to meet this cost of teacher salary supplements. The record shows that the Ministry never was able to meet these costs, neither in 1964 nor in 1965. Instead, the Ford Foundation had to provide these fees each time as a way of inducing the teachers to continue their participation in the course writing activity of the project.

This problem of legal restrictions also applied to the payments of salary supplements to the University scientists for their part in serving as teacher-trainers of the Turkish Science teachers. The result was that the Ford Foundation had to revise the original grant provision and allocate $64,000 for salary supplements for Turkish scientists as well as for the science teachers.

To add to these difficulties, another governmental crisis now broke out in the fragile political situation of Turkey.

The crisis aroused anti-American sentiment (related to the military crisis in Cyprus) that complicated relationships between the Turkish government and the U.S. personnel in the Science Lycée project. For example, one member of the Turkish Parliament actually led a fight to eliminate any further government funds in support of the Lycée project on grounds it represented interference in Turkey's domestic affairs.

The crisis also brought on another series of changes in heads of government departments. Hatipoğlu was removed as Minister of Education and Dr. Ibrahim Öktem was named Minister in his place. Osman Ülkümen was shifted from his post as Director General of Secondary Education to a similar post in the area of primary education, while Kemal Yılmaz was put in the Secondary Education post. These changes led to a noticeable increase in petty, day-by-day administrative problems in connection with running the Lycée project. Ernest Burkman summed up that trying period in these words:

> If the situation does not improve here, I have great fears for the Project. Although there has been a steady procession of what on the surface appear to be minor problems, such as the unwillingness or inability of the Ministry to supply paper and stencils, secretarial personnel, an administrative assistant, an automobile, an agreement to move materials through customs rapidly ... the basic difficulty stems from one simple fact: the Ministry has still to recognize the Science Lycée as being different in kind as well as in degree from other lycées in Turkey.
>
> The Ministry has consistently insisted upon interpreting all requests and necessities of the Science Lycée Project in terms of very restrictive existing regulations. Its response is that the Lycée must prove itself to be different before it can be treated differently. *I am convinced that if the Lycée is treated like an*

*ordinary lycée at this point in its history it will ultimately end
up as little better than an ordinary lycée.*[27]

Burkman went on to plead for special legislation that would set the Science
Lycée apart from other lycées in Turkey. Of course Northrop himself had sought such
special legislation in behalf of the Science Lycée when he first began negotiations on
the project with the Turkish authorities. Although he continued year after year, to
plead for such a special status, to the present day (1974), the Ministry of Education still
has not set the Science Lycée apart from other secondary schools in Turkey. Northrop
once confided to friends that on hindsight he realized it had been a mistake to begin the
project in the absence of such special legislation.

9.   *Final preparatory steps taken*

As gloomy as conditions surrounding the Lycée project appeared to be in the
winter and spring of 1964, they did not prevent progress in respect to the student
selection process. Thousands of 14 year-old students in the middle (Orta) schools all
over Turkey responded to an invitation issued in February, 1964, to take the first
selection examination. The Ministry's Research and Measurement Bureau prepared
the examination which measured scholastic aptitude and science achievement. The
1,000 highest scoring students then took a second battery of tests developed by the
Bureau and administered in May, 1964. These tests and a screening by interview
selected the 100 students to be admitted to the Lycée in September, 1964. Three urban
centers of Turkey—Istanbul, Ankara, and Izmir—yielded 65% of the students enrolled
in that first-year class.

As a contribution to ensuring a high level of quality in that student testing,
the United States AID program provided fellowships for advanced study in
psychometrics at U.S. universities to six members of the Ministry. Furthermore,
Marshall and his Florida State University colleagues also worked with the Bureau staff
in preparing special examinations for that student selection.

The final chapter in the preparatory period before the October opening of the
Science Lycée was a Writing Conference at Florida State University during the sum-
mer of 1964. The thirty science teachers and the nine Turkish scientists travelled to the
U.S. in June, first to New York for a brief visit to the Bronx High School of Science —
which had often been referred to as a model in much of the planning of the Turkish
Science Lycée — then to Florida. There, four U.S. high school teachers, Robert
Carmichael (Chemistry), William Houser (Biology), Ronald Townsend (Physics) and
Allan Weinheimer (Mathematics), joined the Turkish teachers and professors for two
full months of writing course materials destined to become the textbooks for the
first-year classes of the Science Lycée. Three of the Turkish scientists, Professor Okay
(Biology), Nasuhoğlu (Physics), and Ergün (Chemistry), headed the writing groups
composed of the Turkish and U.S. Secondary School Teachers.

During that eight-week period, each group made certain modifications to the
U.S. materials and then translated them into Turkish. Consultants from U.S. science
curriculum projects again participated in the Writing Conference to assist the Turkish
participants. Although they had been tutored in English throughout the preceding
year, the Turkish science teachers encountered severe language difficulties during that
summer, both in their work and in their daily lives.

A clue to the severity of these language difficulties appears in a comment by
Marshall at that time on the Turkish teachers participating in the Summer Writing
Conference: "One of the Turkish science teachers is still in the hospital. *He speaks no
English* and this has created some problems in the hospital.[28]

Upon their return to Ankara at the close of the Writing Conference, half of the science teachers were assigned to teach in the Science Lycée, while the other half were again assigned to secondary schools in the vicinity of Ankara. All continued to participate in in-service courses conducted by the nine Turkish scientists as well as in course writing groups at the Science Lycée.

10.   *The first year of classes at the Science Lycée*
At last, that long preparatory period reached its culmination when, on 12 October 1964, the Science Lycée opened its classrooms and laboratories to the 100 selected students from throughout Turkey. The teaching staff comprised fifteen of the thirty science teachers who had spent the preceding summer at Florida State University. The other half of those thirty teachers took on teaching assignments in other lycées in the Ankara area. Working as consultants at the side of the Lycée staff during that first year were the four U.S. science teachers; Carmichael, Houser, Townsend, and Weinheimer.

There were some unfortunate gaps in the staff complement on that opening day. Unoccupied, for example, were both the librarian and guidance counselor posts. Even more unfortunate for its consequences on the program, of course, was the absence of a Lycée director. And despite repeated pleas from Marshall and Northrop to the Ministry of Education, the directorship post remained unfilled until mid-way through that opening year.

Throughout that first year, the nine Turkish scientists continued to conduct in-service courses for the Lycée teachers to familiarize them with the content and teaching methodologies of the U.S. science curriculum materials which they were using as their text materials. The teachers also continued to participate throughout that opening year in the work of modifying those U.S. course materials. As they completed modifying and translating chapters, these were turned over to the Turkish publisher, Çeviri Yayínevi, for printing.

Even though the Lycée teachers conducted their classes in the Turkish language, Turkish language continued to be a major source of difficulty for both teachers and consultants. For while the scientists and teachers worked together in their own language, the American consultants, with no command of Turkish, had to rely on interpreters in their work with the Turkish science teachers. The only way that the American consultants could examine the curriculum modifications or adaptations of the Turkish professors and teachers was by translating the Turkish language material into English.

A vivid portrayal of events and conditions at the Science Lycée during that opening year appears in a diary-like account written by Robert Donaldson, who had served throughout the year as American Co-director of the Lycée:

> My first recollection of the Lycée was one of astonishment that we would have a chance of opening school in the fall—lots of concrete and many workers scrambling from top to bottom. In the early days I signed a document with Prof. Şenvar recommending dismissal of four teachers who apparently had not contributed much to the Writing Conference. This move was to haunt us for the next three weeks. During the first week in October, I still had some hope that I might be able to learn some Turkish but the tempo was soon reached where I rationalized that I could not devote time to this.

Some time (passed) before a telephone connection could be made. The electricity had been turned on but it was off as much as on for weeks.

Food was prepared in one of the outside shacks and brought into the large hallway for serving. Its quality was questionable because we often had six or eight students lying ill in dormitories.

In the days prior to opening, we could note a cultural difference between Turkey and the United States. Then we found it was difficult to encourage the teachers to involve themselves in settling into laboratories. Some grousing was also heard concerning the proposed in-service training with the professors, with comments made that nothing had been learned in the previous semester. The teachers, in general, kept mentioning English training — but only a hard core of a few teachers really wanted to learn.

In December there were frequent intervals of no electricity, no water, no heat, no telephone. We decided to improvise and maintain the biology lab as a heated place for work. The portable heat units never really did make the laboratory warm but were sufficient for students and teachers to conduct some laboratory periods. Even so, it was difficult to encourage the physics and chemistry people to conduct the physical science laboratories in a room where they had to either borrow the equipment or carry it in.

In February it soon became apparent that it would be difficult to continue the English training program for the Turkish teachers by utilizing our own English staff members. The time was then devoted to extra work with the professors in the afternoon for curriculum development and in-service courses.

In looking back over the year, it would appear as if a great deal of progress was made. The teaching staff apparently was getting stabilized. For me it has been a busy but enjoyable year.[29]

Donaldson went on to describe the insurmountable language barriers between the U.S. science teachers and the Turkish science teachers. Their principal means of communication turned out to be mainly goodwill and shoulder-to-shoulder work together on concrete tasks.

He described dismay and confusion among the Turkish teachers over what they perceived to be a bewildering number of "bosses" over them: the Lycée Director, the Turkish professors, the Turkish and American Co-directors, and the American science teachers. He reported that both the isolated location of the Lycée—several miles from either Ankara or the main METU campus—and the inadequate transportation services contributed to low morale among the Turkish teachers.

These difficulties among the Turkish teachers had a particularly deleterious effect upon the regularity of their performance in the course writing teams. That in turn led to serious difficulties with the Turkish publishing firm of Ceviri Yajínevi which had accepted the responsibility for editing, printing and binding the texts and guides written by these groups. Their irregularity made it almost impossible for the commercially-structured publishing firm to maintain pre-arranged scheduling of work. The result was costly for the project. For example, although the original purchase order covered 6,000 pages of editorial work and 4,000 pages of production and printing, the excess work mounted to upwards of 4,100 pages of editorial work and 1,200 pages of production and printing, causing a budget over-run of $26,500. Or again, although $105,000 had been budgeted for publishing, translating and recording sound tracks on science films for the Lycée, by April, 1966, the total cost of that work had mounted to $202,000.

11.   *The Ford Foundation extends support to the Lycée
         for a second year*
         Midway through that difficult first year, Stanley Marshall prepared a detailed analytical report on the project for the consideration of the Administrative and Advisory Committee. In that report, he pointed out first some of the favourable circumstances surrounding the project:

1. The willingness of the Turkish government to recognize the importance of utilizing the talents of gifted children in appropriating a considerable sum of money for the establishment of a special school for the gifted in science.
2. The willingness of a number of Turkey's ablest professors of science and mathematics to give the project a large amount of time over a period of years.
3. The appearance in Turkey of a talented architect who has developed a serious interest in school architecture.
4. The cooperation and the support of the American scientific and educational communities.

He then drew the Committee's attention to some problems that he saw interfering with effectiveness in execution of the project:

1. Failure to interest professors from universities in Istanbul.
2. Reports have indicated that the teacher selection program was not truly national in scope.
3. It is unfortunate that more serious attention could not have been given to the study of English by all the Project Leaders.
4. The agreement for publishing the textbooks was entered into without a full understanding by both parties of the real nature of the job to be done and of the working arrangements which all parties were to observe.
5. Failure to have the full complement of teachers along with the librarian, the guidance counselor, and others.

He concluded the analysis by suggesting a series of positive steps to be taken in the future:

1. The teachers must continue to increase their understanding of their own discipline and their knowledge and skill in the teaching of modern science.

2. There should be several years of testing the modified American curriculum materials, with results of the testing serving as a basic for continuous revision.

3. The Lycée curriculum materials and new teaching methods should be extended to other lycées in Turkey at the earliest possible moment; the Science Lycée makes an admirable location for summer institutes, writing conferences, and similar activities for other lycée teachers in Turkey.

4. There should be a continuing effort to refine the student selection procedures.

5. Students must be given opportunity to express their creative talents by being provided opportunities to undertake individual project work in science and mathematics.

6. The Ministry of Education should attend to passage of a special law — or establishment of special regulations—that will free the Director and teachers of the Lycée from regulations applying to other lycées in Turkey.

7. The Administrative and Advisory Committee should give increased attention to its responsibilities in behalf of the Science Lycée and the Ministry of Education should give serious attention to the Committee's recommendations.[30]

With this analytical study as a basis, Northrop and Marshall opened an intensive debate on the merits of continuing Ford Foundation support to the Lycée project beyond that year. At one point in this debate, Marshall wrote to Ford Foundation officers in New York headquarters:

> The original plan for the project was to modest; the expenditures of money and effort which all of us are making demand that sufficient attention be given the problems listed here. The failure of any one aspect—teacher education, curriculum, proper equipment—could doom the whole project to failure. I have no doubt that the authors of the original plan foresaw the need for important changes since it would be impossible to plan so far in advance the details of so complex an operation.[31]

Northrop carried the debate to the Ministry of Education in a letter to Dr. Öktem, the Minister of Education. In that letter, Northrop indicated the willingness of the Foundation to continue its support to the Project:

> The present grant funds are inadequate for the purpose because they have been diverted, (a) to pay supplementary salaries up to the present, and (b) to provide an additional $100,000 for equipment requiring foreign exchange. However, a supplementary budget (can) cover present inadequacies and at least two further activities, both of great importance to science education in Turkey. One is a program to improve student selection and evaluation procedures, and the other is a program of summer and in-service workshops (courses) in which teachers from lycées throughout Turkey will profit from the materials and methods being developed in the Science Lycée Project.[32]

127

The Minister replied to Northrop, acknowledging his pleasure over the Foundation position on continued support to the Project and calling attention to contributions of the government to the Project:

Our Ministry has allocated TL 10 million over the past two years for building alone. It can easily be appreciated that triple the amount spent for any ordinary lycée in Turkey has already been spent for the buildings of this lycée.

The completion of the school plant, consisting of a complex of buildings, requires that our Ministry appoint qualified personnel to direct services, and we will exert our utmost efforts in this matter. Thus, in a letter (22 January 1965, No. 423-1322) to the Governor's Office in Ankara, it was requested that, in the case of the Science Lycée the usual limitations on appointments of service personnel to regular schools in the province be waived. Teachers of the Science Lycée and other teachers included in the project have been granted the opportunity to teach less than the compulsory hours required of other teachers. As a matter of fact, in view of the great need for teachers, especially in the field of science, the course taken in this instance is proof of the sincere efforts we are expending for the success of this project.

In addition, the financial liability the Ministry is undertaking in the preparation of tests to increase accuracy of student selection and in travel and per diem expenses for science teachers attending summer institutes, is substantial.

Also, positions such as guidance counselor, librarian, and shop director, which should be included in the staff of such a school for its proper operation, is one of the subjects on which our Ministry puts much emphasis.[33]

At the conclusion of the debate, Northrop submitted a Request for Grant Action to his Ford Foundation colleagues in New York, calling for a supplementary grant to the project. In that RGA, he described two new program components that would unfold under continued Ford Foundation support. Both were to enable the Lycée project to take concrete action in behalf of a wider range of students in Turkey. The first was an effort to extend the student selection process to rural areas:

Selection of scientifically talented students from a rural junior high school with inadequate offerings has proved to be a stubborn and challenging problem. For this new activity, plus research to provide overall program evaluation and guidance, $85,000 is being requested.

The second was an outreach to other Turkish lycée teachers:

Another new activity is a program of summer institutes in 1965 and 1966, through which the programs developed for the Science Lycée will be introduced to some 340 science teachers from all parts of Turkey, each of whom will return to his school not only with new knowledge and insight but also a "kit" of laboratory and demonstration materials. Funds in the amount of $144,000 are requested for this activity.[34]

128

The Ford Foundation awarded this supplementary grant in the amount of $572,000 in March, 1965, to support the Science Lycée project for one additional year.

12.   *Marshall scrutinizes the curriculum development capability*
       of the writing groups

Despite the award of the supplementary one-year grant to the Lycée project, Stanley Marshall grew increasingly sceptical of the true quality of the course writing which was going on among the different writing groups at the Science Lycée. This scepticism had first appeared after the writing sessions with the Turkish teachers at Florida State University during the summer of 1964. After that summer experience, he wrote to Donaldson:

> I feel we must reduce the pressure next summer from the level which seemed to possess the group here last summer, at least in some cases. We must emphasize that curriculum production does not lend itself to a slavish adherence to a time schedule. In the summer of 1965, I hope we can pay less attention to deadlines and in this way improve the quality of the product and the morale of the workers.[35]

At the same time, he wrote to Şenvar:

> Ever since the writing conference of last summer, various ideas about the whole matter of curriculum production and our approach to it have been taking shape in my mind. One thought comes back repeatedly. I have come to the position that we may have made one rather serious error in our approach to this problem. I believe we may have placed too much emphasis on an arbitrary time schedule and as a result have caused the entire group to work under a kind of pressure which may not be conducive to creative intellectual activity.[36]

That sceptism and doubt gnawed away at Marshall until, suddenly, in late February, 1965, he cabled to Northrop in Ankara that he was making an immediate, unplanned trip to Ankara to examine certain matters in the project about which he wanted to satisfy himself. During the few days in early March while in Ankara, Marshall then made a special study of the work being carried on by the course writing groups. During an extraordinary late night session, he drafted a long document which he entitled: "Toward the Improvement of Science Education in Turkey — A Plan." In this, he first described the shortcomings of the existing arrangements by which the course writing was being carried on and then outlined a radically different procedure for preparing materials for the project. The following excerpt from that document presents the gist of his thought on the subject:

> The remarkable success of the construction of buildings may create a false sense of well-being in the project. There is danger that those in the project may mistake excellence of physical facilities for a quality educational program. There is presently some evidence of a certain complacency, a reduction of intense effort which seem to characterize the early stages of the project. (sic).
>
> The job of preparing curriculum materials for the Science

Lycée is certain to demand more time and the talents of more people than was originally planned. There is also the recognition that the writing of textbooks, laboratory manuals, teacher's guides and similar materials is a more formidable task than it appears at first. The meaning of this is that resources in people and money must be provided to produce the high quality materials which the Lycée demands. The modification of these materials for use in other Lycées must be viewed as a matter of urgency.

It appears that anything approaching a real understanding of the nature and the purpose of the Science Lycée has not yet developed in its teachers. Nor is there a noticeable esprit de corps among them. This should not be a surprise in view of a wide variety of backgrounds and educational experience and in view of the part-time training they have received since joining the project.

A Plan for the Future:

Consideration should be given to establishing as an appendage to the Science Lycée a *curriculum development center* which would be housed at the Science Lycée but operate as an adjunct to it. It would have a separate staff of perhaps six full-time people who would be carefully selected and specially trained. It would be their job to develop curriculum materials in science and mathematics for use in the lycées and perhaps, later, at the orta (junior high) and other levels in Turkey. The advantage in having this facility attached to the Science Lycée seems to be clear: it would operate in the atmosphere of an ongoing science-oriented educational institution and would benefit from the physical proximity to laboratories, the library, expertise of the professors, teachers, and the consultants who are part of the Science Lycée Project.

As an illustration of how the Curriculum Development Center would operate, let us suppose that during a given summer, the teachers of say, mathematics, who are enrolled in a summer institute have been chosen from schools of a given type — for example, small village schools whose academic programs and curricula are not well advanced. The assignment of the staff of the Curriculum Development Center would be to meet with the village lycée teachers immediately upon their arrival for the summer institutes and determine from several days of conferences with them precisely the kind of curricula in their schools. Their job during the summer would then be to build upon these curricula as a base in developing improved instructional materials.

A plan would involve the Science Materials Development Center in a close working relationship with the Curriculum Development Center at the Science Lycée so that as new curriculum materials are developed the necessary science equipment is developed simultaneously for use by the teachers in the summer institutes and return to the lycées with them.[37]

The record contains no evidence that he was able to gain a hearing in Ankara for this remarkable plan. His underlying discontent with the curriculum development activity smouldered quietly for only a little while longer, however, for in May 1965, it broke out in a sudden strike at the writing groups in Ankara — at least at one of them. From Florida on 28 May, he wrote to the two Co-directors, Donaldson and Şenvar in Ankara, stating his dissatisfaction over the product of the physical science writing groups and proposing that they abandon their effort to prepare an original product and turn, instead, to translating one of the recently released U.S. curriculum project materials, the "Introductory Physical Science" course.

This proposal shocked and dismayed the Turkish scientists and teachers in the physical science writing groups. In a letter sent to Marshall at that time Donaldson describes the group's reactions:

> The physical science people (professors, teachers, and consultants) spent nearly four hours in discussion on Thursday. Everyone agreed that to throw everything away was most undesirable. The IPS booklet had arrived only two days before, but even with such short scrutiny, all felt that those materials were really not very challenging to the children we have at the Science Lycée — inappropriate for the bright children at our school.
>
> I felt it would be very precipitate action to swing too suddenly to either IPS or to completely cancel out all the efforts expended thus far. Both Dr. Tüzün and Dr. Zengin felt quite keenly about the wasted energies should we have to start all over again.[38]

Northrop also viewed the episode with great alarm, and came to the defense of the physical science writers by sending Marshall this telegram:

ALL PHYSICAL SCIENCE PROFESSORS TEACHERS AND CONSULTANTS UNANIMOUS FOR REDOING PRESENT MATERIALS AND AGAINST IPS MATERIALS.[39]

He then wrote to his colleagues in New York:

> A storm appears to be brewing which could have consequences for the Science Lycée Project.
>
> Marshall has undertaken to secure permissions from the various U.S. curricular projects — BSCS, CHEM Study, PSSC, and SMSG — for translation into Turkish of certain of their materials prior to adaptation for local use.
>
> One of the major undertakings of our group of Turkish professors and teachers and American consultants over the past 12-15 months has been the writing of an introductory physical sciences course that drew heavily upon well-known PSSC and the newer IPS materials. The group here has been working hard in recent weeks to edit them prior to mimeographing 25 copies of 250 pages to serve as a point of departure for the writing conference in July for seven weeks.
>
> Then came the bomb in the form of a memo from Marshall, dated 28 May. The Turks are deeply hurt, needless to say, and I am all for them.[40]

After pondering the meaning of the cable from Northrop, Marshall replied:

The arrival of your cable this afternoon has caused some fairly major perturbations in the system at this end. That there would be some shock among the professors when my memo on the physical science matter arrived was expected; but neither Burkman nor I were prepared for your message. Let me try to register our reactions:

The subject of our concern is a book that is poor by the most modest standards. The reasons are clear to Americans who have seen how it was produced, and I am sure they are clear to the Turks, too. We made an attempt to produce a physical science book by the best method we could come up with at the time — that of borrowing heavily from PSSC and CHEM Study and of filling in some of the blank spaces with materials to be written by the Turks. We recognized from the start that, like any other experiment, it might not work well and we should be prepared to accept anything from complete failure to unqualified success.[41]

In Ankara, meanwhile, the Turkish scientists and teachers worked with the American consultants to find a compromise solution. They finally proposed a set of alternatives to Marshall:

Plan A would throw away all past material and use PSSC and CHEM Study in grades nine and ten;

Plan B would continue work along the lines the physical science group had been following;

Plan C would accept the IPS materials (translated) in the first half of the ninth grade and use PSSC and CHEM Study for the second half of the ninth year and all of the tenth year;

Plan D would follow plan C except that instead of using a translated IPS in the first half of the ninth year it would use a condensed version of the disputed physical science material prepared by the Turkish course writing group.[42]

In replying to their proposal, Marshall stated his preference for Plan C and then apologized for the situation caused by his earlier suggestion. He then wrote to Northrop to explain his commitment to a high quality curriculum development component in the Lycée project:

It is important to produce materials in which the Turks have had a hand and in which they and the Ministry can take local pride. But this must be tempered by two factors: our legal and moral commitments to the copyright owners of the borrowed materials; and our commitment to quality education.

We have not been ... literally translating and not adapting the PSSC and CHEM Study materials, but neither have we modified them to any considerable degree. It is close enough to a translation so that even a casual reader would know that the passages were taken directly from those books. I have been for adaptation and against transplantation and we are still trying to do this in biology and mathematics and to a lesser degree in CHEM Study. In my own mind, I have not ruled out the possibility of doing this in the physical science course as well but I believe that our efforts to date have failed.

This does not mean that they could not succeed if we had all
of the conditions in physical science that we have in the other
fields: people of like competence, more suitable materials to
begin with, and a more realistic approach to curriculum production. But we would also need time, much more time than we have
now.[43]

13. *The Science Lycée Project conducts its first summer institute*
     for Turkey lycée teachers

The supplementary grant awarded by the Ford Foundation to the Ministry of
Education (see Section 11 above) made it possible for the Science Lycée to organize the
first summer institute for science teachers in Turkey. This institute, convened during
the summer, 1965, represented, a significant advance in the history of the Project.
As Marshall noted:

The project in my view is now entering a *second phase* with
new requirements and opportunities. Until now, we have been
involved in the gross problems of getting the Science Lycée in
operation and of meeting deadlines. We must now consolidate our
gains; this means placing the main emphasis on improving the
quality of education — in the curriculum materials we produce, in
the teacher education program, and in the services to be provided to other lycées.[44]

Close to 100 teachers of mathematics and biology from lycées throughout
Turkey attended the institute, receiving a stipend of 20 Turkish lira ($2.00) per day.
The following Turkish university professors served as the lecturers in that first insti-
tute:

Mathematics
  Dr. Tuğrul Taner, METU
  Prof. Esat Egesoy, Ankara University
  Prof. Ali, Ergün, Ankara University
  Dr. Okan Gürel, METU
  Prof. Orhan Icen, Istanbul University
  Doç. Dr. M. G. Ikeda, Ege University

Biology
  Prof. Selâhattin Okay, Ankara University
  Prof. Kâmil Karamanoğlu, Ankara University
  Prof. Yusuf Vardar, Ege University
  Prof. Atif Sengun, Istanbul University

Serving as consultants to the summer institute as well as to the course writing
groups were the following U.S. scientists:

  D. Murray Alexander (Physics), Foothill College, California
  D.M. Ritter (Chemistry), University of Washington
  John A. Brown (Mathematics), University of Delaware
  Claude A. Welch (Biology), Michigan State University

In his address to the assembled teachers, lecturers and consultants on the
opening day of the summer institute, Northrop stated:

Every year the Science Lycée Project takes another major
step forward.

133

The first step was in 1962, when the Project was proposed by a study committee appointed by the Minister of Education.

In 1963 the professors and teachers began their work together of training and writing.

In 1964 the Science Lycée opened its doors to the first class of 100 students.

Now, in 1965, begins still another phase of the Science Lycée Project — the bringing together this summer of additional professors and teachers for writing and training with a view to spreading the responsibilities and benefits of the Project to other parts of Turkey.

Believing with many other people that this aspect of the Science Lycée Project may be the most important of all, I should like on behalf of the Ford Foundation to welcome the new professors and teachers, to urge you all to work hard to make the best of this opportunity, and to wish you every success in the weeks ahead.[45]

14. *The Science Lycée enters its second full year of operation*
The Science Lycée opened its doors in September, 1965 to the second entering class of 100 students recruited from throughout Turkey, to begin its second full year of operation. In a sense, it had now come of age. It possessed buildings with fully equipped classrooms, laboratories, library and student dormitories. Its teaching staff was at hand, and available were Turkish-language textbooks and laboratory guides.

The Science Lycée Project entered that second year under a totally new administrative team. Both Cemil Senvar and Robert Donaldson had left their posts as Turkish and American Co-directors respectively. Taking over as American Co-director (and as the representative in Turkey of Florida State University) was D. Murray Alexander, the physics teacher who had come to Ankara as a consultant for the Summer 1965 institute. The post of Turkish Co-director remained unfilled for many months, however, until the Administrative and Advisory Committee was finally able to persuade Professor Rauf Nasuhoğlu (physics department of Ankara University and leader of the physics course writing team in the project) to serve in that post.

Alexander had served in the position of Co-director for only a few months when he began to encounter severe administrative problems. He quickly sized these up as due to the weakness in the administrative link between the Lycée Project and the Ministry of Education:

> During the two months of my tenure as American Co-director of the Project, it has become increasingly clear to me that progress towards the full achievement of the Project goal is being seriously hampered by the failure to adapt and strengthen administrative procedures which would allow the freedom for experimentation and change which is so vital to any forward-looking education project. Since August the 2nd, 1965, nine meetings of the Administrative and Advisory Committee have been scheduled but only three have taken place — on the other occasions the meetings were cancelled by representatives of the Ministry. It surely indicates a very serious breakdown in the functioning of the Committee when the Project is deprived of decisions which are essential for its progress.

It is clear that for some time the Committee has not been fulfilling the leadership role originally assigned to it. It is particularly unfortunate that the Committee has seen no need to keep abreast of the Project development to the extent of providing a clear organisational framework, for the *operation of the Lycée* on the one hand and the *development of the Project* on the other. The organisational framework provided in 1963 before the opening of the Lycée is out of date and does not reflect the current situation of the Lycée and the Project.

I strongly urge that we should seek a high-level meeting with the appropriate Ministry of Education officials to discuss ways of reorganising the Administrative and Advisory Committee so that it can fulfill the function envisaged for it, when the original understanding was reached between the Ministry of Education and the Ford Foundation.[46]

Alexander pressed the Ministry of Education to recognize the need for stronger, more effective working links between itself and the Science Lycée Project, but to no avail. Consequently, the Project leaders struggled along that year under increasingly difficult circumstances. Northrop was particularly hard hit by this situation, for mid-way through the year, he had the responsibility of preparing a recommendation to his New York colleagues on the question of renewing grant support to the Project for an additional year. Unable to engage in meaningful discussion with the Ministry through appropriate channels for that purpose, and as the deadline neared for a Foundation decision on the matter of grant extension, Northrop finally decided to recommend a minimum grant, what he termed a "tie-off" position which would provide only enough funds to avoid an abrupt break with the Turkish scientists who had remained loyal to the Science Lycée Project. To his New York colleagues he wrote:

We can all look back with considerable satisfaction on the job done to date for the Science Lycée proper. The buildings are up, the equipment installed, two waves of students have been selected and admitted, a good core staff of science teachers has been trained, and new course materials for the Lycée have been written.

I wish we could look ahead with comparable confidence to the second stage originally envisaged for the Project — extension through Turkey of the teacher training activities, the new curriculum, and the new teaching methods. The requisite body of experience and devoted professors and teachers are for it, the American consultants and we in this office are for it, and *only the Ministry of Education seems not to understand the opportunity within its grasp.* (R.H.M.)

Under the circumstances it seems best to plan at this time for only one more year of Foundation support of the project. I believe the Foundation owes it to the Turkish professors and teachers to see the course writing job through to a conclusion.

If this terminal year materializes, it seems clear to me that Florida State University should be asked to continue its role in the project during that year. On balance, Stan Marshall and his colleagues have done a good job, the present difficulties are not of their making.[47]

135

15.   *The Ministry of Education renews its interest
in the Science Lycée Project*

During those dark and difficult days, Northrop and Alexander, in close liaison with the few Science Lycée Project supporters on the Turkish side continued quietly to persuade the Ministry of Education to improve its stance toward the Project. This policy of patience and persistence eventually paid off, for abruptly, on 25 April 1966, the Director General of Secondary Education, İbrahim Cengiz, announced his intention to reconstitute the Administrative and Advisory Committee and to convene it without delay. He followed up this announcement by appointing the following as members of the new Advisory Committee:

Erdal' İnönü
Bahri Domanic .... University professors
Yusuf Vardar
Chairmen:
Hasan Acar .... Member, Board of Education
İbrahim Cengiz .... Director General
of Secondary Education
Rauf Nasuhoğlu .... Turkish Co-director
D. Murray Alexander .... American Co-director
Necdet Onur .... Science Lycée Director

Northrop followed up this display of rekindled interest at once by calling directly upon the Undersecretary of Education, Ferid Saner, to discuss the future course of the Project:

(It was) an occasion to discuss with Ferid Bey with complete frankness and great earnestness, the Ford Foundation's concern over the decreasing interest in the Project on the part of the Ministry, and its reluctance therefore to carry the Project more than one additional year. I made it clear that the scientists and teachers were enthusiastic, as well as the Foundation. It seemed, I went on to say, that only the Ministry of Education failed to recognize the importance of the work done to date and the opportunity it offered for the improvement of science teaching throughout Turkey in the future.

Ferid Bey listened with great attentiveness and sympathy. He was quick to observe that it is easy for a splendid idea of this sort to become lost in the web of bureaucracy in the Ministry with its many severe problems of shortcomings in all areas, and observed that what was needed was an individual or two in the Ministry to keep a special eye out for it. He said he would urge Hasan Acar to pay special attention to the Lycée Project and that he would assign an assistant special responsibility for science education in general and the Science Lycée Project in particular. I came away feeling I had really succeeded in getting through to Ferid Bey, and that his sympathetic interest had in fact been aroused.[48]

Saner demonstrated the sincerity of his interest in the Science Lycée Project by attending the next meeting of the newly reconstituted Advisory Committee on 20 May 1966. That meeting has proved in retrospect to be a turning point in the history of

136

the Project, for in it Ferid Saner expressed the clear interest of the Ministry of Education in extending the results of the Project to schools throughout Turkey. He reviewed with the Committee the regulations of the Ministry governing schools and invited the Committee to prepare a draft proposal for a new program for extending science education innovations to the schools within the framework of those regulations.

The new Advisory Committee then began to convene regularly and to deal decisively with the administrative questions of the day. It lost no time in completing the plans for a second institute for the Summer of 1966. It prepared plans for a special international conference on mathematics education at the Science Lycée. Plans were also approved for a conference on guidance and evaluation. Of the many administrative details it had to clear up, two stood out for their importance to the on-going welfare of the Project: approval of a proposed budget for the continuation of the Project; and a decision that salary supplements would be paid to teachers on the basis of accomplishment of specific additional tasks to the normal teaching loads.

The improving relations between the Ministry and the Science Lycée Project encouraged Northrop to re-open discussions on the topic of extending Ford Foundation support to the Project. Most importantly, through the access he found to the Ministry's thinking, he was able to discern an underlying dissatisfaction on the Ministry's part with the way earlier Foundation grants had been structured. To meet this Ministry objection, he recommended a change in the pattern of the grant at the time of its renewal:

> It became increasingly clear to me that people in the Minis-
> try from the Director General of Education to the Minister him-
> self, were increasingly resentful over having to request of the
> Foundation funds destined to be withheld and used for American
> salaries and services. It is easy for the Minister to understand
> and defend requests for Turkish salaries and services, and for
> equipment — that is, to become the property of the Ministry. But
> in the case of American salaries and services, it is harder for him
> to put his finger on just what he is getting, and that makes it
> difficult — and even politically dangerous — for him to justify.
> Nor is resentment of this sort limited to the Ministry. No matter
> how well disposed the Turkish professors in the project may be,
> they cannot help but make invidious comparisons of salaries, for
> Americans are part of the overall request.[49]

Once again, then, in mid-1966, the Ford Foundation awarded a supplementary grant to the Ministry of Education of Turkey for support of the Science Lycée Project, only this time the award was made in two parts. The first, in the amount of $265,000 went directly to the Ministry chiefly to support continued writing and publishing of the Lycée text materials. The second part of the award went to Florida State University to cover those Lycée Project related costs which it was incurring, such as the salary of the American Co-director and other professional support to the Project.

The Science Lycée Project Directors received a letter from the Ministry of Education in October of that year requesting them to take the first step in the direction of placing the Lycée materials into other schools in Turkey:

> Our Ministry of Education finds it suitable to look into the
> possibility of administering the programs used in the Science
> Lycée and other lycées.

In this context, it is desired that the first experiment start in the Bahcelievler Experimental School during the 1966-67 academic year.

It will be appropriate to get the academic support of the Science Lycée Project personnel, books, and equipment.

Hence, it is desired that a committee be set up, including the Experimental School Director (and) the four teachers in each discipline who will teach the courses, Turkish and American Co-directors of the Project, to conduct these activities in accordance with the desired goals. I request your help and cooperation in this matter and extend my regards.[50]

That first pilot effort in extending the Science Lycée Project proceeded throughout the 1966-1967 school year with Science Lycée staff assisting teachers at the Bahçeliever School to use the Science Lycée materials in all of their science classes. Moreover, that first experience traced the initial outlines of the framework for a future large-scale extension of the Science Lycée materials.

16.   *The Ministry of Education establishes the*
        Science Education Development Commission

Throughout that 1966-1967 period, two initiatives taken by the Ministry of Education set events running along courses that began to converge on an eventual major new program for science education improvement in Turkey. As mentioned above, the pilot program at the Bahçelievlar School was one such initiative. The other was the charge by Ferid Saner to the Advisory Committee at its 20 May meeting to prepare a proposal for a program of large-scale extension of the Science Lycée Project materials. One member of that committee, Rauf Nasuhoğlu, had been specifically asked to draft a paper that could form the basis for such a proposal. He presented his paper at the 11 July 1966 meeting of the Advisory Committee, setting forth the first concrete framework of the future program:

> This experiment of establishing a special school using modern materials and instructional methods, has shown clearly the need to extend similar efforts to the other lycées of Turkey. At first, a few pilot schools should be selected to test the appropriateness of using the Science Lycée materials, possibly at a slower pace and with larger classes, handled by teachers who have been through the summer institute program of the Science Lycée Project and who can be assisted during the year by the Science Lycée teachers. Later the efforts of the Project can be expanded to lycées in other parts of Turkey, and to the development of suitable materials for the orta and lower levels. To establish a framework within which an expanded effort in science education development might take place, possibly with additional Ford Foundation support, the following broad outlines are suggested:
>
> A new official unit should be established by the Ministry of Education. This new unit should include the present Science Lycée Project and be given a title which will reflect its broader scope and avoid confusion with the Science Lycée, which would continue to be the basic experimental science school for selected

students. The unit might be called the Science Education Development Committee, emphasizing the important role to be played by a committee representing a combination of scientific and educational interests and entrusted with administrative authority for the direction of the development program.[51]

This draft proposal from the Advisory Committee went to the Ministry of Education where it added to the reports of the experiences emerging from the pilot project at the Bahçelievler School. Thus, on 11 March 1967, Under-Secretary of Education Ferid Saner wrote to Northrop to report that:

> The success of the programs prepared by the Science Lycée Project has urged us to use these programs at the Bahçelievler Experimental Lycée and the encouraging results have led us to seek the opportunity of using these materials on a wider scale. Therefore, we have decided to establish a special Commission for Development of Science Education, composed of university scientists, to promote science education in our country.[52]

The Ministry of Education followed up this notice from Saner by issuing its official Memorandum Number 1240, dated 28 March 1967, in which it declared its intention to establish a Science Education Development Commission under the organization of the Ministry's Board of Education. The Ministry then prepared a charter for the new institution, setting forth its purposes, functions, working procedures and financial resources. It described those functions as follows:

(1) To promote development of new science and mathematics for pilot schools

(2) To arrange for supply of teaching materials to the pilot schools

(2) To arrange for appropriate training of teachers in the pilot schools

(4) To smooth out problems in the schools related to university entrance examinations.

The charter went on to designate the Science Lycée as the "number one" laboratory school under the academic supervision of the new Commission. It called for the Advisory Committee to terminate its existence and transfer to the new Commission all of its duties and responsibilities and set April 4, 1967 as the effective day for this change.

Finally, the Ministry of Education appointed the following as members of the newly created Commission:

Hüsnü Círitli — Chairman
  (Head of Board of Education)

Bahattin Baysal
  (METU)

Rauf Nasuhoğlu
  (Ankara University)

Ali Ríza Berkem
  (Istanbul University)

Mustafa Uluöz
  (Secretary General of the Scientific and Technical Research Council)

17.   *The SEDC sets up the Pilot Lycée Program*

The new Commission lost no time in planning its future program. Within a few weeks of its formation, the Commission decided to launch a pilot program for extending the Science Lycée materials to other lycées in Turkey. It designated the following nine lycées for participation in this pilot program:

Ankara	Gazi Lycée
	Bahçelievler Lycée
	Balkiraz Lycée
Istanbul	**Kadikoy Kiz Lycée**
	Attatürk Kiz Lycée
	Attatürk Erkek Lycée
Aydín	Lycée
Erzurum	Lycée
Izmir	Attatürk Lycée

An additional nine teacher training colleges were also included in the pilot program.

Hüsnü Círítli, Chairman of the Commission, wrote to Northrop on 8 May 1967, acknowledging the influence of the Science Lycée Project upon science education in Turkey and requesting support from the Ford Foundation for launching the pilot program. His letter is a lucid exposé of the educational strategy of the Commission as well as a heart-warming testimony to the earlier work of the Science Lycée.

The Scientific and Technical Council of Turkey (TÜBITAK) then agreed to act as the sponsor of the pilot program, and at a meeting of its Science Board on 19 August 1967, voted formally to conduct the pilot program as one of its research projects under the title:

> "Research on the possibility of conducting science education at other Turkish Lycées using the courses developed by the Science Lycée Project."

This somewhat unprecedented and highly unconventional arrangement whereby an official scientific body, lying outside the Ministry of Education, would act as the sponsor of a large-scale educational operation conducted by a commission of the Ministry of Education, naturally aroused suspicions and doubts within and without the Ministry and the TÜBITAK. Discussions continued for many months both in TÜBITAK and between TÜBITAK and the Ministry of Education to clarify the precise areas of responsibility between them.

Finally, on 20 October 1967, after a delay of five months from the time the Commission had first submitted its proposal to Northrop, the Ford Foundation awarded a grant in the amount of $150,000 to TÜBITAK, for the pilot program. The Commission then organized a small secretariat to look after its day-by-day affairs and appointed Bahattin Örnekol as its first full-time administrator. His initial responsibilities were to regularize the financial arrangements with TÜBITAK, to assign work orders to the Ankara Equipment Center for manufacturing the equipment to be placed in the nine pilot lycées, and to organize in-service institutes for the teachers from those lycées.

This steady march of events was momentarily halted when, once again, political disruptions in the country brought with them a change in Ministry of Education leadership. This change resulted in a complete turnover in the composition of the Science Education Development Commission. Hüsnu Círítli was replaced by Zekâi Baloğlu as Head of the Board of Education. Bahattin Örnekol took leave of his position as the Commission's administrator. In late December, 1967, Zekâi Baloğlu as Chairman of the Commission (SEDC), met with Cahit Arf, the Secretary General of TÜBITAK, to arrive at a new protocol governing the SEDC and TÜBITAK cooperation. They then confirmed the following as members of the Science Education Development Commission:

Representing the Ministry of Education:

1. Zekâi Baloğlu (Chairman)
2. Remzi Erkoç (Secretary General of the Commission)
3. Hasan Acar

Representing the scientific community:

1. Esat Egesoy, Ankara University
2. Vedat Enüstün, METU
3. Kamil Karamanoğlu, Ankara University
4. Rauf Nasuhoğlu, Ankara University
5. Secretary General of TÜBITAK

In July 1968, the administrator of SEDC, Remzi Erkoç, resigned from his position as Secretary General for reasons of health and was replaced by Sakir Soykal. Soykal then created a General Secretariat of SEDC, which included himself and three Ministry of Education colleagues, Mehmet Bertan, Müslim Pekgöz and Cemil Gür.

It was this group that now carried on the day-by-day work of the SEDC. Their first assignment was to establish working links with teachers and administrators in the nine pilot schools to assist them in obtaining textbooks and equipment needed for their participation in the pilot program. That program continued throughout the school year 1967-68 under a government allocation of 5 million Turkish lira ($500,000). The Ford Foundation provided an additional sum of $150,000 for purchase of translation rights to foreign books and films and to import foreign equipment and supplies for building up the Educational Equipment Manufacturing Center in Ankara.

Next, the SEDC commissioned an evaluation team to study the performance of teachers and students of the nine pilot lycées in their use of the Science Lycée materials over the three-year period, from 1968 to 1970. That team consisted of 14 science professors and teachers from participating universities and lycées, two specialists from the Tests and Measurements Bureau of the Ministry of Education, and a consultant on educational measurements from Hacettepe University, Fuat Turgut. Over a four-month period, the three "staff" members of the evaluation team conducted training workshops to acquaint the 14 professors and teachers with evaluation procedures.

In June, 1970, the evaluation team convened a two-week intensive evaluation seminar at the Science Lycée with teachers from the nine pilot lycées, scientists and Science Lycée teachers who constituted the course-writing groups, members of SEDC and the four SEDC General Secretariat members. The seminar first reviewed three years of experience in the pilot lycées and then recommended that the project be expanded to a broader range of schools throughout Turkey.

In a report in which he summarized the findings of the evaluation team Fuat Turgut points out that:

1. According to the results of the achievement tests, student
   achievement in the pilot lycées varied between 25% and 40%
   of expected achievement, and in the Science Lycée between
   50% and 70%. In other words, results of using the Science

141

Lycée materials in the nine pilot lycées were only half of those attained in the Science Lycée.

2. The general attitude of pilot lycée teachers towards the modern programs was positive. They were able to understand the general spirit of the new materials and found them superior to the traditional materials they had been using.

3. Teachers in the pilot lycées were unable to fit the Science Lycée materials into the limited timetable for science classes which they were obliged to observe.

4. The most important factor in student learning was the teacher's capability, for high-achieving classes invariably were correlated with the presence of better teachers. Another important factor in student learning was thought to be student intelligence, but correlating between the achievement test scores and the scholastic aptitude test scores were so low that it was necessary to conclude that poor teaching accounted for the observed failure to call forth the promise lying in students.

His concluding statement attempted to justify the use of the Science Lycée materials in the proposed extension to all schools in Turkey:

"The application of the modern programs was not as successful as we hoped it would be for a variety of reasons. The factors which affected achievement have been discussed in this report. We may thus safely conclude that within a completely renovated secondary education system, these modern programs could be successfully applied."[53]

An informative report on the collaboration between SEDC and the nine pilot lycées in the period 1967-1970 also appears in a summary of that pilot program prepared by the Chairman of the SEDC Zekâi Bologlu.[54]

18.   *The Commission enlarges the scope of its outreach*

The agenda of the 8th National Educational Congress (Sûra), convening in September, 1970, reviewed the progress made to date in the SEDC-conducted pilot project in the nine lycées. That Congress also reviewed the recommendations found in the report of the evaluation team. These called for major changes in the Turkish educational system, including a re-patterning of the school sequence of grades to a 5-3-3 pattern and the institution of a common ninth-year curriculum for all secondary schools followed by options for the final two years—one leading to higher education and the other a terminal course. The Congress gave its approval to these far-reaching recommendations and, subsequently, the Ministry of Education issued an official decree that introduced them into the educational system of Turkey.

These changes opened the educational system to innovations, particularly those which the SEDC was prepared to introduce in science and mathematics. This confronted the SEDC with an enormous workload, of course, for it represented an enlargement of its work from the nine lycée pilot program level to one that would be dealing with about 400 lycées throughout the country. The Ministry of Education estimated that the expansion would require $5 million in local costs and over $500,000 in foreign exchange costs, primarily for equipment. The SEDC therefore presented a request to the Ford Foundation for a grant of $200,000 to partially offset these foreign exchange costs. The Ford Foundation responded positively to this request awarding a sum of $200,000 in 1972 to TÜBITAK, the Scientific Research Council, which acted as paymaster for SEDC in such matters. That support enabled the SEDC to initiate the first phase of a planned extension of the Science Lycée Project materials which included 100 regular lycées and 89 lycée-level teacher training schools.

At the same time, the SEDC decided to mount another large-scale outreach to the schools by placing a Turkish translation of the Introductory Physical Science (IPS) course (another U.S. National Science Foundation sponsored curriculum program) into the ninth-year classes of these 89 lycées. To provide additional support to the SEDC in this venture, the Ford Foundation then awarded a grant of $32,000 to the organization that had prepared the original IPS materials, the Physical Science Group in Massachusetts, U.S.A. Earlier (at the same time SEDC was contemplating extending the IPS materials to the lycées), the director of the Physical Science Group, Dr. Uri Haber-Schaim, had paid an exploratory visit to Turkey and had agreed to provide useful consultant services to the SEDC in that implementation effort. The Ford Foundation grant to the Physical Science Group represented a distinct shift in its policy of support to the SEDC. The Foundation would now begin placing support more selectively upon specific consultant and training needs rather than continuing to give general program support to the Commission. Through that grant to the Physical Science Group the Foundation also attempted to provide the SEDC a stout "resource base" upon which SEDC could draw for a variety of services. In time, the SEDC did ask for the services of one of the Physical Science Group equipment specialists and also for an inspection visit by Dr. Haber-Schaim to a selected number of the lycées where IPS course materials had been introduced.

The SEDC also received support for its expanded efforts from sources other than the Ford Foundation. For example, in 1971, the U.S.A.I.D. program in Turkey provided for a consultant, Dr. Charles Whitmer from the Washington staff of the U.S. National Science Foundation, to visit the SEDC in Ankara. At the close of his visit, Whitmer prepared a report[55] in which he recommended AID funds to support at least five Turkish teachers as participants in IPS summer institutes in the U.S. as a way of training a corps of IPS teachers for the lycées accepting the IPS materials.

As the SEDC got deeper into the task of disseminating the Science Lycée Project materials and the IPS materials to a large number of lycées spread over a vast area of Turkey, it gained increased awareness of the problems entailed by such an effort. Its administrative position as an advisory arm of the Board of Education of the Ministry placed it in a favorable position to foster cooperation among the various Ministry departments necessarily involved in dissemination of materials to the lycées. In addition to the departments on teacher education, primary and secondary education, examinations, and textbook publishing, the Educational Materials Development Center of the Ministry of Education became more and more central to that dissemination. That Center, originally established in 1961 under a grant to Turkey from the Organisation for Economic Cooperation and Development (OECD), began in 1972 to manufacture many of the IPS equipment items required by the SEDC for its dissemination activity.

19. *The Science Lycée declines in importance as a creative center of innovations*

An anomaly in this general scene of increasing effort by the SEDC to carry the benefits of the Science Lycée Project to all of the schools of Turkey is the decline of the Science Lycée itself as a source of innovations in science education. The charter for the SEDC issued by the Ministry in March, 1967, clearly specified that the Science Lycée was to be the "number one" laboratory school of the Commission. However, the record reveals that a deterioration in the quality of the work carried on at the Science Lycée set in shortly after that charter was written and that the SEDC has, in fact, not relied on the Lycée as its laboratory school. The Science Lycée seems to have reached its zenith in 1967 at the time of graduating its first class of students. At that high moment, Northrop wrote:

> Of the Science Lycée's first graduating class of 100 students, 73 passed the entrance examinations at Middle East Technical University.
>
> Among these 73, the top scores in physics, chemistry, mathematics and engineering were Science Lycée graduates. In sum, of 40 top places, Science Lycée graduates occupied 20, or exactly half of them.
>
> Note also student career choices. About half of them still elected engineering, to be sure. But what warms my heart is that *no more* than half elected engineering, that only 10 elected medicine, and that 25 chose teaching and research, 4 physics, and 4 mathematics. Not a bad first-year trend away from engineering and medicine and toward natural sciences.[56]

A year later, however, following his visit to the Lycée, a Ford Foundation officer described the low morale among the Science Lycée teachers in these words:

> The teachers feel they are doing more work than is required of teachers at ordinary lycées, but they are not being paid extra for their labor. They are forbidden to teach at private schools, but some of them are doing this at night anyway.
>
> In addition, they feel the Ministry is applying pressure on them by assigning new graduates of teacher training institutes to serve as apprentice teachers at the Science Lycée. The Science Lycée teachers fear that these younger teachers are being trained to become teachers in the Science Lycée and that their introduction on a large scale would ruin the Science Lycée. But once these young people are trained, the Ministry will be able to hold them as a threat against the Science Lycée teachers.
>
> If SEDC does not approve the salary supplements, many of them [Science Lycée teachers] will resign at the end of this school year.[57]

At the present time (1974), the Science Lycée occupies a sentinel-like view from its hillside site on the edge of the METU campus over the rapidly encroaching gecekondus (these shanty-towns that surround all large cities in developing countries) lying between it and the main part of Ankara some three or four miles distant. From the outside, its building still appear imposing and unique for a secondary school in any country. Yet, once inside those buildings, and especially once in contact with the present staff members, the visitor soon realizes that the Science Lycée is now an ordinary secondary school, struggling against the same problems of niggardly budgets, inadequate equipment, and indifference among teachers that afflict most secondary

144

schools in most economically-deprived countries. There is here and there a still-glowing ember of the original fire that burned as the "great" Science Lycée praised by Northrop on that halcyon day in June, 1967. Those embers are the one or two teachers who still hold, with unbelievable personal commitment, that original vision for a special high school of science for gifted students in Turkey. Their lot is made difficult by lack of equally inspirited colleagues, lack of spare parts (now almost unobtainable due to foreign exchange costs) for equipment which, as a result, must be shelved, and their own lack of involvement in wider creative tasks such as course-writing.

This foregoing epitaph on the Science Lycée means that the SEDC is now unable to turn to it for fresh inputs to the dissemination activities which the SEDC is managing so successfully. This poses a problem. Changing educational and sociological conditions in Turkey are creating needs for new science materials in the schools of the country. The SEDC lacks, however, a dynamic and creative source of such materials.

TURKEY FOOTNOTES

1. METU — Middle East Technical University.
2. Memorandum of 27 October 1964 by E. P. Northrop, Ford Foundation files.
3. Letter of March 10, 1959 from Celâl Yardimci, Minister of Education in Turkey to Forest F. Hill, Vice President, The Ford Foundation, New York.
4. Letter of May 11, 1959 from E. P. Northrop to Celâl Yardimci, Minister of Education.
5. Letter of February 8, 1960 from Atif Benderlioğlu, Minister of Education to E. P. Northrop.
6. Letter of September 30, 1960 from E. P. Northrop to Professor Râtip Berker, Istanbul University.
7. Sahap-Bey refers to Sahap Kocatopcu, Minister of Industry, mentioned in the previous paragraph.
8. The ruling General, following the military coup of May, 1960.
9. Letter of January 27, 1961 EPN to Dr. Nejat Eczacibasi of Istanbul.
10. A position paper dated 10 February 1961 entitled "Science in Turkey" submitted by Northrop to Ford Foundation in New York.
11. M. S. Bilman: Stable Characteristics of the Turkish Lycées, Maarif Basimevi, Ankara (1960).
12. Northrop's notes of discussion with Tahtakilic on 21 April, 1961.
13. Northrop actually did visit some of the building sites suggested by the Ministry of Education but found all of them unsatisfactory.
14. Translation of section of Ministry of Education paper presented at Seventh National Educational Congress (Sûra), 5 February 1962.
15. 22 March 1962 letter from Northrop to F. Champion Ward, Ford Foundation, New York.
16. Attesting to this, for example, is the following statement found in a January 15, 1965 Memorandum prepared by Marshall: During the weeks preceding my first visit to Ankara, I studied the Report of the Committee Studying the Subject of Establishing a Science Lycée in Turkey. (It) had considerable influence on my thinking both with respect to the project which I was about to undertake and in regard to my approach to the problems of education generally. The Report of the Committee has continued to provide the guiding philosophy for the Project as viewed by the American Co-director. It is clear that the Permanent Administrative and Advisory Committee, the Turkish Co-director, and others in the Project have likewise been influenced by the Report. To the extent that the Project has succeeded, its success must be attributed to our adherence to that philosophy; and where obstacles have appeared to delay and to thwart progress, these obstacles have deterred us only when we have failed to follow closely the guiding philosophy expressed in the Committee's Report. (January 15, 1965 memorandum, Marshall to Administrative and Advisory Committee).
17. Report, page 4.
18. Appendix 2 to the Report, pages 7 and 8.
19. Request for Grant Action, dated September 28, 1962, submitted by Northrop to the Ford Foundation.
20. May, 1962 letter, Northrop to F. Champion Ward, Ford Foundation, New York.
21. Hereinafter referred to as the "Project Document."
22. 19 December 1962 letter from E. P. Northrop to Sevket Hatipoğlu.
23. 28 December 1962 letter from Northrop to F. C. Ward, Ford Foundation, New York.

145

24. Request for Grant Action, dated September 28, 1962 and submitted by Northrop to the Ford Foundation, New York.

25. 21 January 1963 letter, Northrop to Harvey Hall, Ford Foundation, New York.

26. 3 July 1963 letter, J. S. Marshall to Northrop.

27. Letter of 6 May 1964 from Burkman to Northrop.

28. 8 July 1964 letter Marshall to Northrop.

29. 26 August 1965 summary report by Robert Donaldson.

30. These statements are adapted from the 15 January 1965 memorandum by Marshall addressed to the Administrative and Advisory Committee.

31. 6 July 1964 letter J. S. Marshall to Harvey Hall, Ford Foundation, New York.

32. 24 Nov. 1964 letter EPN to Minister of Education.

32. 1 February 1965 letter Dr. Ibrahim Öktem, Minister of Education, to E. P. Northrop.

33. From 12 February 1965 Request for Grant Action.

34. 12 January 1965 letter from Marshall to Robert Donaldson in Ankara.

35. 13 January 1965 letter from Marshall to Cemil Şenvar.

37. Excerpts from a March, 1965 memorandum for the files written by J. S. Marshall.

38. 4 June 1965 letter, Donaldson to J. S. Marshall.

39. 4 June 1965 cable, EPN to Marshall.

40. 10 June 1965 letter, E. P. Northrop to Harvey Hall, Ford Foundation, New York.

41. 7 June 1965 letter, J. S. Marshall to E. P. Northrop.

42. 4 June 1965 letter from Robert Donaldson in Ankara to J. S. Marshall in Florida.

43. 18 June 1965 letter from Marshall to Northrop.

44. 8 March 1965 memo Marshall to Osman Ülküman.

45. 19 July 1965 Opening Remarks by E. P. Northrop.

46. November, 1965 Memorandum, D. M. Alexander to E. P. Northrop.

47. 1966 letter from E. P. Northrop to Thomas Scott, Ford Foundation in New York.

48. 11 May 1966 memorandum to the files by Northrop.

49. 4 March 1966 letter from E. P. Northrop to Stanley Marshall.

50. 7 October 1966 letter from Director General of Education Ibrahim Cengiz to Science Lycée Project Co-directors.

51. Draft proposal for Future of Science Lycée Project, meeting of 11 July 1966.

52. 11 March 1967 letter from Under-Secretary of Education Ferid Şaner to E. P. Northrop.

53. From an English language translation of Turgut's report, "An Evaluation of the Pilot Lycée's Experimental Mathematics and Science Curricula."

54. Available from its author, Zekâi Baloğlu, Chairman, Board of Education, Government of Turkey, Ankara.

55. April 14, 1971 report by Charles A. Whitmer to the NSF, "Visit as Science Education Consultant to the Turkish Ministry of Education, March 28--April 9, 1971."

56. 4 August 1967 letter, Northrop to J. D. Kingsley, Ford Foundation, New York.

57. 22 December 1968 memorandum for files by James Curley, Ford Foundation office, Ankara.

PART II
Analysis and Conclusions

Introduction

The preceding case histories, just as they stand as descriptive and interpreted accounts, throw a surprising amount of illumination on the two principal subjects of interest in this study, viz., innovating in science education and providing technical assistance needed for innovating in science education.

To illustrate, on the first topic, they describe the background to many of the more important decisions that were taken on curriculum matters. They describe details of procedures followed in devising educational innovations. They reveal problems encountered in bringing about change in educational systems in developing countries. Of particular interest is their portrayal of personalities, styles, convictions and, on occasion, even emotions, as forces that often direct the flow of events in a project. This was true in the Brazil Case History, for example, where the zeal and imagination of a single scientist, Isaias Raw, carried that project from its earliest "one-man" stage to its present-day form as a national-level unit with an outstanding record for innovation.

Those accounts also have much to say on that other topic, providing the technical assistance required for innovating in education. Throughout the case histories there are "lively" presentations of internal debates among Ford Foundation officers on critical issues in providing technical assistance. Even without being interpreted, the case histories convey an awareness of salient features of the Ford Foundation commitment to meeting the technical assistance needs of the projects: responsiveness to changing circumstances arising in the projects, comprehensiveness of coverage, timeliness, generosity, etc. Thus, those uninterpreted accounts do indeed have a useful side, a fact that supplies much of the justification for my having prepared them in the first place. In light of all the foregoing, why, then, an analysis as a second stage in this public review?

For all I might say in support of those purely descriptive and uninterpreted accounts, there is nevertheless a strong case to be made for a systematic and critical analysis of the experiences of these five projects as the task of a second stage. In my judgement, only through such analysis can those many deeper-lying meanings and conclusions contained in that experience be drawn out and given voice as lessons taught by the authority of experience.

To bring to light the full range of conclusions contained in this collaborative experience between the Foundation and the leaders of these projects, I examine that experience from two points of view. First, I look at it from the viewpoint of the educator concerned with improving science education. In this way I draw out those conclusions that bear upon innovation and change in science education, especially in the

147

context of developing countries. This makes up Chapter 1, which I entitle, "Lessons on Innovating in Science Education." I then shift my angle of vision to look at this collaborative experience from the point of view of the agency providing support to educational innovators. From this vantage point, I am able to bring to light conclusions that bear on the tasks of assistance agencies in meeting the technical assistance requirements for innovation. This I do in Chapter 2, under the title, "Lessons on Meeting the Technical Assistance Requirements of Innovation in Education."

On consulting the literature on innovation and change in education for guidelines to follow in my analysis of these science education programs from the point of view of educational innovation, I find three studies of particular helpfulness.

The first, a report of a UNESCO seminar on educational innovation and change, states that "case studies should aim at explaining the way in which changes occur; at describing the goals intended; and at analyzing the facilitating factors and obstacles."[1]

The second, an exhaustive review and analysis of the literature on development of innovation, looks at innovation and change under the following three headings:[2]

1. the organizational setting conducive to innovation and development;
2. identities and characteristics of successful innovators;
3. procedures used in innovation development.

The final study, carried out by Sloan Wayland, would analyze educational innovation under these headings.[3]

1. the content of change;
2. the process of implementation;
3. the role of the leader.

These suggestions lead me to organize the first chapter of this analytical part, "Lessons on Innovating in Science Education," under two sub-divisions. The first, "The Content of Innovations" corresponds to suggestions in the above studies that an analysis of innovation should "describe the goals intended" and should also consider "the content of change." The second sub-division "The Process of Innovation" then corresponds to the remaining items on the above lists, all of which refer to various dimensions of a "process" (q.v.).

The conclusions of Chapter 1 are directed primarily at educators and government authorities responsible for educational quality in their school systems. Those of Chapter 2 may interest not only the Ford Foundation, but other international assistance agencies engaged in promoting innovation and change in the educational systems of developing countries.

1. Report of a Seminar on Innovation in Education, International Bureau of Education (UNESCO) Geneva, March 1973.
2. Ellen Corcoran, Ph.D. Thesis, University of New Hampshire, 1973.
3. Sloan Wayland, In Lawler "Strategies for Planned Curricular Innvoation" Teachers College Press, New York (1970) page 100.

CHAPTER 1
Lessons on Innovating
in Science Education

Section a. The content of innovation.

1. *Introduction*

A thorough-going critical analysis of the products of these five science education projects is clearly beyond the scope of this study. Such an analysis requires
extensive technical procedures—control groups, test instruments, testing of null
hypotheses, measuring student achievement levels and attitudes, to reach conclusions
on the products at statistically significant levels, etc. To do these things is important,
and indeed has been done, not by this study but rather by highly competent evaluation
teams in each of these projects reviewed. This study, however, aiming as it does to
place the experiences of these projects into wide public review, has a different obligation: to call attention, inter alia, to such psychometric studies as may have been carried
out "within" the projects being reviewed and to offer them as evidence of the vitality of
the projects and of the quality of their products.

A number of critical questions can be addressed to the products of these five
projects. The answers lead to lessons taught by these projects on the characteristics of
innovations in science education. Thus, these questions ask: What specific changes
were felt to be needed in the way science was being taught? By whom? For whom?
What characteristics did the project specialists consider that the innovations should
have in order to effect those changes? And, to what extent did these innovations bring
about those intended changes?

2 *Changes intended at early period in these projects*

The five projects give an answer to our first question at the time of their
outset which is most striking and informative. The case histories show that all five
perceived the need for change in an identical way in that early period: a need to change
the way science was being taught *at the secondary-school* level in their countries. The
explanation of this remarkable fact lies in the origin of these projects, in the 1950's,
among educational and scientific leaders who, at that time, held a particular conviction
about the potentialities in modern science and technology for the development of their
countries. That conviction, widely shared among leaders throughout the world in that
early post-World War II period, held that science and technology, almost as miraculous
forces, would soon abolish the remaining vestiges of disease, hunger and poverty that
still afflicted mankind. That sentiment was especially appealing to the leaders in developing countries who saw the promise of a quick solution to their many persisting
problems.

In the grip of this sentiment, these leaders understandably joined in efforts to plan specific action that would harness these miraculous forces for the good of their countries. That planning led them to recognize the need for a sizable corps of well-trained scientific and technological manpower. They assigned the task of preparing that corps to their educational systems. At that point, however, they came in for an unexpected shock. On looking more closely at those systems, they soon saw how unprepared they were to take on a task of such magnitude. Curricula and textbooks were ill-adapted and out-dated. Grave deficiencies afflicted the corps of teachers. They were too few in number; they lacked training along modern scientific lines, etc. A most vivid summary of the situation at that time appears in a report prepared by a special committee of the Philippine Senate in 1960, just prior to the establishment of the Science Teaching Project in that country:

> Our educational system is ineffective as a steady source of competent scientific and technological manpower. Most science teachers lack **competence**. There is a dearth of qualified teachers in science and mathematics. Science teachers are poorly paid. Laboratory facilities are inadequate. Supply of science textbooks and references is deficient.

Faced with these facts of systems totally unprepared to raise up the urgently-needed corps of scientific specialists, those leaders took historical decisions to make science courses at the *secondary-school level* in their countries the prime target for educational change.

In discussions I held with some of those leaders, they told me that they had given much attention at that time to this question of the "best" place to initiate project activity. They had considered the primary school level as none too early a place to begin, insofar as making an early impact on the training of future scientists was concerned. But on reviewing the enormity of the task, if undertaken at that level, and on counting their available resources, they had backed away from that beginning point out of a fear of becoming so overwhelmed that nothing would be accomplished. On the other hand, they saw the university level as clearly too late a period in the training of a future scientist to compensate for shortcomings in the lower levels of his schooling. Their decision to initiate science education improvement at the secondary school level was a clear compromise between a desire to begin as early as possible in the training of a scientist and a need to be realistic about the resources they had for mounting educational improvements.

3.   *The innovations chosen to bring about change in the schools*

When I pose the question, "What kind of innovation did these projects consider would best serve to up-grade science instruction in their secondary schools at that time?," I again received a most striking reply. Essentially all of those projects decided to employ the then just-released course materials from the large national-level science curriculum projects in the United States—PSSC (Physics), BSCS (Biology), SMSG (Mathematics) and CHEM Study or CBA (Chemistry) as their innovations. These U.S. materials had been produced by curriculum development groups in which some of the leading scientists of the U.S. had participated, giving characteristics to the materials that made them ideal for use with students who were aiming to enter careers in the scientific professions. Thus, their content was recognizably modern; they stressed the study of scientific principles over rote memorization of disjointed facts; they engaged the student in actual scientific enquiry to assist him to gain some idea of science as a process. Intensely concerned that their educational systems should train scientific manpower, the leaders of these projects at that early period found these characteristics of the U.S. materials highly appealing to them.

That all of these project leaders (all, that is, except those in the Lebanon project who did not commence national-level work in Lebanon until much later) selected these U.S. materials as the chosen innovation, calls for an explanation. The single most likely factor that can account for this uniform choice is the predominance of scientists in the leadership of each of the groups making these decisions. Thus, in Turkey, E.P. Northrop, an eminent professor of mathematics, worked closely with scientists from Turkish universities and the Turkish Scientific and Technical Research Council (TÜBITAK) in setting up the Science Lycée project. In Brazil, Isaias Raw, a professor of biochemistry from the University of São Paulo, made most of the early decisions in the programme of IBECC. In Argentina, the Nobel laureate, Professor Houssay and his colleagues in the Argentine National Council for Scientific and Techni-cal Research (CONICYT) planned and executed the early educational activities in that project. And, finally, in the Philippine case, Delores Hernandez, although a science educator, reached her decisions in close cooperation with the influential science educa-tion sub-committee of the National Science Development Board. As leaders gravely concerned over the need to increase the ability of their educational systems to produce scientific manpower, these scientists, in making the decisions on innovations, quite plausibly found the recently-developed U.S. science education materials as the ideal solution. As scientists, they were undoubtedly drawn to those materials which had been prepared by teams composed of other scientists. As the case histories show, the Ford Foundation aided them in reaching their decisions on innovations by bringing them together with those scientists from the United States who had participated in the development of the materials. This undoubtedly swayed their minds even further in the direction of those materials.

As I interpret the decisions on need for change and on the selection of innova-tions at the earliest period of these projects, I conclude that both of those decisions were strongly swayed by the value judgments of men who were scientists. Their belief in the power of science led them to pinpoint the need for change as being at the secondary-school level. Moreover, the intrinsic appeal of the U.S. materials to them as scientists led them to choose those materials as their innovations. Most thoughtful educators are no doubt little surprised at this, since they recognize that the value judgments of those who are responsible for guiding innovation and change in education are likely to exercise a crucial influence on the direction of educational effort for change. This conclusion proves to be a helpful explanatory principle in interpreting events in these five projects at a later stage.

4.   *Evaluation of this choice of innovations*

At this point, where I am about to inquire into how successful were those innovations in bringing about the changes intended, I hear the protesting cry of an educator-critic. Those scientists, he protests, in their understandable and even com-mendable concern to act in behalf of improved teaching of science in the schools, stepped beyond their realm of competency into an area requiring the insight of an educator. In their choice of innovations, argues this critic, they took too narrow a view of the matter. He, as an educator, would only make such a decision, especially one that concerns the improvement of teaching at school level, after applying the following five criteria to an innovation under consideration:

151

1. An innovation should fulfil the value-orientation of those employing it so that, when adopted, it effects that change towards the "better" which they desire;

2. Especially in science education, an innovation should pass the scrutiny of the scientific community in respect to the accuracy and recency of its scientific content as well as the logical coherence of its development of topics;

3. An innovation should possess pedagogical validity, not only utilizing effective techniques but also gearing them to the pupil level for which the innovation is intended;

4. An innovation should slip readily into the school system without clashing violently with constraints of a legal or cultural kind; and

5. The costs associated with adopting an innovation should fall within an acceptable range, so that the system can "afford" the innovation.

Plainly, this critic charges, those scientists who chose the U.S. materials displayed concern for only a narrow range of criteria. By satisfying only the first two of the criteria above, the U.S. materials so reassured those scientists that they ignored the other criteria.

The evidence from the case histories supports the charges of this critic. First of all, it shows how perfect a match existed between the desire of those scientists to orient the teaching of science in their schools to training of scientific manpower and the characteristics of those U.S. science education materials. They had been expressly prepared to accomplish a similar purpose in U.S. schools. Those materials fully met the criteria on value congruence and scientific adequacy. That alone "sold" the scientists on them.

The evidence also supports the critic's charge that the scientists ignored the other criteria, viz, on pedagogical validity, on constraints in the school system and on costs, when choosing the materials. As matters turned out, however, this neglect led to few difficulties, because the U.S. materials were used primarily with highly selected university-bound students. They were able to cope, it appears, with what little mismatching was present in the materials. As highly motivated students, they found the newly-developed U.S. materials far more challenging and appealing than their earlier traditional textbooks. Because I am confident that the scientists who chose the materials were aware of this, I would exonerate them in their choice of these materials as the innovations for that time.

It is interesting to note that, in effect, the Ford Foundation grants and those of other foundations and agencies to these projects permitted them to ignore the criterion on costs (No. 5). First, in several cases, an outright grant of funds lowered the real costs of the initial materials to an apparent cost that then fell within an acceptable range. Second, U.S. publishers and curriculum projects made significant concessions to the projects, such as reducing royalty charges, providing photographic plates for printing low-cost versions, etc., and in these ways reduced the costs of the project materials to a level that was acceptable.

This critic's charges against these scientists become more serious when we consider the longer-range impact of these early choices. In Turkey, reliable measurements have been carried out on the project's curricular impact in a full-scale study by a competent team of psychometrists. The results of this study are reported in the Turkey case history. The study measured achievement among two groups of students who used the Turkish adaptations of the U.S. materials; one group was in the special Science Lycée where, in addition, teachers had been specially prepared to teach with the materials; the other group was in nine selected lycées whose teachers also had some although less special training.

The psychologist who directed the study, Fuat Turgut, had this to say about the outcome of the testing:

> According to the results of the achievement tests, student achievement in the pilot lycées varied between 25% and 40% of expected achievement, and in the Science Lycée, between 50% and 70%. In other words, results of using the Science Lycée materials in the nine pilot lycées were only *half* of those attained in the Science Lycée.

Turkish educators react in two different ways to the Turgut findings. One group sees a serious problem in any continued use of U.S. materials. They argue that, although the materials may have worked satisfactorily under the highly favorable conditions existing at the Science Lycée, between 1968 and 1970, those materials have proved to work only half as well in the nine pilot lycées. Therefore, when, as is now happening in Turkey, the Ministry of Education decides to place the materials into the remaining 189 secondary schools, they may be even less successful, perhaps causing achievement levels to drop below 25%.

The other group takes the position that, despite low levels of student performance, the materials are so great an advance over the older traditional materials previously in use, that their continued use is justified. Unfortunately, no psychometric findings are available to help decide between these two interpretations.

In the above discussion I have both exonerated the scientists from the critic's charge and admitted grounds for questioning the long-term soundness of their decisions. There is, in fact, a third interpretation of their decisions which deserves to be considered. In this view, I defend the scientists' choice of the U.S. materials because, although that choice compromised pedagogical validity and systemic constraints, it gave the scientists a chance to demonstrate to the educational authorities in their respective countries that their fledgling projects could respond decisively and constructively to an emergency. In the judgment of these scientists, the advantage in demonstrating that response capability outweighed the disadvantages in using less than perfectly fitting materials in their schools. Each of the project leaders affirmed, in conversation with me, that such *timely* and *effective* action had gone far to gain for their young projects the important advantages of recognition and legitimacy among the educational authorities in their countries. Moreover, this proved crucial for the projects. The authorities soon began bringing them requests for additional innovations in science education for the schools. Put pithily, these scientists acted as they did out of a realization that nothing succeeds like success! These episodes teach a clear lesson for newly-organized projects for innovation in education: Demonstrating a capability to meet demands quickly and decisively can prove crucial to the continued existence of a project insofar as the educational authorities are concerned.

The leader of a project for innovating in education is called upon to exercise judgment in this matter of demonstrating the capability of his project in the eyes of

153

authorities. In some of these projects, for example, demonstrating that capability required a leader to sacrifice certain desirable educational qualities in the materials prepared by the project as well as to incur a corresponding degree of criticism from educators.

5.   *Contemporary vision of need for change*

When I apply these fundamental questions on discerning need and selecting innovations to the experiences of these projects a decade later, in their current involvement as centers of creative curriculum development with finding solutions to problems now arising in the teaching of science in schools of their countries, I obtain quite different responses from those found earlier.

Thus, their views on the changes needed in school science have broadened greatly. Whereas earlier, they saw a need for change that would fit the schools to prepare a scientific elite, today, without abandoning that earlier concern, they now also see change needed that would fit those schools to contribute, through science and mathematics instruction, to the modernization of the thought patterns of the entire school population. This is, of course, one of the most complicated and burdensome tasks before the schools in these countries. It faces them because deep changes of a socio-economic kind have swept over these countries in the decade or more since these projects were first established. Those changes have flooded the schools with pupils in ever-increasing numbers and altered the class-bias of the student population toward the rural and lower-income groups.

The shift in the center of gravity of these projects' concern reflects a corresponding shift in the value judgments of those who lead these projects. For today, leadership of these projects rests squarely in the hands of science educators while the direct influence of scientists has waned, though in the better projects, arrangements exist for meaningful consultations with these scientists in recognition that their knowledge and perspective are among the necessary inputs to sound curriculum development in science. The science educators who now lead these projects are showing a distinct sensitivity to circumstances and the different kinds of learning needs now prevailing in the schools. This corroborates the conclusion reached above at the end of Section 3 about the value judgments of those who determine the direction of change and innovation in education.

6.   *Contemporary perspective on these projects on*
      innovations in science education

What innovations do these contemporary leaders now consider to be appropriate, in the light of their perception of the changes needed in the schools today in these countries? Let the answer to this question come from the current experience of these projects, from the "living experience" recorded in the case histories.

I begin with the Brazil account for in that case history I find information that helps me to interpret the other projects as well. I find there certain criteria on the new types of science courses that are intended to meet the mass education demands now being made on the schools in these countries.

The year 1971 saw sweeping changes overtake the educational system of Brazil, as the Ministry of Education instituted a complete restructuring of the system. Compulsory education was extended from four to eight years. At the same time, eight-year primary schools (first level or *primero grau*) were instituted in place of four-year schools, and four-year secondary schools (second level or *segundo grau*) in

154

place of the former middle schools (*ginasio*) and higher schools (*colegios*). These changes suggested an entirely new set of circumstances under which instruction in the schools would take place. Larger numbers of students would enter the schools and remain for longer periods of time. A rise in the demand for teachers would mean hiring many unqualified teachers and decreasing the quality of teacher training. The government would have to lower the cost of schooling per pupil, to make its limited budget stretch further. And so on.

These circumstances contrast sharply with the conditions that prevail in academically-oriented schools for the elite groups. The contrast is bound to grow sharper as time goes on and it will pressure on science educators to devise more appropriate kinds of science courses for the new circumstances.

The Federal Council of Education of Brazil, anticipating these pressures, passed Law No. 6592 in 1972, calling for the availability of new forms of science courses in the secondary schools. A rough translation of the relevant portion of this law reads as follows:

> Diversified science offerings in a developing country such as Brazil are now considered desirable for future professionals during their middle and upper levels of secondary schooling. Two different groups of students are: those who do not go to university but leave school for employment; and those who do go to university but not to continue studies along technical or scientific lines. The time for science study for these students is one year, owing to course requirements for other areas.
>
> Science courses should contribute to general education. The student should have the option of taking a basic science —chemistry, physics, or biology—or an 'integrated' science course. This integrated science course is the preferred option. Pedagogical, scientific and citizenship points of view should be reflected in this integrated science course. Separate chemistry and physics courses for the general student are inferior to an integrated course which gives a better global view of science.
>
> Integrated science should develop interest by presenting science as a story of human progress and by involving students in *solving problems* drawn from the surrounding community —pollution, for example. An integrated course should provide a base for the training of a future citizen in taking decisions of questions of community interest which involve a basic comprehension of science but not a specific knowledge of physics, chemistry or biology.

I deliberately chose this Brazilian example because this law describes well the characteristics of a course intended for mass education purposes. One characteristic is a *wide spectrum of objectives*. These range from achieving basic comprehension of science to involving students in problem-solving and decision-making on questions of community interest. This wide range was no doubt considered necessary to satisfy the demands of mass education. For a course of instruction that embraces such a wide range of aims as this, I apply the term "relevant science." Incidentally, the currently popular "integrated science" course may or may not fall into this "relevant science" category, depending upon the range of its aims.

Under a contract with PREMEN, FUNBEC has agreed to prepare a relevant science course that satisfies these government criteria. That contract asks FUNBEC to "prepare a course that presents to students basic concepts of science and their implications in a modern world; see to it that students acquire a capacity for solving problems; see that students understand the interaction of man and his environment; and give to students basic science information in order to comprehend the fundamental principles of this branch of knowledge." The contract then lists topics to be developed:

- the great steps of science
- the materials used by man
- living species and man
- the energy used by man
- the human population
- modern man and science

During my recent visit to Brazil, I talked with the writing team at FUNBEC about these contract specifications and guidelines. They see the extreme difficulty in their assignment, realizing that there is a fundamental contradiction in the above specifications. They know that science is both a body of organized information and a closely related methodology, termed scientific inquiry or research, and that a student learns science by gaining a comprehension of its concepts and logical structure as well as by becoming familiar with the process of inquiry. They see that "problem-solving," on the other hand, is a characteristically *different* discipline. It involves the exercise of human judgment and has reference to values and constraints. Learning "problem-solving" places radically different demands upon teachers and students from those required in learning science. Little wonder, then, that the FUNBEC team is examining the possibilities in game playing as a pedagogical device for combining these diverse and contradictory course specifications.

Now I let "living experience" out of the Lebanon account speak to this problem of devising a "relevant science" course. The Science and Mathematics Education Centre at American University of Beirut (AUB/SMEC) has prepared textbooks and teachers' guides for science courses that fit the prescribed "relevant science" requirements. The SMEC team takes a highly pragmatic view of their encounter with relevant science. They replace *some* of the logical development of scientific content in the traditional courses by "relevant" topics, such as population, ecology and environment, health, natural resources, food supply, etc. Their rationale is that this sacrifice of logical development is a price that must be paid to "purchase" student interest and motivation. Including relevant topics in the course is, in their judgment, the only way to motivate the kind of students who fill today's classrooms so that they will study at least *some* of the logical development of science still remaining in the textbooks. The science educators at SMEC find it necessary to exercise great care and judgment in arriving at an optimum "mix" of these two kinds of topics in their materials.

Relevant science courses must not only include topics of societal interest in order to meet the demands created by the new circumstances of mass education; they must also meet stringent cost constraints set by these mass circumstances. One of the best illustrations of how these science education projects are currently facing this cost problem appears in the Philippine case.

Two different integrated science courses are being developed at the Philippines science education project, University of the Philippines, Science Education Centre (UPSEC): the Integrated Science Program (a Philippine adaptation of the Intermediate Science Curriculum Study (ISCS), Florida, U.S.A.) and an Environmental Science course. Both aim at the seventh and eighth years of school; both attempt to meet the conditions for mass education courses. Both are "relevant science" in that they include a wide spectrum of objectives. One course employs the scientific themes of energy and matter as keys for opening up understanding of everyday areas: the environment, human nutrition, hygiene, and drug abuse. The other leads the pupil into a study of the physical aspects of the earth and atmosphere and the relationships between living organisms and their environments (ecology). UPSEC declares that it intentionally offers schools a choice between two courses with different topical interests. Along with this choice of topical treatments, the courses also offer low unit costs in the classroom. In offering these two, UPSEC, conscious of the cost factor in education, is searching along two different paths for ways to meet this factor. The Philippine adaptation of ISCS is built around a school room equipment kit costing 1,000 pesos (about U.S. $200). One kit serves a teacher's needs with 150 students. The cost of a textbook added to this amount (about seven pesos or U.S. $1.50) brings the unit cost (per student cost) of this course to approximately U.S. $2.00. The Environmental Science course, on the other hand, requires a school to purchase a few simple pieces of apparatus totalling 200 pesos ($40.00) per class of 40 students and a textbook costing eight pesos. The unit cost thus works out also to be about U.S. $2.00. The ISCS course places a well-stocked kit in the classroom; the items are manufactured locally in the Philippines. The Environmental Science course expects the teacher and the students to find suitable materials for the student experiments at home or in the market. School authorities choosing between these courses have to weight the equipment cost factor against the willingness of a teacher to do the additional work of hunting for materials. UPSEC expects to obtain responses from the schools to these choices and to formulate guidelines for further efforts to reduce unit costs.

7.   *A fresh issue emerges: academic or relevant science?*

Competent science educators in these five projects have made the decision to employ these relevant science courses as innovations to bring about change in the schools of these countries. They undoubtedly took fully into account those criteria on innovations outlined earlier on page 151. Their choice, therefore, leaves little room for my educator-critic of that earlier section to find fault. Yet, in putting forth these relevant science courses as they have, the science educators have triggered a fresh controversy.

This centers around the question of how best to meet mass education learning needs. Which course of instruction, they are asking, best serves the learning needs among those in these societies who are crying out for the school to be relevant, to say something helpful on topics such as population growth, environmental pollution, public health, etc.: the traditional "academic science" course, or the so-called "relevant science" course?

Those who consider "academic science" courses to be the soundest answer hold that only *authentic encounters* with science have meaning for students. In their view, these encounters occur only in science instruction that places the student in genuine "inquiry" situations and, in addition, asks him to master the logical development of major concepts and theories. These advocates of academic science fear that the "mixed modes" of thought found in relevant science courses will confuse a student and rob him of these authentic encounters.

8.   *Current trends in curriculum development by these projects*
These relevant science courses are but the initial attempts by these projects to satisfy the new types of learning needs in science now arising out of mass education. Other, more powerful, innovations will certainly follow, given the degree to which the science educators who now staff these projects are attuned to those needs. Many of these educators are taking steps to fit themselves more fully for the inventive work they see ahead. The Philippine case history illustrates this well.

When UPSEC recently took on the responsibility of preparing a course of instruction in science for the primary schools in the Philippines, its leadership realized that something should be done to add certain additional competencies to UPSEC's complement of skills. Consequently, Delores Hernandez approached the Ford Foundation with a request for travel funds that would permit selected UPSEC staff members to travel abroad for advanced study in such fields as psychometrics and child development psychology.

UPSEC then took another bold step to increase its state of preparedness for this new area of curriculum development; it opened a dialogue with scholars in anthropology and social studies, seeking through this interchange of viewpoints a deeper insight into the problem of cognitive growth in children of the Philippine culture and society.

In one discussion I attended, a prominent Philippine anthropologist talked about the learning of science among children in these words:

> The abstractions of science are universalized: gravity, momentum, atom, stoichiometry, rate, natural selection, gene, etc. The learning path may be rooted in more culturally influenced perceptions—but ultimately learning must lead a student from his *pre-conceptions* to these universally formulated abstractions (concepts).
>
> The processes of observation, classification, etc. may be heavily culturally-colored—as well as the pattern of processes: observe, classify, conceptualize, test, and discover new relationships, properties, etc., inherent in the concept. This holds the interest there is in making instruction more culturally linked, through children's games, for example.[1]

The UPSEC staff members are also opening dialogue in another direction with agricultural specialists who can help them to adapt science course materials to the classroom environment of villages and rural areas in the Philippines. UPSEC hopes to ensure the potency of its innovations in science at the level of the remotest village. UPSEC has also recently convened a group of twenty science teachers from villages throughout the country to collaborate as a team with linguists in the development of a glossary of scientific terms for the science textbooks under preparation.

In fact, in each of the projects one sees the leaders and staff members taking steps to prepare themselves for the curriculum development tasks that lie ahead as changing conditions in the schools pose fresh challenges for new teaching materials. These relevant science courses will, as time goes on, be followed by innovations in

158

science education of even greater efficacy and relevance to the learning needs of the students.

Section b. The process of innovation

1. *Introduction*
    Bringing about planned change in as complex a social entity as an educational system requires extraordinary skill on the part of an innovator. That is why I find the extensive changes brought about by these five projects so convincing as witnesses to their acumen as innovatory centers of action in their educational systems. Moreover, it is why I find the record of those accomplishments so valid a source of lessons to be learned on innovation and change in education.

    As pointed out earlier, suggestions from the literature on innovation and change identify the following topics with the process of innovation:

Topics	Dimensions
The organization setting of change	organizational setting
Characteristics of innovators;	
role of the leader	personnel
Procedures used in innovation development;	
the process of implementation	procedures

These dimensions now serve as principal elements of comparison among the five projects in the analysis which follows. By their use, I bring to light some of the more important conclusions on the processes of innovation and change in educational systems suggested by the experiences of these five projects.

2. *The organizational dimension in the process of innovation and change*
    In a study of planned change in an educational system, Rogers and Shoemaker hold the view that such change alters both the structure and function of that social entity. They see the process of social change as occurring in three sequential steps: (1) invention, (2) diffusion, and (3) consequences.[2] This suggests a way of classifying the five projects under study that opens the door on exploring relationships between the organizational dimension of a project and the level of its innovatory activity in science education.

    This comparative tabulation leads me at once to a finding of great importance for understanding the influence of organization on the level of innovatory activity of a project. In the three countries where that activity is highest, viz., Brazil, Lebanon, and the Philippines, the functions of invention and diffusion take place in *separate* and *distinct* units. In marked contrast in Argentina, one of the countries where overall innovatory activity is currently low, INEC (now DIEPE) tends to carry on both tasks. In the other case, Turkey, where activity is also low, although the two tasks are in principle allocated to separate units: invention to the Science Lycée and diffusion to the SEDC in the Ministry of Education - only the latter is performing its assigned task. The Science Lycée ceased many years ago to serve as a source of new and applicable science materials. Consequently, despite the work of SEDC in coordinating diverse parts of the Ministry bureaucracy to ensure distribution and adoption of science educa-

TABLE I
OrganizationalPatterns of Science Education Activities

Step in Process of Change	Units Responsible for Carrying Out Steps				
	Argentina	Brazil	Lebanon	Philippines	Turkey
1. Inventing Innovations	INEC*	FUNBEC	SMEC	SEC	SCIENCE Lycée (inoperative as Invention Unit)
2. Diffusing Innovations	INÉC*	PREMEN together with the CECIs	CERD	Regional Science Teaching Centres	SEDC
3. Adopting Innovations	Ministries of Education**				

*INEC is the single unit responsible for both tasks.
**In all cases, the Ministries of Education, through their official boards, or textbook boards, hold responsibility for decisions on adoption of new science courses and materials.

tion materials among schools in Turkey, innovative activity in Turkey is hampered by the absence of a unit that can produce fresh inputs of Turkish-created and Turkish-related science materials for dissemination to the schools.

This finding suggests the following conclusion: the likelihood of success in carrying through change (at least, instructional change) in a complex educational system appears to be greater *when change is organized so that the two processes –invention of innovations and diffusion of innovations—take place in separate (but cooperating) units of the system.*

Strong corroboration of this conclusion appears in recent studies of sustained efforts to promote change in social systems:

> Specialization of function and personnel is required. Research, development, and testing should be assigned to specialists who operate in organizations designed for that purpose. Information dissemination should be manned by different kinds of specialists, operating in their own particular organizations, separate from, but with definite systemic ties to, the research sources. Neither is expected to possess and exercise the skills of the other to operate effectively in the role of the other. Although the specific nature of the organization for research and diffusion of information is open to question, there is no doubt about the need for specialization. Skills and academic specialities needed for research include services of psychologists, social psychologists, sociologists, statisticians, and others in addition to educational specialists. Both experimental testing and basic research should be a function of the research unit.

160

The diffusion function is the second basic requirement for which special organization and personnel are needed. This activity must serve the needs of the adopter clientele, whether they be individuals, groups or formal organization. Close liaison must be maintained between research sources and the adopter clientele.[3]

The Philippines project introduced this division of labor in its innovatory activity for improving science education at the very outset, that is, when UPSEC (then the Science Teaching Center) was established.

In the improvement and reform of science teaching of the country, the University does *not* propose to undertake the training of large numbers of students and teachers in the field, or to conduct studies on the administration of the program. Rather, the University can best meet its obligation and produce significant results with maximum impact by producing graduates who can provide leadership, and (by) furnishing the educational authorities, teachers, teachers' schools and other entities with suitable instructional materials, tools, models and examples of good teaching practice.[4]

To this day, the Science Education Center at the University of the Philippines (UPSEC) restricts its responsibilities to research, development of curriculum materials, and testing of these materials. When authorities in the Philippines decided to accelerate the spread of the materials prepared by UPSEC they organized a nation-wide network of Regional Science Teaching Centers to diffuse these materials and to train teachers in their use. At the same time, they held UPSEC to its limited role of inventing and testing the innovations. This combined Philippine program is proving its effectiveness. In my judgment, it is one of the most valid models for emulation by science educators and government authorities elsewhere.

The Brazil case also provides support for this lesson on division of labor. There, the efficacy of the project has gradually increased by differentiating tasks and establishing specialized units to accomplish each of them. When Isaias Raw first took up the task of placing equipment into the hands of Brazilian youth through IBECC, he worked at a wide range of tasks: he designed the kits; set up a factory for producing regional units called CECI's as units for dissemination of innovations. Now FUNBEC, as well as other creative centres in Brazil, are able to concentrate on developmental work while they cooperate with PREMEN to ensure that a growing number of innovations in science education are disseminated to schools throughout Brazil.

regional units called CECI's (see p. 00 of Brazil account) as units for dissemination of innovations. Now FUNBEC, as well as other creative centres in Brazil, are able to concentrate on developmental work while they cooperate with PREMEN to ensure that a growing number of innovations in science education are disseminated to schools throughout Brazil.

The program in Lebanon also showed little differentiation and specialization of functions at its earlier stages. The returning Wisconsin-trained science educators became involved in efforts across the entire gamut of Ministry of Education responsibilities for science education. For example, on their return in 1967, Namek and Haddad accepted teaching assignments at the American University in Beirut as well as assignments to conduct National Council-sponsored summer courses for teachers. And for Haddad, government service as coordinator and executive secretary of the powerful Science Advisory Committee set up by the Director-General of Education, Joseph Zarour, drew him even further afield. Fortunately for this program in Lebanon, the founding of the Science and Mathematics Education Centre at the American University of Beirut (AUB/SMEC) in 1969 introduced an organizational pattern of divided responsibilities. This change soon brought about a noticeable increase in the level of science education innovation in Lebanon.

The by-laws of AUB/SMEC clearly restrict its functions to those appropriate to a creative centre:

1. The preparation of prospective science and mathematics teachers on both the undergraduate and graduate levels, in cooperation with the science and mathematics departments.

2. The training of teachers in-service by means of institutes, conferences, workshops and evening classes.

3. A consultation service of schools and governments regarding textbooks, curriculum planning, equipment, laboratories and methods of evaluation.

4. Research and development in the fields of science and mathematics education.

5. The production of textbooks, experimental curricula and instructional materials for science and mathematics education.[5]

In 1971, this differentiation of function went one step further when Wadih Haddad left AUB/SMEC to assume the Directorship of the newly-created Centre for Educational Research and Development. As a nerve-centre in the Ministry of Education, the initial task of that centre has been to bring about a profound reorganization of the entire educational system. A somewhat fluid situation exists at present in the Lebanese educational system as Haddad struggles to restructure the Ministry for its task of disseminating innovations to the many different kinds of schools in Lebanon. Meanwhile, AUB/SMEC, under the leadership of George Za'rour, continues to provide innovations in science education. Haddad plans to encourage the formation of similar centers in other subject-matter fields.

As stated earlier, the currently-experienced difficulties in the Argentine project (INEC) appear to be clear consequences of an organizational plan that does not respect differentiation and specialization of function. INEC encompasses responsibilities for disseminating as well as creating science education materials. In my judgment, this undifferentiated role places too heavy and diverse a set of burdens on the INEC staff and thereby reduces its overall level of performance.

In the Turkey case the educators have options either to restore vitality to the Science Lycée through, for example, adding new staff, providing a budget for development work and enacting legislation setting it apart as a "pilot" or "experimental" unit; or, for example, to organize *de novo* a curriculum development center perhaps at one of the universities in Turkey. Until one of these options is chosen by SEDC, it is limited to disseminating the older Science Lycée materials, or materials brought in from other countries—a less than satisfactory way to meet the changing educational needs in Turkey.

162

Those programs that are most successful and show the highest levels of over-all innovatory activity place invention and diffusion in separate specialized units, but at the same time establish close working links between those units. The inventive units are autonomous and frequently located at a university while the units of diffusion are integral parts of the official educational systems that they serve. The diffusion units coordinate various parts of those systems: curriculum divisions, textbook boards, school supply divisions, examination boards, etc. (SEDC in Turkey is an excellent prototype), to promote action in concert that ensures efficient and far-reaching dis-semination of the innovations to the schools of the system. The list below shows how these diffusion units can operate through various components of an educational system:

Components	Possible actions by diffusion units
Teachers:	Organize and conduct in-service courses for teachers of science and mathematics in use of innovations.
Materials:	Arrange publication of textbooks, and design and manufacture of equipment in proper quantities and on schedule.
Curriculum:	Revise official curriculum so that sequence of science courses is appropriate and time alloca-tions to science instruction are realistic.
Examinations:	Introduce examination questions reinforcing the content and modes of learning in the inno-vations.
Codes, statutes, and laws:	Influence legislation and Ministry regulations to encourage adoption of innovations.

My examination of the experience of the three most successful projects of this study reveals that close liaison between the invention and diffusion units is a two-way street that leads to educationally-significant influences operating in both directions and benefitting the overall system. In one direction, information about the learning needs and conditions for learning among pupils in the schools flows from the schools through the diffusion units to research and curriculum development specialists working in the unit for invention. In the other, opportunities for advanced study at the centers for invention become available to personnel who work in the diffusion units. This latter situation occurred in Brazil and the Philippines programs.

In Brazil, a Ford Foundation grant brought fifteen university professors and staff members from the CECI's to serve as interns in leadership training in FUNBEC for periods of several months. While at FUNBEC they participated actively in cur-riculum development as well as in the evaluation and testing programs. They also provided leadership for the in-service training of teachers from the schools of Brazil.

In the Philippines, a similar leadership training program took place at UPSEC under financial support from UNICEF. Educators from the Regional Science Teaching Centres, the units of the diffusion network, were able to earn Master of Arts degrees from the University of the Philippines, which added to their professional competence for the crucial part they play in the spread and adoption of UPSEC innova-tions throughout the Philippine educational system.

These beneficial consequences of close liaison between the separate units illustrate the influence of organizational setting on the overall innovative activity of a project. There are other features of "organizational setting" which also have a definite influence on the overall level of inventive activity of a program. For example, during my visits to AUB/SMEC, UPSEC and FUNBEC—all specialized units for invention of innovations—the directors referred constantly to the importance of "autonomy" for their units. They explained this autonomy as administrative and intellectual "free space" that is vital to inventiveness in their work. This space allows them freedom to include untested or untried components in course materials during the developmental and trial period. It prevents external *administrative or bureaucratic interference* with their setting of priorities, deciding on sequence, or placing relative weights on topics in the new course materials. It allows them to assign work loads among their staff in consultation primarily with those staff members rather than with outsiders whose views on priorities on a staff member's time or talent might differ from their own. In short, these project leaders consider freedom of action essential to ensure high quality and originality in curriculum development, and insist that the only way to ensure it is to assign an appropriate degree of *autonomy* to an inventive unit.

Before exploring internal aspects of the organizational setting of a unit for invention, that is, its "structure," I refer to one last consequence of what I might have been calling the "external posture" of the relations between a unit and its surroundings. Rogers and Shoemaker state:

> The social structure of a formal organization can be made to work for effective communication, rather than to impede it. One method is to create an adaptive unit as part of the organization's structure. It may be called a research and development unit or some such euphemistic title. The purpose of the adaptive unit is to sense the changes in the environment, to determine the need for changes in the organization, to identify suitable innovations, and to evaluate innovation.
>
> Perhaps what every corporation (and every other organization) needs is a department of continuous renewal that would view the whole organization as a system in need of continuing innovation.[6]

The directors of these units for invention of innovations hold, I found, precisely this conception of their role in the educational system. They are deeply conscious that their privileged autonomous status obliges them to accept responsibility for ensuring continuous renewal of learning opportunities in science in the schools of their countries.

My observations up to this point on organization and innovatory efficacy among these projects lead me to conclude that an inventive unit must be free from arbitrary external control and enjoy good working links to related external groups in order to make its full creative contributions to continuous renewal of an educational system.

Equal to its external organizational setting, its "posture" as I have called it, as an influence on the creativity of an inventive unit is its internal setting, or "structure." That structure and the relationship it implies powerfully influence the well-being and effectiveness of an organization for inventive work. According to Rogers and Shoemaker,[7] that structure influences an organization by bestowing these qualities on it:

1. Predetermined goals;
2. Prescribed roles;
3. Authority structure;
4. Rules and regulations governing decision-making; and
5. Informal patterns of relations and practices.

The following checklist of dimensions of "organizational health" prepared by Miles[8] introduces a systematic way to study the influence of structure on behavior. I use a version of Miles' list suggested by Michael Huberman for study of innovative units:[9]

1. *Clarity and acceptance of goals*. In a healthy organization, members are reasonably clear about goals and their acceptability. Goals must be achievable with available resources and be appropriate, i.e. more or less congruent with the demands of the environment.

2. *Adequacy of communication*. This involves distortion-free communication vertically, horizontally and across the boundary of the system to and from the surrounding environment.... People have the information they need and have gotten it without exerting undue efforts.

3. *Optimal power equalization*. Subordinates can influence upwards, and can do the same with their superiors. Units stand in an interdependent relationship to one another, with less emphasis on the ability of one unit to control the entire operation.

4. *Resource utilization*. A healthy organization, like a healthy individual, works to its potential.... People have a sense of learning and developing while in the process of making their contribution to the organization.

5. *Cohesiveness*. The organization knows 'who it is.' Its members feel attracted to membership. They want to stay with the organization, be influenced by and have an influence on it.

6. *Morale*. The sense of well-being or satisfaction, as judged from individual sentiments or responses. Despite the vagueness of this concept, behavioral scientists have isolated some of the components of high and low morale.

7. *Innovativeness*. 'A healthy system would tend to invent new procedures, move towards new goals, produce new kinds of products, diversify itself and become more rather than less differentiated over time. In a sense such a system could be said to grow, develop and change rather than remain routinized and standard.'

165

8. *Autonomy*. A healthy organization is independent from the environment in a sense that it does not respond passively to demands from without, nor destructively or rebelliously to perceived demands. Like the healthy individual in his transactions with others, the school system would not treat its responses to the community as determining its own behavior.

9. *Adaptation*. The idea is that of being in realistic, effective contact with the organization's surroundings. Its ability to bring about corrective change should be faster than the change cycle in the community.

10. *Problem-solving adequacy*. 'The issue is not the presence or absence of problems, but the manner in which the person, group or organization copes with the problems...(in) an effective system, problems are solved with minimal energy; **they stay solved; and the problem-solving mechanisms used** are not weakened, but maintained or strengthened.' Conflicts are treated as an indicator that changes are needed.

Huberman points out that the first three dimensions on Miles' list are related to tasks, organizational goals, the transmission of messages and the way decisions are made; the second group (4 to 6) to the structure proper; and finally, there are four dimensions which deal with growth and changefulness.

By their small size, these five science education improvement projects meet the first group of criteria. The case histories show how staff and committee discussions enjoy immediate message transmission and intimacy of relationships among the members of each unit. During my visits to these projects, I was able to observe directly such characteristics as goal-awareness and communication adequacy. I saw that even the physical circumstances in which these units work appear to play a part in maintaining high levels of communication and goal-awareness. Crowded work and office spaces only seemed to heighten the sense of participation in the creative work going on among their staff members. A photograph of the crowded space in which the UPSEC carries on its daily operations would reveal a large room housing seven or eight staff members at desks. In that same room there are several large tables around which, at any moment during the day, small conferences convene with outside groups of consultants or teachers. I witnessed one of these in which a group of specialists from an agricultural experiment station came to discuss with UPSEC staff members the outline of topics for a science course for rural schools. I took particular notice of the door to Delores Hernandez office—open most of the time, permitting staff members to come and go at will! In a similar way, Myriam Krasilchik's office in FUNBEC (Brazil), serves more as a staff conference room than as an executive's retreat.

Items 4, 5 and 6 of the above list refer to the spirit present among staff members of an organization. I found that spirit remarkably high among these creative science education units, reflecting satisfaction among staff members with respect to the first three dimensions on Miles' list. Motivation and interest were surprisingly strong among the individual staff members as were loyalty, a sense of identity with their units, and morale. The only exception to this last—the kind of startling exception among these cases that provides a lesson by its sheer contrast with the other cases—was that at INEC in Argentina. There, staff members actually admitted to me their anxiety over future job security in view of the reorganization of INEC and DIEPE. I find in this a strong argument against locating an innovatory unit within the official ministry of education. That location seems to compromise the unit's autonomy at its very roots. One Ford Foundation officer, Peter Hakim, commented after a visit to review INEC's activities: "INEC's ties to the Ministry have not resulted in the effective distribution of its materials, but may have had a stifling effect on its creativity."

In a study of the literature on innovation and change, Ellen Corcoran lists organizational constraints and pressures that affect innovation development. One of these which is relevant to this topic of spirit and morale is the perceived status of authority of the potential innovator: "If the potential innovator perceives himself, or is perceived by others, as having high status and authority, he may well decide to risk developing an innovation." My conversation with individual staff members of these science education projects gave me a distinct impression that they found mere membership in the unit a factor in keeping their determination and diligence in work at high levels. It was clear to me that, by himself, a staff member probably would not have performed to the same extent and quality. There was little doubt in my mind that putting people together in a formal organization helps to define patterns in their roles and induces characteristics in their behaviour that are different from the mere sum of their individual intrinsic characteristics. The overall effect derives from that grouping itself, and accounts for much of a project's effectiveness in meeting its assignment.

I conclude this particular section by describing one last impression of the consequences of institutionalization resulting from my visits to these projects. When these competent science educators came together and organized themselves in the patterns of relationships characteristic of these projects, certain consequences occurred.

First, scattered and non-interacting individuals, although competent in their own right, found themselves with others of similar ability and interest in an organizational setting which was task oriented. This focusing of concern enhanced their abilities and inventiveness, and provided them goals and resources to apply these meaningfully to recognized needs in their educational systems.

Then, at some point in its development, and largely through support from a benefactor (in these cases, the Ford Foundation) each unit acquired that requisite number (what is it?) of staff members for "critical size" which, in itself, for reasons little understood, endows a project with competence, effectiveness, and stability.

Finally, over and over again, I saw evidence in these countries that these projects are the only groups with competence in curriculum development to whom their educational authorities can turn for fresh inputs to their educational systems. This leaves no doubt in my mind that the act of institutionalizing these projects was a crucial event in the educational history of these countries. Had this not occurred—as was nearly the case in Lebanon—these individuals would undoubtedly have dispersed, leaving a country without that critical mass of inventive educators which alone can ensure continuous renewal of its educational system, at least in respect to science learning opportunities.

Last on Miles' checklist of dimensions of organizational health are items which, as Huberman says, deal with growth and changefulness. Plainly, any group displaying a spirit and morale as described under items 4, 5 and 6 would likely be highly innovative. This quality rests upon more than a buoyant spirit (item 7), however, as the case histories of these science education projects reveal so well. I defer further discussion of this quality of innovativeness until the last part of this section where I shall examine the procedures employed by the projects in their work of inventing innovations.

The actual record of accomplishments by these projects is sufficient proof of their problem-solving ability (item 10). And items 8 and 9, of course, require no comment beyond that which I have made earlier in this section.

3.   *Crises in organizational development*

In the Philippines, a Presidential Commission to Survey Philippine Education has set up an Education Task Force in 1971. That Task Force wants to create a Curriculum Coordinating Unit in the Philippine Department of Education. It would put UPSEC at its core, with responsibility for overseeing invention of innovation in *all* subject fields. UPSEC would then be linked to a greatly strengthened network for diffusing those innovations to Philippine schools. This proposed scheme is of deep concern to the director of UPSEC, Dr. Delores Hernandez. She sees its merits but at the same time fears that it threatens the future of UPSEC.

She expressed these anxieties to me repeatedly during my visit in the Philippines without indicating what alternative she would suggest as a future programme of educational innovation in a country where reform of all educational disciplines is urgent.

In Lebanon, Wadih Haddad, former Director of AUB/SMEC, is now Director of a powerful new Center for Educational Research and Development (CERD) in the Lebanese Ministry of Education. Traditionally, by mutual agreement among the diverse religious and political communities in Lebanon, the Ministry of Education had been maintained at a modest level of political power. Now Wadih Haddad plans to center many of the educational development functions in his new CERD, where he is building up strong and sophisticated groups in educational measurements and testing, educational research, etc. Even now, CERD has already embarked upon measuring student achievement with science materials prepared by AUB/SMEC using CERD-designed classroom tests. Such activities would enhance the power of the Ministry of Education and could unbalance the political detente.

Such activities of CERD disturb AUB/SMEC Director George Za'rour who is uncertain about the "fit" between his testing of materials during the trial period (formative evaluation) and this national-scale, summative evaluation by CERD. In return, Wadih Haddad himself faces a difficult political problem. In commissioning AUB/SMEC to prepare science educational materials for Lebanese schools, he asks a legal entity of a U.S.-supported university to make inputs to an official ministry of the Lebanese government, whose mandate is to serve school needs among all the diverse religious, cultural and ethnic groups in Lebanon. Thus, both men are uncertain at the moment how to reduce the awkwardness of the situation they face in Lebanon.

In Turkey, the Science Education Development Commission is today functioning as a unit of the Ministry of Education to disseminate science education materials to schools throughout Turkey. It has come to its present position from that day in 1966 when the then Undersecretary of Education, Ferid Saner, wrote to Eugene Northrop of the Turkey office of the Ford Foundation as follows:

> The success of the programs prepared by the Science Lycée
> project has led us to use these materials on a wider scale. There-
> fore, we have decided to establish a special commission for the
> Development of Science Education (SEDC).

SEDC works through a Secretariat composed of four science educators who coordinate the various bureaux of the Ministry to ensure dissemination of science materials to schools in the right quantities and on time as well as to provide teachers in-service training in the use of the new materials. Two fundamental problems cloud this otherwise encouraging picture of SEDC. One is its inability to provide indigenously prepared science materials to the lower levels of Turkey's schools, an ability which stems from the failure by the Science Lycée to function as a unit for invention. The other is a mismatch between the composition of SEDC's advisory body and that of its secretariat. The advisory group consists of scientists drawn from the Universities and TÜBITAK, the Turkish Scientific and Technical Research Council. I witnessed some of their working sessions in which they were deliberating problems facing the SEDC Secretariat. These high level scientists were trying to think through constructive solutions to administrative problems within the bureaucracy of the Ministry of Education where their secretariat is located. Their time would have been better used counselling a Turkish unit for *invention* of innovations rather than the Ministry of Education-connected secretariat of the SEDC. On the other hand, that Secretariat needs the advisory help of a panel of educational specialists in administration, planning, finance, and pedagogy.

Mounting organizational problems are also afflicting the projects in Brazil and Argentina, as reference to the case histories will show. But rather than lengthen this catalogue of these problems, I conclude the commentary on this particular issue by observing that all these difficulties point up the inevitability of change in the life history of an organization. As one writer put it, "Management problems and principles of organizations are rooted in time."[10]

Although these mounting difficulties pose grave challenges to the directors of these projects, if they can view these problems simply as symptoms of organizations which are passing into a new and more mature phase of existence, then there is hope. Their bold and imaginative leadership can carry these projects to even higher levels of innovatory performance. On my visits to the projects, I found these leaders fully aware of this challenge. I saw that they are indeed consulting the literature on organizational development and that they are seeking assistance along lines of management counselling. However, in my judgment, these leaders are not as fully appreciated as leaders in creating innovations for the schools of their countries as they might be, at least not by their own educational authorities.

4.   *The contributions of leadership and professional competence*
        to the process of innovation

The previous section related the influence of the pattern of organization on the level of innovative activity in these projects. Now I wish to give appropriate acknowledgement to the influence of talented leaders and trained specialists on that performance. The directors of these projects possess qualities that are acknowledged prerequisites to leadership of a unit for inventing innovations in education. One such quality is the ability to manage the affairs of a creative group within a complex educational system. In conversations with Myriam Krasilchik at FUNBEC, I found her almost consumed by concern over the managerial dimension of her task as leader of FUNBEC: What should be the composition and role of her advisory board? What mix of full-time and part-time staff would give FUNBEC maximum effectiveness? How far should FUNBEC go in divesting itself of its inherited earlier involvements in manufacturing and distribution of science education materials? Her questioning went deeper than the merely operational level. I found her asking repeatedly, Should FUNBEC even exist any longer? If so, in what form and with what mission?

I found George Za'rour no less preoccupied with managerial matters. Since AUB/SMEC is a component part of the School of Education of AUB, Za'rour and his colleagues lead complicated lives. First of all, they teach and carry on research as professors of AUB. Then, they must perform the developmental duties of SMEC staff members. And as time goes on, they take on more and more duties as Ford Foundation consultants in science education throughout the Middle East. Za'rour is fully aware of the limited size of his staff as well as of the obligations that pull them in all these different directions. In fact, the attention he must give to the resulting administrative and managerial problems is becoming a very real distraction to his fundamental research investigations to which he brings exceptional insight and competence. A glance at the publication schedule which AUB/SMEC has set itself gives some clue to the magnitude of the managerial dimensions of Za'rour's role as director of AUB/SMEC. The day does not seem far away when good judgment would dictate that he add a full-time administrative assistant to his staff.

Angel Hernaiz, Director of INEC, has demonstrated remarkable managerial skill in mobilizing the large amount of talent in science education from among professors and instructors of teacher training colleges and universities throughout Argentina. Because of this skill, he could assign INEC a heavy load of in-service teacher education not only for Argentinian teachers but for teachers from other Latin American countries (through OAS financing) as well. He was particularly skillful in mobilizing resources from other institutions in Argentina in ways that led to cost-sharing. As the case history shows, this skill caused misunderstanding between him and the Ford Foundation officers, who at first interpreted his modest use of their funds as a failure to perform. Later, of course, they saw this in a different light. In a private conversation with Hernaiz on this matter, I discovered that he holds deep convictions about his responsibility not only to mobilize talent, but to do so in ways that would cause his colleagues in other institutions and sections of the Ministry of Education in Argentina to feel a greater sense of obligation to support educational innovation. This vision, and his stout commitment to it, marked Hernaiz as the right leader for an organization with such a broad mandate.

This commentary on the managerial skill of these leaders would be incomplete without reference to the consummate managerial ability of Delores Hernandez. Even at UPSEC's inception, she showed uncanny insight into her management responsibilities as director. Thus, one of her first decisions was to set up two types of advisory bodies for UPSEC: a Steering Committee and an Advisory Board. The first comprised administrative officers at the University of the Philippines as well as the science education supervisor from the Ministry of Education. Its task was to assist her in day-to-day administration of UPSEC. The Advisory Board, on the other hand, represented a wide range of institutions in the country with interests in science education improvement. It gave these many different communities a definite sense of involvement in UPSEC's affairs, brought UPSEC a great variety of ideas for its educational work, and helped ensure wide acceptance of UPSEC's products once developed.

In addition to this quality of managerial ability, these directors displayed an astute professional judgment in curriculum development matters. Dwayne Huebner characterizes this judgment among curricular leaders in these terms.[11]

Responsibility for Awareness
As a decision maker, the curricular leader must have all necessary information at his finger tips. As any executive, he must be aware of all available conditions and values which might

influence his own field of action. It is essential that an aspect of his role or his office be devoted to intelligence—to determining what is going on in the world. Because the educational environment is an aggregate of educational conditions patterned to maximize value, he must recognize existing educational conditions. Knowledge of educational conditions implies awareness of:

(a) educational technology;
(b) conditions of teachers;
(c) educational and social values within his educational community; and
(d) all the streams of thought which might influence his designing of an educational environment.

Political Responsibility

The curricular leader is a leader; that is, he is an eventmaker and a shaper of an environment. By vocation he is a politician. He has consciously chosen to use his working time to shape a human institution. Consequently,

(a) he must operate within the realm of differences of opinion;
(b) he must make decisions which reflect economic awareness;
(c) he must influence others; and
(d) he is always held accountable for his action.

Aesthetic Responsibility

Aesthetic responsibility requires a responsiveness to the conditions of the environment—to the givers which determine the educational possibilities. Judged aesthetically, the significant educational environment has meaning, beauty, and truth and reflects vitality and purpose.

Using this list as a checklist against which to measure the quality of curriculum decisions taken by the leaders of these science education projects, I find those decisions standing out as remarkably responsive. First of all, they reflect the conditions that shape the learning environments of their pupils. In the Philippines case, for example, I find Delores Hernandez fully alert to the possibilities in science education for modernizing the social and cultural fabric of society. This alertness has led her to open a vigorous dialogue between her staff at UPSEC and specialists in such disciplines as rural sociology, anthropology, and linguistics. In this same spirit of alertness, Myriam Krasilchik is carrying educational evaluations on FUNBEC-produced science kits beyond São Paulo and Rio de Janeiro to villages in rural Brazil. In Lebanon, George Za'rour is pursuing studies of the influence of the Lebanese home on a child's interest in science in an unmistakable manifestation of this alertness. In Argentina, INEC (now DIEPE) carries the testing of preliminary versions of its new instructional materials in biology to schools in the far northwest of the country as well as in Buenos Aires.

These project leaders display sound judgment in curriculum development matters in yet another way: by showing an openness to the influence of scientists upon the preparation of their materials for science instruction. In all cases, they have provided mechanisms for drawing upon the expertise of the scientific communities in their

171

countries. For example, I saw this liaison with scientists in Brazil where Dr. Ernesto Giebrecht, despite the heavy burden of his duties at the chemistry faculty of the University of São Paulo, nevertheless devotes an unbelievable number of hours each week to his work as an advisor to FUNBEC and CECISP.

In Argentina, I witnessed a similar situation under particularly enjoyable circumstances. I spent many hours in thoroughly rewarding fellowship with Dr. Ariel Guerrero, Professor of Chemistry of the University of Buenos Aires, as he explained to me the details of the Chemistry 30 project in which he has invested much time and thought as an INEC advisor.

No less dedicated to INEC are biologists, physicists, and mathematicians from the scientific community in Argentina. Only in Lebanon did I fail to find such strong cooperation between scientists and these science education projects. Although a scientific advisory panel of science faculty members at AUB exists, it does not appear to be active in the AUB/SMEC program.

Against this checklist, these project leaders show that they have a remarkable sence of *political* responsibility. They are fully aware that key decision-makers in the educational systems of their countries must be influenced if the innovations produced in their projects are to have impact on classrooms. They demonstrate this political consciousness in several ways. One is their determination to maintain strong working links between their creative units and groups outside their units that are likely to serve as resources to their creative work or that facilitate diffusion and adoption of their innovations.

During my visit to Brazil, I had an exceptionally good opportunity to witness this leadership quality of political responsibility. I accompanied Myriam Krasilchik, director of FUNBEC and CECISP, on a visit she paid to the director of PREMEN in the Ministry of Education. She discussed with him the question of coordination of tasks between inventive centers such as FUNBEC and governmental units for diffusion —PREMEN itself and the CECI's through Brazil. They reached agreement on many areas, while on others they found differences of opinion. This showed me that mutual adjustments between FUNBEC and the Ministry of Education are still being worked out. Their goal is to reach an eventually harmonious program of invention and diffusion on innovations in science education that will ensure change in the furthest reaches of the educational system of Brazil.

As planning rationalities enter the decision-making and allocating of funds in each public sector, the educational innovator must be able to state the "need" for his activity in economic terms so that funds are channeled to it in proper proportion. He must evaluate the relative importance of his sector to all others that contribute to social and economic improvement and assign an appropriate weight to his demand for funds. In that weighting, the educational innovator must also judge the proportionate part of allocations to the educational sector that should go to innovative effort as compared with efforts for maintaining on-going aspects of education.

One clear example of this economic sense of responsibility appears in the way Delores Hernandez leads UPSEC in pursuing a search for curriculum materials at lowest possible unit cost.

Finally, the above checklist suggests that a leader in curriculum development should display responsiveness to the aesthetic dimension, that in his design of an educational environment, he should create meaning. Thus Huebner writes:

"Meaning isn't something which simply exists in the world.
It is man-made, what man is or what man makes himself to be. To

ignore the creation of meaning is not simply to let natural meanings come to the fore, but to let meaning emerge out of the careless and routine activity of man. The educational environment has meaning; it is the significance of those people who have responsibility for it.

"Monotony can rule supreme; things and schedules can be more important than students and teachers; plans can be of greater concern than the creative outbursts of students. Joyful discovery can also be the meaning. Enthusiastic responsibility of young people can be manifest. Knowledge as truth and possibility rather than grades and promotion can be the meaning. Community rather than isolation and division can be reflected in the design. What would the curricular leader have man be? The school is that place where man is that which he would be."[12]

Huebner challenges curriculum development leaders to create learning environments that are both durable and, as it were, alive: "The curriculum must always be in process. The design is never a one-shot job with a state of completion; it is always in process. It must reflect the life of the people responsible for it and the life in the surrounding communities of knowledge, social action and technology." By this comment, he opens a vista on curriculum development in the sciences in which lively and authentic experiences in science, essentially the observation of natural phenomena together with the intellectual ordering of these in concepts and theories, exert a powerful influence on the affective and cognitive learning of the student.

Such aesthetic vision gripped Isaias Raw in the early era of IBECC as he sought to bring to Brazilian youth the opportunity to handle scientific equipment and to perform their own experiments. In fact, that aesthetic vision possesses all directors of these science education projects. George Za'rour exhibits this when he writes in the preface to one AUB/SMEC textbook:

"To the Student

"We like to build upon your curiosity and encourage it. Practically, most of the book consists of student activities. This reflects what we strongly believe in. You—the student—should be the center of attention.

"*Physical Science 1* presents an approach to the teaching of science which emphasizes *understanding through activities.* You have to do, think and arrive at answers by yourself in order to understand. This process of getting at the answer is probably more important at this stage than the answer itself. Thus, it does not matter if you have studied some of the topics at the elementary stage. These will be dealt with in a different approach and in greater depth.

"Activities in science help us to see relationships between what we observe and other problems. In doing the activities you follow the steps of other people and learn what they have discovered. You begin to share with them an understanding of basic principles. However, if one day an experiment does not turn out as expected by a book, a teacher or other students do not give up easily. If you have done your work properly, you may be right and everybody else including the authors of a book may be wrong. This is not very common but it does happen. In fact, many advances in science take place when one is patient enough to repeat his observations carefully. If he still gets the same result, he looks for sources of disagreement with others. If he is wrong, he learns much from trying to know why. And when it turns out that he is right the satisfaction is great."[13]

To the contribution these leaders make to the efficacy of their projects must be added that made by their staff members. Chiefly, these staff members bring various specializations in various scientific and pedagogical disciplines to bear on the creative power of the projects. One area of their competence that deserves special mention is that of psychometrics. Just how great a bearing this descipline has had on the course of curriculum development in these projects shows forth in this list of their reports:

1. Report on the Evaluation of the Argentine Version of the IPS Course. Prepared at INEC by Señora Marta Maraschi.
2. Report on the Evaluation of the Pilot Lycée's Project in Turkey. Prepared by Fuat Turgut.
3. Two reports: "Evaluation of the Brazilian Adaptation of the BSCS Green Version" and "Science Investigation in Elementary School; an Evaluation of Level I Kits" by the FUNBEC evaluation team, Señoras Faria, Chippari, Manfredi and Araujo.
4. An abstract of the Ph.D. thesis completed at the University of Texas by Miss Rosalina Villavicencio, "An Analysis of the In-Service Training Programs for Biology Teachers in the Philippines."

Another area in which staff members have contributed with exceptional originality and hence increased the inventiveness of these projects is in the design and production of prototypes of laboratory apparatus. The most widely acclaimed examples of this activity are, of course, the kits produced by IBECC and FUNBEC.

Since it is not my purpose, in this analysis, to catalogue details about these projects (I attempted to do that in the case histories), I shall not elaborate further upon these staff accomplishments, but simply underline once more that these competencies among the staff members of these projects underlie their creativity and inventiveness. What should be pointed out here is that this kind of talent in organizations carries with it special obligations for those who lead and support such organizations. I like to refer to this as their responsibility for the "care and feeding" of an innovative group. Enabling those specialists to find opportunity for professional growth is one of the most important of these obligations. Hence, the Foundation grants almost invariably contained funds for travel by staff members for short-term study or observation of new techniques and practices.

Even more significant as part of this professional "care and feeding" of the creative individuals in these projects were the long-term training opportunities provided by the Ford Foundation grants. A comparison of the projects in respect to this provision shows very strikingly how critical it has been to the very survival of these creative units. The Turkey case unhappily illustrates an absence of such long-term study awards. Turkish science educators failed to complete higher degrees in specializations related to curriculum development, thereby, as I have explained earlier, bring-

174

ing on the decline of the Science Lycée as a creative, inventive source of innovations in science education.[14]

In Argentina also, failure to provide long-term training opportunities appears to be a possible cause of some of INEC's current difficulties: too few full-time staff members are available to shoulder the enormous number of burdens which INEC is otherwise commendably attempting to carry. One Ford Foundation officer, after a visit to INEC in 1972, commented on Hernaiz' refusal to use Foundation funds earmarked for training of staff members:

> "Besides the director and technical secretary, INEC's staff currently consists of 16 persons, all part-time and mainly trained as secondary school teachers. Seven staff members work in substantive areas of biology, chemistry, physics and mathematics, principally in the organization of training programs; three are assigned to the annual mathematics contest and science fair. One is a translator; three have evaluation responsibilities and two coordinate the preparation of teaching materials.... I was surprised by the number that had not received any special training outside of Argentina and were not familiar with the work of the other centres (even FUNBEC), especially since our grant contains funds for staff travel abroad. To encourage INEC to expand its very inadequate permanent staff, the Foundation, contrary to its assertion in the Request for Grant Action 'not to use for local staff salaries' allocated $20,000 in staff expansion under the modification. INEC has used only about $6,000 so far to contract three part consultants."[15]

The policies in the other projects, in Brazil, Lebanon and the Philippines, however, have always stressed the long-term education of key staff members. For example, a statement on "Faculty Development" from the 1972 Annual Report of UPSEC states:

> "During the year under review the Center continued its policy of a strong faculty program for its staff. Among the accomplishments in this area are:
> A. Degree program completed:
>   1 M.A.
> B. Ongoing programs (1974):
>   3 Ph.D.'s
>   1 apprenticeship in art and publication
> C. Scheduled for early academic year 1972:
>   2 short-term on Ford Foundation
>   3 short-term on UNESCO-UNDP
> D. Requested for the near future:
>   5 degree and short-term fellowships
>   9 degree and short-term fellowships (UNDP)

The Lebanon case provides the classic illustration of the importance of long-term training. When Pella could not find satisfactorily-trained talent on which to build a project in the Middle East, he recommended that the Ford Foundation invest in the training, to the doctorate level, of six science educators from Middle Eastern countries.

175

Attesting to Pella's wisdom is the fact that nearly all are today engaged in curriculum development at SMEC. These experiences of long-term investment in creative talent teach a fundamental lesson on developing organizations with a creative or inventive function to perform: in building such organizations, it is essential to invest in the training of key personnel up to the point where they become self-confident members of the team through their mastery of a useful specialization.

5.   *The "procedural" dimension in the process of innovation*

Earlier, I explained that to improve science education in the schools of a country, a unit for invention of innovations needs to be linked to one for dissemination of these innovations. This latter unit must also bring about adjustments to the system's policy, legal and administrative factors that affect the distribution and use of innovations by the schools. In this analysis, however, I have focussed my attention on the invention of innovations, the dominant feature of these five projects (except for Turkey). To study the diffusion or adoption of the innovations would require a study of far greater scope than I have given mine. Some impression of the information needed to study models of change at that larger system level is given in Huberman's review of the literature on innovation and change, especially in his Chapter VI, "Planning and Executing Change."[16] There he states that "case studies (on innovation in education) are justified in that one of the objectives was to identify a *natural process of change.* By tracing the sequence of events, we can isolate the phases of change as they took place naturally, in order to take account of these interactions when drawing up a planned sequence."

My case studies can contribute only in part to this search for the "natural process of change" in the way outlined by Huberman because I have focused on the units for invention and merely acknowledged the existence of a network for diffusion with its associated dynamics, as a *context* for these inventive units. Despite this limited scope of my work, however, the cases I have prepared do make an essential contribution to that larger mosaic; these five case histories and my analysis of them provide an understanding of one tile of that mosaic—a tile quite central to that larger picture.

The final topic then, is that of the *internal* procedures by which these inventive units prepare innovations in science education. Those procedures refer to steps taken by these projects within the organizational structures outlined earlier. Hence, to the extent that these structures give direction to those steps, they supply a starting point for understanding those steps of innovatory work.

In taking those steps, science educators in these projects attempted to modify one or more of the following six determiners of the curriculum: teachers, pupils, subject matter, methods, materials, and time.[17]

They aimed their action most directly on that constellation of subject matter, methods, and materials which make up instructional materials. Less direct was their effort to modify teacher behavior in the classroom; this came primarily through teacher participation in in-service courses for which these projects supplied guides and trained teacher-educators. Least direct was their effort with the individual pupil. Again modification at that level was a result of classroom use of materials prepared by the projects.

The case histories provide three detailed descriptions of the actual pattern of steps followed by these science educators in developing curriculum materials. The Argentina case history supplies this statement by Fischler, the consultant to INEC:

I suggested a development model to Professor Hernaiz:

(1) each writer prepare a lesson lasting 3 or 4 days;

176

(2) the writer then teaches the lesson in a classroom. He does this to get a feeling for the children and to be in a better position to revise what he wrote initially.

(3) the writer re-writes on the basis of his own experience and then finds a teacher who will teach it for him;

(4) the evaluation team members work with the writer all this time to develop items for the test;

(5) the lesson is finally typed and tested in twenty schools. The evaluation team produces tests for this stage.[18]

The Lebanon case history states that in writing the texts, SMEC proceeded in the following manner:

1. *How the writing is done*

One or two senior editors are responsible for each textbook and guide book. The editors assign writers who are chosen among (sic) qualified teachers and/or other people qualified and working in science education. The writers work in close cooperation with the editor(s) and are responsible for writing the text and choosing illustrations, activities, reading, etc. ... Editors are entitled to suggest or require possible changes in the text and/or illustrations submitted by writers. Each writer is responsible for one or more units in the book according to this specialization, background, and ability. The editor may himself write units. An artist and photographers are available for illustrative material.

A contract is made between the writer and SMEC; this contract stipulates the honorarium to be paid, the deadline for submission of manuscripts and the responsibilities of writers and editors. The Ministry of Education keeps the copyright for all manuscripts. The average honorarium for writing is 35 Lebanese pounds per printed page of the students' text and 45 Lebanese pounds per *printed* page of the teachers' text. Writing for intermediate texts is done in either French or English and later translated. Intermediate textbooks are produced in two versions: English and French. Elementary texts are written and produced in Arabic. SMEC consults language specialists to assure the level of language is appropriate for the various classes.[19]

In an annual report prepared in November 1965, Delores Hernandez described the procedures followed by the Philippine project as follows:

1. *Organization and Administration*

An interdisciplinary approach has been adopted in the organization of the three committees who have overall responsibility for the production of curriculum materials: Advisory Board, Steering Committee, and Work Groups.

Direct responsibility for this lies with the Work Groups, each consisting of technical people, teachers in the field, subject specialists and educators. There are five such Work Groups: Physics, Chemistry, Biology, General Science (including elementary science) and Mathematics (first grade through fourth year high school). Each Work Group is headed by a professor who is a subject specialist.

There are from 9 to 35 members in each Work Group, all of them either writers or reviewers. There are a total of 116 writers representing 21 different educational institutions.

Manuscripts prepared by the writers are submitted to the Steering Committee who not only review the materials and suggest improvements, but also help the director administer the project.

An Advisory Board reviews the manuscripts approved by the Steering Committee. The involvement of many different agencies is designed to secure the ideas and contributions of all who are concerned with instruction in science and mathematics. This insures the acceptance and use of the curriculum materials produced.

Development of the foregoing outlines into manuscripts for textbooks, laboratory manuals, and teacher's guides will be accomplished by the writers of each Work Group. Success of the project depends primarily on the quality of manuscripts produced. The Work Group are the most important members of the organization. This is the reason for the rigorous care exercised in their selection.

Before being accepted, all manuscripts undergo no less than two, three, or even more revisions to insure quality. It is a difficult task involving searching analysis to determine adequate coverage and unity, accuracy, and pedagogical soundness.

To secure a wider and more significant range of judgment, a meeting was held with 27 elementary school teachers from five nearby provinces (besides those from Manila and Quezon City) selected to represent different types of schools according to size: large central (regional) schools, city schools, rural schools (big town, smaller towns, and barrios); and according to type: complete primary schools (I-IV), complete elementary schools (I-VI). They read all the sample manuscripts, and were asked to respond to a questionnaire prepared by Dr. Ward. It was felt that the reaction of teachers from different types of schools and different provinces would provide the Science Teaching Center staff with useful information and fresh insights which could be passed on to the writers.[20]

These three procedures are not identical, but do suggest similar paths in the preparation of science materials. In more recent years, of course, all of the units for invention of innovations have introduced formative evaluation through adding staff members trained in psychometrics, contributing to even closer similarity in their basic work patterns.

A convenient summary of the pattern followed by the four projects in creating innovations is this:

1. Identification of aims and objectives of a particular course.
2. Restatement of these aims in cognitive and behavioral terms.
3. Use of a table of specifications to match these aims with spe-

cific subject-matter components—facts, concepts, theories, historical material and experimental activities—laboratory exercises, demonstrations, field trips, etc.

4. Arrangement of this conceptual and experimental material in a sequence and pattern that gives coherence and pedagogical efficaciousness in the light of current theories on learning and knowledge about concept development in children.

5. Utilization of appropriate instructional techniques (audio-visual, materials, diagrams, programmed instruction, etc.) in preparing classroom materials.

6. Preparation of a first provisional "package" for trial in a small number of schools. (This step usually was accompanied by preparation of materials for the guidance of teachers in the trial schools.)

7. (Formative) evaluation of teacher and pupil response (achievement and attitudinal) to the provisional materials, collection of feedback information and a next round of writing of course materials.

8. Eventually, publication—by a commercial publisher or by the Ministry of Education—of large quantities of a first edition of the course materials.

The overall process outlined here is the *design process* that puts ideas and materials together in the light of the desired learning objectives, resources (subject-matter content, experimental activities, learning techniques) and constraints (first of all, costs, then legal or statutory requirements, learning behavior in pupils at the age concerned, customs and cultural patterns, and teacher preferences). On my visits to these projects, I saw the dynamics of this design process: first, thought and study by individual members of staff followed by vigorous, contentious but constructive group discussion and debate. A word about both of these is illuminating.

I stated earlier that staff members of these projects found stimulation for their work through belonging to a group with an acknowledged reputation for accomplishment. On my visits, I saw how this identity with a group greatly enhances an individual's ability to contribute to this design effort. Each is an inveterate scholar of his discipline—science education, psychometrics, or of a science discipline. Each knows and loves young people—often having begun his career as a classroom teacher. But as a member of a project for improving science education, those individuals go out of their way to keep in close touch with teachers and pupils in the classrooms of the schools in their respective countries. In addition to social interactions with the teachers and school authorities, some hold teaching responsibilities as a way of remaining in contact with classroom conditions, while others carry on their research into the classroom, focussing inquiry on some aspect of the learning or teaching process.

On my visits, I saw how a vital spirit animates the group discussions. Each project director encourages and promotes an openness within the group and maintains lively contacts outward. These contacts extend to the scientists of a country, usually through formalized advisory committees, to specialists in such relevant fields as psychology, linguistics, computer science, etc., and to the educational world—Ministry of Education authorities, school teachers and principals.

Other factors also help to sustain the vitality and effectiveness of the design process. Consultants are used to bring in new ideas on curriculum development and to provide valuable criticism of the emerging products of the design process. Most importantly, the commitment among these projects to research that is closely tied to their main mission of improving science instruction in the schools reassures me that these projects will continue to play a useful role in the educational systems of their countries as these societies continue to change. Thus, whether it is George Za'rour's sensitive and brilliant studies of the home and its influence on attitudes to learning of science among Lebanese children or the cold competence of the FUNBEC evaluation team in using sophisticated psychometric techniques to determine the learning potential of FUNBEC kits with rural children in Brazil, there is no question that basic research occupies a meaningful place in all of these projects. How it became implanted there and subsequently received careful nourishment is one of the more exciting stories revealed by the analysis of the following chapter.

REFERENCES

1. Remarks by Professor Jocano, University of the Philippines, May, 1973, at the Regional Science Teaching Center, Ateneo de Davao, Davao City.

2. Rogers and Shoemaker. *Communication of Innovations*. Free Press (Macmillan): 1972. For my purposes in this section of analysis, the consequence of main interest is the *adoption* of the innovations.

3. Herbert F. Lionberger, "Strategy Implications for Curricular Changes in Education," in Marcella Lawler, *Strategies for Planned Curricular Innovation*. New York: Teachers College Press, 1970, p. 81.

4. Philippines Case History, p. 10. (From 1964 programme statement on the "Proposal to Establish a Science Teaching Project," University of the Philippines.)

5. By-Laws, AUB/SMEC, Beirut, Lebanon (1969).

6. Rogers and Shoemaker, *op. cit.*, pp. 314, 315.

7. *Ibid.*, p. 314.

8. Miles, M., "Planned Change and Organizational Health" in *Change Processes in the Public Schools*. Eugene, Oregon: University of Oregon, 1964, pp. 11-36.

9. As presented by Huberman, M., "Understanding Change in Education: An Introduction." UNESCO. Geneva: IBE, 1973.

10. Larry E. Greiner, "Evolution and Revolution as Organizations Grow," in *Harvard Business Review*, July 1972.

11. Dwayne Heubner, "The Leadership Role in Curricular Change." Department of Public Instruction, State of Wisconsin. Paper presented before the Kenwood Conference on Curriculum Leadership, May, 1966.

12. Dwayne Heubner, *op. cit.*, p. 149.

13. Preface to the Intermediate Physical Science Textbook, AUB/SMEC, Beirut, Lebanon.

14. Professor Uri Haber-Schaim was a recent Ford Foundation consultant to the Science Education Development Commission in Turkey. After a study of the problems of primary and middle school science education improvement there, Haber-Schaim expressed to me his opinion that unavailability of trained capability in science curriculum development in Turkey was a severe limitation to further educational improvement there.

15. Memorandum, Peter Hakim to Dr. R. E. Carlson, March 3, 1972.

16. Huberman, *op. cit.*, p. 61 ff.

17. Gordon N. MacKenzie, "Curricular Change: Participants, Power and Processes" in Miles, Matthew B., *Innovations in Education* (New York: Teachers College Press, 1964), pp. 402-407.

18. A 1969 memorandum written by Dr. Abraham Fischler, describing his discussion with Angel Hernaiz.

19. 8 August 1973 letter, Samir Makzoume of AUB/SMEC to Robert H. Maybury describing SMEC procedures.

20. Science Teaching Center Annual Report, November 1964 to November 1965.

CHAPTER 2

Lessons on Meeting the
Technical Assistance Requirements
of Innovation in Education

I now shift my focus from science education and its improvement to the Ford Foundation effort to meet the needs for technical assistance arising in these projects. A critical examination of that decade-long experience of the Ford Foundation as a donor agency directs these basic questions to that effort: What assistance was given? In what manner? And with what consequences to the projects and their capability for innovatory action?

This questioning brings to light highly informative conclusions on fundamental issues in technical assistance programs such as these:

1. the influence of organizational structure of the donor agency on its effectiveness in meeting the technical assistance needs of innovative projects;
2. the technical assistance requirements for institutionalizing an innovative project;
3. criteria to determine the appropriate time to terminate assistance; etc.

Two preliminary matters require attention before I take up the analysis proper. First, I need to point out some advantages and disadvantages of these case histories as a basis for reaching conclusions on technical assistance efforts. Second, I need to describe the main lines along which I proceed in the analysis.

Although the case histories draw heavily upon documents and correspondence found in the files of the Ford Foundation and present events in the projects primarily from the point of view of the Foundation, any bias this might give the accounts is offset in part, I hope, by my visits to the projects where I could observe their work and obtain the viewpoints of their leaders on the historical development and present-day activities of the projects. Alternate versions of these events could of course have been written by someone with an entirely different involvement in the projects, such as one of their leaders, for example. Such versions would provide desirable complementary views to the one I take and would undoubtedly broaden the understanding of issues raised in my analysis. One such complementary account is, in fact, available: a historical account of the project in Turkey by Zekai Baloğlu, the principal government officer who is involved in that project at the present time[1]

On the other hand, the case histories offer several distinct advantages for such a critical analysis as this. One is their factual accuracy resulting from the abundance of direct quotations from documents in the Ford Foundation files. That same use of Foundation files also gives a desirable concreteness of detail to their descriptions of the Foundation effort. And of even greater significance for this analysis are two other advantages they possess. First, by recording events over a time-span that covers two decades (significant decades at that, having been termed the "decades of development"), these case histories make it possible to trace long-term consequences of the Foundation's performance. Second, by presenting accounts of that performance in five widely different countries, they facilitate comparison of the Ford Foundation performance and its consequences among these different countries, thereby highlighting certain cultural and other country-specific influences on that effort to assist.

Some may question the usefulness of these accounts as sources of conclusions on technical assistance, when they cover only a limited sector of the Foundation's total international program. In reply, I assert that, just as a particular prism can yield highly valuable information about the energy in a light beam, so can these case histories, covering a single sector of the Foundation's program, yield useful information about features of its performance as a donor agency.

Turning now to the analysis that follows, I outline briefly the following main lines along which I proceed. First of all, I examine the reasons given by the Ford Foundation for supporting science education improvement in these countries. In that connection, I note that views on education and development held by Foundation officers today pose a sharp critique on these earlier initiatives in supporting science education. Next, I probe into the relationship between the Ford Foundation as a donor agency and its recipients. This leads me to recognize that "aid giving"[1] occurs within a definite framework, which I term the "aid relationship." I then examine the dynamic interactions between the Foundation as a donor agency and its recipients that go on within that framework. That brings to light the critical roles of field and headquarters officers of the Foundation in effective aid-giving. My inquiry turns next to the problematical situation that arose with the decision to institutionalize these innovative projects. Upon examining the decisions and actions taken by the Foundation in that situation, I draw some highly useful conclusions pertaining to a donor agency's contribution to institutionalizing an innovative project in education.

Finally, I consider that ultimate, and sometimes painful, issue, "When has the time come to consider terminating an aid-relationship?" Although I find a defensible reply to that question in the experiences of the Ford Foundation, I also discover there a surprising reason for continuing that relationship beyond that defensible terminating point.

A. *Purposes before the Ford Foundation in supporting*
    science education innovations
    Logic itself dictates that I begin by considering the question of purposes, i.e. the reasons found by the Ford Foundation for supporting science education improvement projects in the first place. In attempting to evaluate a given action, it is necessary to know why the actor took that particular action. When that reason is known, that action (and actor) can then be fairly judged by comparing actual consequences with the intended ones.

The early records on these projects suggest that the Ford Foundation first supported the improvement in science education in these countries out of an interest in economic and social development. Along with other major international agencies, the Foundation subscribed to a premise, widely held in the decade of the 1950s when these projects were initiated, that aid to education would necessarily accelerate the rate of development in these needy countries. Science education became a particularly favorite target of the aid programmes in those years owing to its clear connection to preparing technical manpower on which economic growth in those countries seemed so closely dependent. Improving science instruction, so went the generally accepted view, would turn out more qualified scientists and technicians and also raise the level of their competence. These outcomes would in turn then necessarily speed up development.

Today, the Ford Foundation and many other aid agencies as well, are questioning that earlier optimism concerning the contribution of education to development. The intervening decades have shattered their optimism, as, in country after country, hopes for development have failed to materialize despite large investments in education. Today therefore, they still assign a crucial development role to education, but they are more modest in their expectations of its contribution. They now understand better how education must work in concert with other social and economic forces in order to advance a country's welfare.

Looked at against this view on education and development, that earlier purpose held by the Foundation for supporting these projects now appears overly ambitious or, perhaps, too simplistic. Consequently, were I attempting to analyse the Ford Foundation support to science education as a contribution to economic and social development in these five countries, I would be called upon to explore further the consequences of this too-simplistic goal. As it is, however, my study does not have that wide a scope. It is limited to determining the influence of that support on the capacity of a project to take innovative action in education. I leave to another, complementary study, one with much wider terms of reference, such questions as whether or not the Ford Foundation *should* have invested in science education improvement for the purpose of advancing economic development or whether or not it should have done certain other things in close liaison with aiding these projects in order to promote the development of these countries. What I can say, though, as far as the contribution of these projects to development is concerned, is this: No matter what else that wider, complementary study might conclude in regard to these five projects, it would have to acknowledge their remarkable achievements in raising standards of science education in the countries where they function. In my judgment, these achievements in themselves justify all the investment made in the projects, even in the light of today's views on education and development. For these views, I note, still see essential developmental roles for highly trained scientists and technicians of these countries. Since poor science teaching hinders a country from preparing its required number of these trained individuals, improving science education does indeed make a contribution to a country's development.

Looking at this question of purposes, at the level of the individual project, I find a surprising diversity among the reasons given for supporting science education improvement. This diversity, incidentally, does not mean that there was conflict with the Foundation's overall purpose to advance economic and social welfare in these countries. It simply shows that there were different viewpoints on how best to fulfill that purpose through science education improvement.

To illustrate this diversity of purposes with examples from the case histories, I begin with the Turkey account. Eugene Northrop's earliest writing on the idea of a National High School for Science in Turkey argued that a special institution to identify and nurture the gifted science students of Turkey would assure that country a future supply of highly trained scientists. The Ford Foundation officers at New York headquarters awarded the grant to Turkey on the basis of this rationale although an earlier, rather different rationale had motivated the Foundation to appoint a scientist as representative in Turkey in the first place. That earlier rationale, the view of two senior officers of the Ford Foundation, F. Champion Ward and John Hilliard, put forward the following four arguments:

1. Turkey would soon (i.e. within twenty years) develop a sophisticated industrial sector which would require an indigenous scientific base;
2. other agencies would tackle short-term needs but would probably not assist in the science field; hence, the Ford Foundation would have a comparative advantage in science;
3. unlike education in "culture-specific" subjects, science education is neutral and therefore an acceptable field for external assistance;
4. the "mentality" of Middle Eastern people is rhetorical and "pre-scientific," making "modernization" difficult.[2]

A similar reasoning lay behind the decision of the Ford Foundation officers in the Beirut office to support a programme of science education improvement in the Arab countries of the Middle East. There, two Foundation officers, Harvey Hall and Hugh Walker, were convinced that pre-scientific modes of thought among the peoples of those countries held back their progress. They decided to support improved teaching of science in the schools of those countries in the hope that it would bring about a modernization of that self-limiting mentality.

In the Philippines, yet another rationale drew the Foundation into support of science education improvement. The Foundation representative in the Philippines at that time, Harry Case, firmly believed in the potential of universities to act as agents for change in a society. Accordingly, soon after taking up his appointment in the Philippines, he invited a university president, John Warner, to come to Manila to advise the Ford Foundation on its educational and scientific programmes of assistance to that country. It was Warner who then recommended support of a project for science education improvement that the University of the Philippines had proposed to the Foundation.

Finally, in Latin America, it was a concern over supply of scientific manpower that drew the Ford Foundation into support of science education improvement. Illustrating this concern is a statement made by the Foundation representative in Rio de Janeiro at the time of awarding the first grant to Isaias Raw:

> "In view of the Institute's (IBECC) unique role in developing scientific and technical manpower in Brazil, a Foundation grant of dollars 125,000 is recommended for a period of approximately three years."[3]

Out of this review of purposes, I conclude that the aid-giving performance of the Ford Foundation should not be judged against that original, perhaps overly-ambitious or too simplistic aim to contribute to a nation's development, but rather against its determination to improve teaching of science in the schools of these five countries. In the subsequent analysis, then, I understandably limit my assessment of the Ford Foundation aid-giving to its impact on the innovative capability of each of these projects.

B.   *The Aid-Relationship*
        Regardless of the reason that may have moved a particular one of these

184

Foundation offices to support science education improvement, once the decision to move in that direction was made, that office faced a challenge of demanding proportions: to meet the critical and continuing needs for technical assistance in projects these countries would have to organize in order to innovate in science education. That challenge drew the Ford Foundation, as a donor agency, into a collaboration that lasted over many years with the governmental, educational and scientific leaders in each country. At its core, that collaboration engaged both donor and recipient in a great variety of transactions related to the transfer of technical assistance from donor to recipient. Those transactions were necessarily complex since they had to match the needs arising on the part of recipients against resource possibilities lying with the donor. They depended heavily upon cooperation and mutual understanding between the two parties. An analysis can do justice to the subtlety and complexity of those transactions and explain their influence on the projects only if it is put into some appropriate conceptual framework. A suggestion from Lester Pearson's well-known study of aid-giving, entitled "Partners in Development," provides that framework in its reference to a relationship between donor agency and its recipients, using the most apt and felicitous term, *aid-relationship*:

> The aid (or development) relationship is at the heart of efficient aid policy. It must be based on a clear division of responsibilities which meets the needs of both partners. These needs arise from the proposition that a main purpose of economic aid should be to promote self-maintaining growth, and from its corollary, the proposition that aid should be linked to performance. On the donor's side, these needs, or interests, lie in its funds being effectively used to reach acceptable development goals. In other words, the donor wants the recipient to make sincere efforts. But the recipient, too, has legitimate needs or interests. Clearly, any such relationship, with its reciprocal rights and obligations, must involve advice, consultation, persuasion. Above all, there must be clear and accepted channels for this and an equally clear distinction between the responsibilities of the partners.[4]

C.   *The structure and dynamics of aid-giving*

C.1.   *The role of a resident field officer*

This concept of an aid-relationship proves immediately useful in analyzing the Ford Foundation aid-giving. By pointing out that a donor agency and its recipients must necessarily collaborate in a great variety of intricate transactions, it stresses the need for close supervision over those transactions by the donor agency in order to achieve effective and satisfactory aid-giving. An examination of the Ford Foundation record of collaboration with these projects in meeting their needs for technical assistance shows that supervision has been present. What is more, it has been in the hands of officers of the Foundation who were *resident* in these countries where the projects being aided were located. The record leaves no doubt in my mind that these officers, by being resident in those countries, made a decisive difference in the effectiveness of the Foundation's aid-giving with these projects. That resident status gave to each of them certain relevant advantages in his role of watching over the Foundation's interests in the aid-relationship. It enabled him to acquire a wide knowledge of local conditions in the country—its politics, social and economic structures, educational patterns and levels, etc. and to become acquainted with leaders in government, educational and

185

scientific circles. It clarified his perception of a country's needs related to the Foundation's aid-giving. And it increased his sensitivity to the most likely points where pressure for educational change could be applied.

Examples drawn from the case histories give convincing support to this assertion that the resident status of its representatives give the Foundation's aid-giving exceptional effectiveness. In Turkey, Eugene Northrop had to negotiate the science high school project with a whole series of different Ministers of Education over a three-year period of constantly changing governments. Only this persistence, made possible by his resident status there, brought ultimate success in the form of a signed agreement with the Ministry of Education.

The Brazil case history carries the following statement regarding the contribution of a resident Foundation officer in that country:

> "We have been working for the past six months with Dr. Isaias Raw on a proposal to assist in the training of leaders and directors for vacation period institutes in the sciences in Brazil. Dr. John Baxter, our Science and Science Education advisor, has carried the full responsibility in developing this project. It has the enthusiastic support of the Director of Secondary Education of the Federal Ministry of Education and his top science aides. It also has the full support of the Directors of these Science Institutes."[5]

This comment is a reminder that sporadic, short-term visits by some officer from the distant headquarters of a donor agency would have been most unlikely to prepare a project plan drawing "the enthusiastic support" of a high government official and, at the same time, "the full support" of a group of scientific institute directors. Nor would such visits have favoured that close supervision of aid-giving which enabled a Ford Foundation officer to write, four years later: "FUNBEC staff consider the internship programme to have been highly successful."[6]

A letter to me from one of the original participants in the Philippine project contains the following testimony to the significance of resident status of a Foundation representative:

> "The overseas representative is a key figure in the application of development assistance funds to country programmes. He can be very effective, as in this case, when he can involve himself and his staff in significant ways in the development stages mentioned above. He can do so, given professional competence in the subject field and skill in the management of the development process, if he has intimate knowledge of the local situation, familiarity with working styles, capability to respond flexibly and quickly to specific needs and opportunities, and enough freedom to take risks as well as to roll and adjust to meet changing demands.
>
> I do grant the representative the wisdom of perceiving the potential of the mix and the acumen of knowing the local people who also did and could employ development assistance funds to use the mix to advantage. The overseas representative was a crucial determinant in the investment of funds, and a key figure in this particular case in the design and conduct of the project."[7]

One final example of the importance of the resident status of the Foundation officer comes from my direct experience during the period when I was gathering information for this study. On my visit to Beirut, Lebanon, I witnessed this importance at first hand. There, I accompanied Courtney Nelson, the Foundation representative, and his associate, Thomas Olson, on their visits to university and government officers to negotiate various details of Ford Foundation grants. The reception they were granted and their intimate knowledge of relevant details gave eloquent testimony to their privileged status as residents of Beirut, an asset of great worth in their aid-giving to projects in that area.

These examples provide overwhelming corroboration of my assertion that the *resident* status of Foundation officers in each country has made a crucial difference to the effectiveness of its aid-giving. That resident status has enabled them to maintain an alert, continuous and knowledgeable watch over the Foundation's interest in the aid-relationship with its recipients, accounting for the effectiveness of the Foundation's effort in providing assistance.

C.2.   *Collaboration between field and headquarters officers*

Up to this point, analysis reveals the crucial importance of resident status on the part of the Ford Foundation representative to effective aid-giving in each of these countries. This resident officer is one component in what I might term the "structure" through which the Foundation has conducted its aid-giving.

Further examination of the record soon brings to light an additional most significant feature of that aid-giving: these resident field officers have not kept the Foundation's aid-giving at high levels of effectiveness by working alone. The record shows instead that it has been a remarkable collaboration between them and their colleagues in the New York headquarters of the Ford Foundation that accounts for these high levels of effectiveness.

To understand how that teamwork or collaboration enhances the Foundation's aid-giving, it is necessary to probe into the underlying dynamics of the process of meeting technical assistance needs. Those dynamics proceed through a vigorous and continuous interplay of ideas, judgements and skills between the field officer and his headquarters colleagues, and continue throughout all stages to that aid-giving. These are: initial stage prior to and including the decision-making in regard to awarding a grant to a project; a stage marked by actual delivery of technical assistance to recipients; and a closing stage. In each of these stages, the interplay between field and headquarters takes on a characteristic form related to the principal aid-giving activity in that stage.

In the initial stage, the chief aid-giving activities are identifying leadership and planning and organizing the envisaged project. Hence, that interplay takes the form of debates between the field and headquarters officers in which the two sides can supply complementary ideas and judgements. That initial stage reaches its climax at the moment of decision-making on the award of a grant to a project. At that moment, the debates between field and headquarters become particularly sharp and incisive.

In the middle stage of aid-giving when the chief function is to supply technical assistance to the recipients, that interplay combines the skills of field and headquarters in mobilizing the resources for technical assistance.

In the closing stage, the Foundation has to ponder the question of continuing or terminating assistance. Since evaluating the progress made by a recipient under the Foundation's grants is a basic step in considering that question, the interplay between field and headquarters officers in that final stage centers on conducting this evaluation.

In making his contribution to this interplay, the field officer takes full advantage of his resident status in a country. Accordingly, he brings up-to-date information on the needs and problems there and a deep understanding of cultural and political conditions as they relate to the Foundation's aid-giving responsibilities.

From their side, the headquarters officers make inputs that reflect their position at the center of policy-making. Their contributions have just as legitimate a bearing upon the interests of the Foundation in the aid-relationship as those made by the field officer. Since these headquarters participants are usually senior officers who are scholars of the development process, they bring to this interplay such long-term perspectives on aid-giving as concern for a balanced distribution of the Foundation's aid among the different sectors of a country's economy, for the possible political implications of Foundation aid, and for the policies that have been set by the Board of Trustees of the Ford Foundation.

Rather than to elaborate further on these stages and the forms of field-headquarters officer interplay associated with them, I prefer to draw upon concrete examples from the case histories allowing them to illustrate the impact of that interplay on the effectiveness of the Foundation's aid-giving. These examples can be found in each of the three stages of the Foundation's aid-giving. The evidence of the dynamics of this interplay appears in the voluminous files of correspondence between the Foundation field and headquarters officers. A culminating moment in it occurs at the time of decision-making on award of grants. One Ford Foundation document called "Request for Grant Action" (RGA) figures centrally in that decision-making by carrying the viewpoints and judgments of the field officer to the decision-making arena. In preparing the RGA document, the field officer, in the manner of an advocate, pleads the cause of his client, the prospective recipient, using all the eloquence and cogency at his command.

One of these RGA documents, referred to in the Philippine case history, illustrates how a field officer engages in this interplay during the preliminary stage of aid-giving. That particular RGA document written by the Foundation representative in Manila at the time he was preparing to recommend the second grant to the Science Education Centre (UPSEC), contains his argument for including in that grant two items not found in the original grant: an augmented programme of staff-training at UPSEC and a long-term and systematic evaluation of the UPSEC curriculum materials. His persuasive and knowledgeable arguments are based on his intimate acquaintance with UPSEC's need for the items requested. I have little doubt that his argument, as conveyed by the RGA document to the decision-making session at New York headquarters, played a major part in the decision to award the second grant to UPSEC. In retrospect, it is clear that those two items—the staff training and the evaluation programme—have contributed greatly to UPSEC's continuing leadership as a center of innovation in Philippine education. Thus, debate between this field officer and his headquarters colleagues led to a specific improvement in the grant and significantly benefited the recipient.

To illustrate this interplay between field and headquarters officers during the second stage of aid-giving, when the chief task for the donor agency is to supply technical assistance, I choose an example from the Lebanon case history. There I single out an episode that, while actually occurring in the period *before* the award of a grant, illustrates this interplay during that second stage. It occurred in connection with the Ford Foundation effort to place a resource base[8] at the avail of science educators in the

188

Middle East. Upon recognizing that such a base was needed, the Beirut office appealed to officers in New York Headquarters to scout around in the U.S. for a suitable institution that could serve. The headquarters officers immediately set about to obtain this needed resource. They actually travelled to the institution of their choice (the University of Wisconsin) to explain the nature of a resource base to the officials there and to negotiate a suitable agreement. This illustrates one of the advantages held by the headquarters officers as partners in this interplay: their proximity to important potential resources for technical assistance needs in the field. The record indicates that this initiative by the headquarters officers did in fact expedite the establishment of a highly valuable resource base at the University of Wisconsin for the science educators in Lebanon. That resource base has since proved of inestimable value in the development of the Science and Mathematics Education Centre (SMEC) in Beirut, illustrating again how the interplay between field and headquarters can bring benefits to these projects.

The last example illustrates the interplay between field and headquarters officers during the closing stage in the Foundation's aid-giving with a project. It was in that stage that a decision had to be made either to continue or to terminate assistance. The characteristic responsibility on the Foundation was, then, to evaluate achievements, both in its aid-giving and on the part of its recipient. I choose an example from the Brazil Case History to illustrate the interplay in this closing stage.

As the time was approaching for the third grant to the IBECC/FUNBEC project to terminate, its director, Isaias Raw, wrote to the Foundation as follows:[9]

> "Sometime ago I discussed with you the future of IBECC
> and other initiatives we are taking. I have decided to go ahead
> and even enlarge our area of action."

Because there were many and persisting difficulties in the internal management of IBECC/FUNBEC, this prospect of a large expansion in its activities caused immediate apprehension among Ford Foundation officers in both Rio de Janeiro and New York. After a period of mutual consultation, they decided to submit IBECC's programme, as well as their own aid-giving, to evaluation. As its contribution to that, the Brazil office prepared a comprehensive historical review of the project from the date of its inception to that moment. Meanwhile, New York officers, in particular K. N. Rao, put their minds to evolving a suitable evaluation scheme that could be used to measure IBECC's performance and finally proposed the following criteria for that purpose:[10]

1. Division of labor and setting of priorities.
2. Distinction between translation and genuine innovation.
3. Decision on size and purpose.
4. Management improvements and commercial spin-off.
5. Evaluation of FUNBEC materials.

Through this collaboration, the field and headquarters officers were able to carry out a thorough evaluation of the IBECC/FUNBEC project that resulted in a profound improvement in its situation.

In response to their efforts, Isaias Raw decided to re-work his entire plan for IBECC's future, shortly thereafter presenting to the Foundation a plan that contained carefully chosen targets and priorities:

a) a series of new and original projects (including an integrated
general science course)

b) improvement of operating conditions in FUNBEC

c) evaluation of the educational impact of FUNBEC productions.

Even today, years later, the improvements in IBECC/FUNBEC's position, with its more tightly drawn plans and better-focussed efforts, owes much to joint effort in 1968 by Foundation officers in New York and Rio de Janeiro to confront Isaias Raw with a full review of his plans.

These above examples of teamwork between the Foundation's field and headquarters officers and the impact this has had on the effectiveness of the Foundation's aid-giving are sufficiently convincing to lead me to draw the following general conclusion on the Foundation's aid-giving:

THE FORD FOUNDATION HAS ATTAINED HIGH LEVELS OF EFFECTIVENESS IN PROVIDING TECHNICAL ASSISTANCE TO THESE INNOVATIVE PROJECTS BY MAINTAINING A DYNAMIC INTERPLAY OF IDEAS AND JUDGMENTS BETWEEN ITS HEADQUARTERS OFFICERS AND ITS OFFICERS WHO ARE RESIDENT IN THE RECIPIENT COUNTRY.

EACH PARTY MAKES ESSENTIAL AND COMPLEMENTARY INPUTS TO THE INTERPLAY. THUS, FROM HIS SIDE THE FIELD OFFICER IDENTIFIES NEEDS IN THE RECIPIENT COUNTRY, FINDS THERE THOSE MOST LIKELY TO USE GRANT FUNDS WISELY AND EFFECTIVELY IN MEETING THOSE NEEDS, AND GUIDES THE DELIVERY OF TECHNICAL ASSISTANCE TO THOSE RECIPIENTS.

FROM HIS SIDE, THE HEADQUARTERS OFFICER SETS OVERALL POLICIES TO PROVIDE A FRAMEWORK FOR AID-GIVING, ENGAGES IN CRITICAL DEBATE WITH HIS FIELD COLLEAGUES WHEN PLANNING AS WELL AS EVALUATING THE FOUNDATION'S ASSISTANCE, ACTS TO KEEP A BALANCE IN THE OVERALL AID IN A GIVEN COUNTRY AND BACKS UP HIS FIELD COLLEAGUES WITH ADVISORY SERVICES AND RESOURCES, BOTH HUMAN AND MATERIAL.

In the following checklist, I summarize the various aspects and dimensions in this teamwork across each of the stages of the aid-relationship.

A CHECKLIST
Collaboration between field and headquarters officers of a donor agency

Stage of Aid-giving	Characteristic aid-giving functions	Form and content of interplay between field and head-quarters officers
1. Preparatory stage up to and including the time of decision-making on award of grant.	Identifying leadership Advising with indigenous project leader on organizational structure and work plan. Preparing schedule of technical assistance delivery. Advising on statutory or legal provisions. *At time of decision-making on award of a grant:* Reviewing project plan and proposed donor agency contributions to it.	Interchange of ideas and viewpoints (debate)
2. Stage of actual delivery of technical assistance.	Delivering technical assistance to recipient. Advising on use of resources supplied. Monitoring recipient's use of funds under specific grant items.	Identify and mobilize resources for technical assistance (Resource bases, curriculum projects and their materials, consultants, suitable sites for fellowship study, etc.) Maintain up-to-date inventory of potential resources in donor country. Assess their usefulness for field applications. Interaction with field officers.

A CHECKLIST

Collaboration Between Field and Headquarters Officers
of a Donor Agency

3. Closing stage.	Evaluate progress of project under assistance provided.	Develop evaluation criteria on donor agency's aid-giving as well as recipient's performance.
	Evaluate impact of aid-giving on project.	
	Weigh question of continuing or terminating assistance.	

D. *Indigenous creative talent: a pre-requisite to institutionalizing an innovative project*

The preceding analysis has identified the basic structure and dynamics of Ford Foundation aid-giving, at least as it has been practised on behalf of the recipients in these five science education projects. This information alone proves quite adequate to explain much of the influence of the Ford Foundation aid-giving with these projects, especially in contributing to their capacity to generate innovations. As I continue to examine individual steps in that aid-giving in order to discern their impact on the projects, then, I keep always in mind that those steps were taken by the Foundation through these structures and dynamic processes.

At the time the Ford Foundation offices in these five countries first resolved to throw support behind science education improvement, and before any of the steps of aid-giving had been taken, they stood before the basic issue of identifying the best way to apply technical assistance to efforts for science education improvement. The various options open to them might be expressed as questions that arose in their minds:

1. At what point in the educational system should technical assistance be applied to achieve the greatest leverage for change?

   On the formal class-room system or

   On non-formal means for bringing knowledge and skills in science to the youth of a country?

2. What is the most suitable way to modernize the teaching of science?

   To revise the curriculum and teaching materials?

   To upgrade teacher education?

   To improve the conditions of employment of teachers?

3. What strategy of reform should be followed?

   Commission surveys on the needs in science education?

   Underwrite basic research into educational problems?

   Provide advisors to assist the educators to overhaul the system?

Train future educational leaders for the country?

Organize a comprehensive science education improvement project?

Choosing among these options was a particularly difficult assignment in view of the nature of the effort to be promoted—namely improving education in *science*. As the record shows, in practically every case, that difficulty apparently led these Foundation officers to seek the advice of consultants who were either scientists or science educators.

Interestingly enough, in every case, these consultants then proceeded to narrow down the Foundation's choice of options to two: either to move directly to institutionalize a project for science education improvement, or, as a preparatory effort, to first identify and train indigenous science educators who could later organize a project in science education. The record of the actual choices then made by the Foundation between these two options and the consequences of those choices ultimately on the projects appears in the five case histories. Submitting that record to a critical examination brings to light a profoundly significant lesson on the responsibilities of a donor agency when initiating a technical assistance programme with a project that has an innovatory mission to perform. That examination and conclusion follow.

In Argentina, Brazil and the Philippines, the three countries where indigenous and competent leadership was available at the very outset, the Ford Foundation took up at once the task of promoting the institutionalization of units for producing innovations in science education. In fact, in Brazil, where Isaias Raw's unit already existed, the Foundation's assistance went immediately to strengthening certain institutional features of that project, IBECC. What the case histories show clearly is that, in each of these countries, those indigenous leaders took firm command of the institutionalization of their units, directing the technical assistance provided by the Ford Foundation to critical areas of need in the fledgling organizations under their guidance.

In the case of Lebanon, where such indigenous leadership was lacking at the time the Foundation first wanted to initiate a program of technical assistance to science education improvement, the consultant to the Foundation, Milton Pella, displayed what in retrospect turns out to be great wisdom in counseling the Foundation *against* initially embarking upon efforts to institutionalize a unit for science education improvement. Instead, he urged the Foundation to invest heavily in a long-term program of advanced training for a small group of young science educators who would become future leaders of innovation in Lebanon. The Foundation did, in fact, follow his advice. Six years later, after acquiring doctoral degrees in science education, those young science educators returned to Lebanon to establish the highly successful AUB/SMEC project there.

In the Turkey case, the record of this Foundation choice and its consequences tells a most disturbing story, one that, when taken together with the preceeding accounts, leads one to a significant conclusion on aid-giving. Over a period of years, Foundation consultant-representative in Turkey, Eugene Northrop, together with the science education consultant Stanley Marshall, strove valiantly to institutionalize a centre for creative production of science education materials, the special National High School for Science. Unhappily, as the case history reveals so plainly, their efforts failed at least as far as building a creative curriculum development unit is concerned.[11] For, today, that centre is completely inactive as a curriculum development unit.

The explanation of this failure is the following: Northrop and Marshall fully intended to staff the High School with individuals capable of carrying on curriculum development tasks as well as of teaching the selected, highly-gifted students. Unfortunately, they never succeeded in attracting such individuals to the school. As I study this case history, I can only conclude that they overlooked the seriousness of their failure to recruit—or, alternatively, to train—a corps of competent specialists in curriculum development. That failure was quite clearly the result of pressures on Northrop and Marshall to open the doors of the Special High School as a fully operational secondary school. The heavy burdens associated with institutionalizing an instructional unit somehow drew their attention away from the responsibility to provide a sound base for the school's creative and innovative capability. Had they been fully attentive to the need for this kind of base, they would surely have embarked upon a long-term training program similar to that which was undertaken in the Lebanon case.

The foregoing analysis of this particular chapter in the Ford Foundation aid-giving experience with these innovative projects leads to the following conclusion on institutionalization:

> BEFORE A DONOR AGENCY TAKES THE STEP OF EN-COURAGING THE INSTITUTIONALIZATION OF A PROJECT FOR INNOVATION IN EDUCATION, IT WOULD DO WELL TO ASCERTAIN THAT THERE ARE ON HAND SUFFICIENT NUMBERS OF INDIGENOUS AND QUALIFIED SPECIALISTS IN THE VARIOUS DISCIPLINES RELATED TO THAT INNOVATING ACTIVITY. OTHERWISE, THAT AGENCY MIGHT MORE FRUITFULLY PLACE ITS AID-GIVING BEHIND IDENTIFYING AND TRAINING THE NEEDED TALENT WITH AN EYE ON ESTABLISHING THAT INSTITUTION AT A FUTURE, MORE PROPITIOUS, DATE.

E.   *Supplying technical assistance for institution-building
      with innovative projects in education*

With a capable, indigenous leader placed at its helm, each of these projects entered a critical period of institution-building that has lasted, in most cases, for over a decade. In that period, those leaders had to devote much of their attention to institutional matters related to forming stable and enduring organizations. The Ford Foundation stood at their side throughout that period to meet the peculiar requirements for technical assistance that arose in institution-building with such innovative projects. The case histories record that aid-giving experience and the impact it had on the projects and their capability for innovative action. Understandably then, that record is a rich source of conclusions on aid-giving in promoting institution-building among such projects. These important conclusions emerge in the analysis that follows through my addressing certain questions to that Ford Foundation aid-giving experience, questions that touch upon critical issues in aid-giving for institution-building purposes. These questions, three in number, ask:

(1)   What extent of collaboration with these indigenous leaders
      has marked the aid-giving effort of the Ford Foundation?

(2)   What were the primary targets and the main ingredients of
      that technical assistance? and

(3)   How has the Foundation handled those two basic dimensions
      of aid-giving—time and money?

194

E.1.   *Collaboration with indigenous leaders*

My first question about collaboration directs attention to a highly critical element in sound aid-giving: the extent to which a donor agency conducts its efforts through collaboration with the leadership in a recipient country. My examination of the case histories reveals that extensive collaboration of Foundation staff with these indigenous leaders has marked the institution-building epoch of these five science education projects. In fact, that record shows that the Foundation followed a policy of placing all basic decisions on institutionalizing the projects in the hands of those leaders. It was they, in consultation with Ford Foundation officers and consultants, who drew up the blueprints and timetables for institutional development of their projects. It was they who also took major decisions on policies governing the scope of effort of their projects. Hence, as already pointed out in Chapter 2 of this analysis, it was these indigenous leaders who made the fundamental decision to use innovative curriculum materials in science as the entering-wedge in modernizing their school systems. Moreover, it was these same leaders who adopted the policy for their projects of limiting them to generating innovations while leaving dissemination to others. The exceptional quality of their leadership at this critical period of institutionalization is worth describing here.

First, in the Philippines account, I observe that the original plans for the structure of UPSEC that were drawn up by Delores Hernandez are still in force to this day, serving as UPSEC's basic organizational pattern. That structure, comprising an administrative committee, an advisory council and a series of subject-area working groups, has provided UPSEC an adequate basis for responding to every demand and emergency that has come to it to date. This attests to the exceptional leadership given to UPSEC by its director, Delores Hernandez, and corroborates the wisdom of the Ford Foundation policy of trusting indigenous leaders to make the basic decisions bearing on the institutional blueprint.

A second example of exceptional leadership at the time of a project's institutionalization, appears in the Argentina case history. There, in his letter to the Minister of Education, Professor Bernardo Housay outlines a brilliant conception of jurisdictional arrangements for a creative unit in science education as follows:

"Mr. Minister:

On the 18th of January I had the honour to visit your Excellency to specifically refer to the project which originated in this Council for the establishment of a *National Institute For the Teaching of the Sciences*, designed to promote the improvement of that teaching on a secondary level. On that opportunity, I left with you a memorandum showing the objectives of the institute (organization of courses and seminars, study of plans and programs, production of publications and laboratory equipment, etc.), wherein was shown that the Institute should be established with the participation of the Ministry of Education, this Council, and the National University. At the same time it was mentioned that the Ford Foundation is prepared to make an important contribution for financing the project.

It is obvious that the Institute would have to work closely in conjunction with that Ministry, because its work will especially benefit the educational establishments which function in your

195

jurisdiction and will only be effective if it can count upon all necessary facilities to enable it to work within that environment.

According to this project, the Ministry would participate in the direction of the Institute, with a representative of the Ministry on its Executive Committee, the Ministry would contribute to its work and support, thus allowing for the appointment of teaching personnel of its dependency for service in the Institute: the aquisition of laboratory equipment produced by the Institute for distribution in secondary schools; and the grant of an annual subsidy."

This excellent plan was unfortunately dropped during the long delay in concluding an agreement between the National Council and the Ministry of Education. Angel Hernaiz abandoned it in favour of one that placed INEC under direct jurisdiction of the Ministry of Education. I cannot help but speculate on how different might have been INEC's fortunes had Houssay's original insight on jurisdictional arrangements prevailed.

Additional examples of such leadership lie at hand in the Brazil and Lebanon case histories. I need not use space here to describe them, however, for the conclusion of this section of my analysis is already quite clear:

THROUGHOUT THE INSTITUTION-BUILDING STAGE OF ITS AID-GIVING WITH THESE INNOVATIVE PROJECTS, THE FORD FOUNDATION TOOK CARE TO PLACE RESPONSIBILITY FOR DECISIONS CONCERNING SUCH CRITICAL ISSUES AS ORGANIZATIONAL STRUCTURES, PROGRAM POLICIES AND STRATEGIES OF ACTION FULLY IN THE HANDS OF THE INDIGENOUS LEADERS OF THESE PROJECTS.

E.2   *Organizational health: a principal target for aid-giving with an innovative project*

My second question above asks about the principal targets of the Foundation's technical assistance to the projects during this period of institution-building. A critical examination of the record reveals that assistance—largely in the form of direct funds, consultant advice, and travel awards and fellowships for project staff members—has gone primarily to building up what I term the "organizational health" of these projects.

To build up this organizational health, the Foundation had to channel technical assistance to three components in a project as follows:

a) to improving its internal structure or organizational pattern:

b) to forging better external links between a project and its surroundings: and

c) to ensuring the problem-solving adequacy of a project through enriching its store of resources for creative work, such as the specific skills held by its staff members, its supplies of equipment and tools, and its "intellectual capital."

The case histories show that Foundation efforts to improve the internal organization of a project centered mainly on up-grading its administration and management. Thus, the Brazil case history records a Foundation attempt, early in IBECC's development, to improve its internal management. Isaias Raw, IBECC's director,

196

sought Ford Foundation assistance for IBECC, an institution to which he had already given organizational form. He admitted to its administrative short-comings for, typically, he preferred to count upon dedication to creativity and hard work to pull it through to success. After having supported IBECC for several years, the Ford Foundation officers recognized that its "financial difficulties are principally the result of a rapid, disorderly growth (annual sales have risen over the past eight years from dollars 10,000 to dollars 400,000) coupled with poor internal management." They then took note of the fact that, although Isaias Raw had only recently taken several steps to alleviate the worst of these administrative problems, "these measures, of obvious significance for the development of the organization, will not help to alleviate IBECC (FUNBEC) of its immediate financial strains. To lessen these strains, the Foundation would provide assistance for partial salary payments for a new manager."

Because officers at the Foundation's New York headquarters had been collaborating closely with their colleagues in the Brazil office in this evaluation of IBECC's management difficulties, one of these headquarters officers, K.N. Rao, was in a position to comment on the above recommendation from the field office in Brazil as follows:

> "I am pleased to see the emphasis you are placing in strenthening the management of the operation as I consider this is one of the weakest parts of the FUNBEC operation. I think it would be useful to consider modestly increasing the provision under "Strenthening Management Capacity" to provide for management services beyond the salary supplement for the new manager."

These earliest efforts by the Foundation to shore up IBECC-FUNBEC's management were unfortunately unsuccessful. The Brazil office had to admit, two years later, that "the business manager contacted about two years ago has left FUNBEC without making a significant impact. Apparently it was not possible to separate the managerial from the substantive aspects of FUNBEC's labors and the presence of an administrator who did not understand the functions and objectives of FUNBEC was the source of considerable tension."[12] However, later Foundation efforts along the same line met with greater success. When, in 1969, political events forced Isaias Raw to flee Brazil, the leadership of FUNBEC fell abruptly upon the shoulders of Myriam Krasilchik, Raw's assistant. At once, the Ford Foundation stepped in and awarded her a travel grant so that she could tour curriculum projects and related activities in the United States. That trip enabled Myriam Krasilchik to familiarize herself at first-hand with organizational and operational details of several major U.S. curriculum projects, an experience that added considerably to her competence and self-confidence as the manager of FUNBEC's complex enterprises. On her return to Brazil, she soon put her newly acquired knowledge and competence into practice. FUNBEC added important new projects in curriculum development and initiated an evaluation of the educational validity of its products for the first time in its history.

Another example of a Foundation effort to improve the management of a project exists in the Philippine case history. In 1966, after UPSEC had been operating for two years, the Foundation awarded a travel grant to its director, Delores Hernandez, so that she could travel abroad to Japan and the United States to observe educational projects and to discuss curriculum development matters with leading educators and scientists. She states as the purpose of her travel: "Evaluation; administration; and observation of science education projects and educational research foundations." Her increased managerial and other leadership abilities showed up almost immediately upon her return to UPSEC. New programme lines, including initiation of a major evaluation, appeared, and UPSEC's Steering Committee began important discussions on a new organizational plan. Those Steering Committee meetings, taking place throughout the winter of 1966-67, produced a draft legislative bill entitled, "An Act to Define the Functions of the Science Teaching Centre, Provide for its Support and for Other Purposes." When finally enacted into law as Republic Act 5506, that bill established UPSEC as a permanent but autonomous unit of the University of the Philippines and earmarked an annual budget of L.250,000 (US dollars 40,000) from the National Special Science Fund for support of UPSEC. This legislation defines, in my judgment, an outstanding model for the legal and structural dimensions of an innovative educational unit.

The Foundation matched its concern for better internal management of the projects with vigorous efforts to help them forge stronger and more useful working links with their surroundings. In the Philippines for example, this effort took the form of a grant to pay for a survey of teacher education institutions, a vital step that prepared the way for establishing the large Philippine Science Education Project. Once that project was established, it placed the Science Education Centre (UPSEC) at the heart of a nation-wide network of Regional Science Teaching Centres which desseminates the innovations created by UPSEC to teachers and schools throughout the Philippines.

In Brazil, meanwhile, a similar action by the Foundation succeeded in placing FUNBEC at the heart of a dissemination network. A Ford Foundation grant to the University of Recife in 1964 led to creation of a teacher in-service training centre known as CECINE. This encouraged the Brazilian Ministry of Education to establish similar centres (CECI's) in other Brazilian cities, forming a network of such centres for disseminating educational innovations, including those developed by FUNBEC.

The Lebanon case history furnishes yet a third example of the Foundation's efforts to strengthen the links between a project and its surroundings. There, Ford Foundation assistance enabled Wadih Haddad to move from AUB/SMEC into a position of leadership in the Ministry of Education of Lebanon. He at once set about reorganizing the Ministry especially its dissemination activities (teacher training, curriculum revision, textbook distribution, etc.). This is increasing the use of AUB/SMEC's science education materials as well as its influence on school science instruction throughout Lebanon.

One additional component of Foundation technical assistance in building up the organizational health of these projects was ensuring their problem-solving adequacy. It was Miles, in his classic work on institutions, who first identified this quality as one of the necessary conditions for the health of an organization. Foundation assistance has gone to reinforcing the following three factors that give rise to a project's problem-solving adequacy:

a) the specialized competencies among staff members;

b) equipment and tools required in creative tasks of curriculum development—collections of technical documents, laboratory apparatus, tools for producing kits and prototypes of school apparatus, specialized machines for preparing printed material, etc.; and

c) the intellectual capital of a project, i.e. its store of ideas and knowledge related to curriculum development.

Staff competencies:

A high proportion of the funds in the Ford Foundation grants that have been awarded to these projects has gone to meeting needs along these three lines: large sums have gone to travel awards and fellowships to enable staff members to acquire needed specializations related to curriculum development; other amounts have gone to the purchase of capital items of equipment and machinery for the projects; a considerable outlay for consultants has served to keep the projects informed on recent advances in curriculum development. Three examples from the case histories (Argentina, the Philippines, and Brazil) illustrate exceptionally well how grant provisions for staff-training have raised the levels of problem-solving ability in these projects. In requesting a grant for specialized training of one of his staff members, the Director of the Argentine project (INEC), Angel Hernaiz, wrote to the Ford Foundation as follows:

> "As you may know, among our activities for the improvement of secondary school teachers in the basic sciences, we will attempt to train qualified staff in the specific area of Educational Testing.
>
> This aspect of teaching, so essential to the effective modernization of teaching in our country, must be initiated rationally, developed in different stages, and carried out in accordance with our actual necessities.
>
> We believe it is necessary to send to the Educational Testing Service of Princeton, a professor with genuine interest in educational evaluation and statistics.
>
> We request Foundation assistance to fulfill this important objective. On returning, this professor will be in charge of INEC's Educational Testing Department, and at the same may develop short courses to train more teachers in this field.
>
> INEC proposes to organize a technical assistance service for schools in order to attend to their requirements concerning test construction (selection, development and analysis of tests); permanent evaluation; curriculum and statistical studies; analysis of related educational problems."

The Ford Foundation responded to his request by awarding a travel grant to Señora Marta Maraschi of the INEC staff for study abroad in evaluation and testing. On her return to INEC, she initiated the work outlined in the above letter. In her first major endeavor, she prepared ten issues of a special bulletin entitled "Medición Educativa" (Educational Measurements), which INEC then distributed to over 3000 secondary science teachers throughout Argentina. This stands as one of the most unique and creative undertakings to be found among all these science education projects. It also represented a phenomenal rate of return on the Foundation's investment in an INEC staff member. The Argentine case history goes on to record additional examples of the important contributions to INEC's innovative output by that Educational Testing Department under Marta Maraschi's capable direction.

The Philippine case history provides another example of enhanced problem-solving ability through Foundation support to staff-training. The Philippine case history describes training that Delores Hernandez, Director of UPSEC, requested the Ford Foundation to support. She asked for "short-duration trips by staff members seeking some immediate information or wishing to acquire some specific skill;

199

and year-long (or longer) study grants for staff members desiring to earn advanced degrees."

This Foundation support of staff-training at UPSEC enabled Dr. Aurora Minoza, on her return from an intensive tour of evaluation projects in the USA, to assume leadership of the first major effort by UPSEC to evaluate the educational validity of its products.

The Brazil case history provides the third example of Foundation assistance to staff-training to reinforce the problem-solving ability of a project. Here again, the specific competence introduced into the project was technique of evaluation. A Request for Grant Action, prepared just prior to the award of the grant to FUNBEC, describes the plan to introduce that capability into FUNBEC:

"First, the most important, is the establishment in FUNBEC of a permanent team of behavioral scientists and educators to evaluate curriculum development processes and related instructional materials. FUNBEC has already identified several social scientists and present staff members of FUNBEC who will constitute the evaluation group. The mandate of that group includes: (1) analyzing the effectiveness of curriculum materials in meeting instructional objectives; (2) evaluating the integrated use in the classroom of texts, workbooks, and experimental kits and suggesting optional combinations of these devices; (3) assessing the needs for an effectiveness of various methods of preparing teachers to use the new instructional materials effectively; and (4) estimating the present diffusion of FUNBEC materials and the market for new materials.

To assist FUNBEC in mounting the evaluation team, the proposed grant would provide support for the full two-year salary of a team leader, and for the part-time employment of up to four additional staff members over the two-year grant period. Funds would also be provided to enable FUNBEC to secure the services of senior consultants now associated with the Carlos Chagas Foundation and the University of São Paulo, and short term consultancies of U.S. curriculum evaluation specialists."

Under this grant, FUNBEC recruited and trained its present evaluation team. One of its first tasks was to determine the educational impact on children of a set of primary school science kits that IBECC had developed at an earlier period. As a result of findings of this evaluation team, FUNBEC's developers are now making major improvements in those kits. One consultant, after working with that team for a month, gave this testimony:[13]

> "I found the organization (FUNBEC) and its staff impressive. I believe that the new emphasis on evaluation encouraged by the Ford Foundation grant will be extremely useful in improving the curriculum produced and the manner of its production and dissemination."

It is a particularly eloquent testimony to this team's role in ensuring the problem-solving adequacy of FUNBEC.

Material means.

The case histories also record Foundation contributions to problem-solving adequacy through meeting costs of needed capital equipment. In doing this, the Foundation relied upon the indigenous leaders of the projects to define needs for technical documents, laboratory apparatus, workshop tools, and machinery for preparing instructional materials. In the purchase of these materials, the convertibility of the U.S. dollar often proved helpful. Particularly helpful has been the ability of the Foundation to make these purchases in a timely manner. Illustrating this last point is an incident in the Brazil Case History. At one point in IBECC's early period, Isaias Raw saw a need to demonstrate the capability of IBECC to the Brazilian Ministry of Education. In his judgment, this required IBECC to prove that it could act quickly in placing translated editions of certain U.S. science curriculum project materials in secondary schools throughout Brazil. The Foundation's response to his request for funds enabled IBECC to translate and arrange for printing of one-half million school textbooks. This successful demonstration established IBECC's reputation with Brazilian educational authorities as a successful center of innovation.

A similar example of timely response to a project's material need occurred in the Philippine project. There, UPSEC's large-scale trial programme required it to produce large quantities of interim editions of its science materials. UPSEC struggled to produce these interim materials with office equipment that was totally inadequate for a task of that magnitude. On seeing this, the Foundation lost no time in purchasing and installing certain appropriate electrically-operated machines that enabled UPSEC to keep up in its development schedule. This enlarged capacity has been no small factor in its attaining a position of leadership in Philippine education.

Intellectual Capital.

The third way in which the Ford Foundation assisted these projects to reach a state of problem-solving adequacy was by investing in what I call their intellectual capital. This refers to their store of ideas and information on curriculum development in the sciences, including their repertoire of strategies and procedures for such work. Visiting consultants have proved absolutely essential in these projects' effort to gain new ideas and to bring their strategies constantly under review. In effect, by keeping the projects in frequent contact with similar work in progress elsewhere, consultants have made vital additions to their intellectual capital.

In meeting these particular technical assistance requirements of the projects, the Ford Foundation has shown great virtuosity as a donor agency. It has identified consultants, persuaded them to devote time to the projects, and provided fees and travel costs. Indeed it took full advantage of its position in the U.S. to attract consultants from the U.S. science education reform movement just then reaching its zenith. Among those consultants brought to the Philippines in the second and critical year of UPSEC's growth were several who were the leaders of the U.S. science curriculum movement. The other projects benefited similarly from work by consultants from the U.S. curriculum movement. In a very real sense, by providing these consultants, the Ford Foundation carried out an efficient "transfer of technology" to these projects.

The Foundation effected this transfer of ideas and information to the projects through both long-term and short-term consultants. Through short-term consultants, it could pin-point highly specific needs in the programmes and supply specialized techniques and knowledge to meet them. Through long-term consultants, who could pay recurring visits to the projects over a period of years, it was able to assist the projects in the areas of policies, organizational structures, personnel training, etc. The following examples from the case histories illustrate this long-term contribution made by consultants furnished through Ford Foundation grants.

201

Visits to INEC in Argentina over a period of several years enabled the Foundation consultant, Abraham Fishler, to win the confidence of INEC's Director, Angel Hernaiz. As a result, Fischler could discuss with Hernaiz even as sensitive a matter as the basic organizational pattern of INEC.

In the Philippines, the Foundation consultant to UPSEC, Robert Ward, found the long-term character of his appintment as *resident consultant* to be a major asset. That feature of his appointment (and, of course, his personality and competency as a science educator) won him respect and confidence among UPSEC personnel to such a degree that they invited him to become a member of their Steering Committee.

Perhaps the classic example of a long-term consultantship is Milton Pella, who has served the project and Arab science education over a period of a decade or longer. In that time, he has trained the entire staff of the AUB/SMEC in Lebanon, assisted them in organizing that centre, and provided advice on its programme of research, teacher training and, most importantly, curriculum development. In fact today, his trainees are serving as consultants, under Ford Foundation grants, to science educators in other Arab countries of the Middle East. In their work with these other science educators, the AUB/SMEC staff members are drawing on their strong backgrounds received at the University of Wisconsin as well as upon their years of experience at AUB/SMEC. Their ability to serve in this wider way is clearly an extra dividend of the Ford Foundation investment in Milton Pella. Pella's service to Arab science educators in Lebanon and the Middle East has gained intensity and focus through membership in his own university department, which has been a resource base for Arab science education. In addition to supporting Pella when he was in the field, with a full range of services and resources, that department also provided Arab science educators opportunity to earn Ph.D's, under the guidance of Pella and his associates. In negotiating the agreement with the University of Wisconsin, Foundation officers urged the University to utilize Foundation grant funds to strengthen its ability to play this role of resource base:[14]

> "Some may look upon this as a contract for services to be rendered, whereas we look upon it as a grant. If it were a contract it would be quite appropriate to measure our action by what the Foundation expects to get in return. This is not, however, the sole measure of a grant, where benefit to the grantee is a prime consideration. With respect to the present example, this means that the development of Wisconsin's interest and competence in the problems of science education in Arab countries is an integral part of our concern.
>
> Some may expect Wisconsin to produce the answers and development materials for improved science education in the Arab countries. Actually, however, our objective is to develop Arabs with the competence to do this, and eventually to work with them in the establishment of some kind of a center through which they can be effective. An essential ingredient in attaining this objective is the strengthening of American competence in terms of individuals at the American university, specifically Wisconsin."

Milton Pella and his colleagues have indeed provided many valuable services to the Arab science educators in fulfillment of this responsibility as a resource base. It is regrettable however that Pella has not utilized the funds set aside so imaginatively by the Ford Foundation for University use in developing its potential as a resource base for Arab science education.

The Brazil Case History supplies another example in which the Ford Foundation has relied upon a resource base to focus and intensify its effort to supply technical assistance to one of these science education projects. In 1971, when FUNBEC recognized its need to initiate a long-term evaluation of its products, the Foundation turned to one of the U.S. national-level science education projects, the Biological Sciences Curriculum Study (BSCS) to place its services at the avail of FUNBEC.[15] BSCS accepted this invitation to serve as a resource base for the Brazilian science educators. A Foundation grant to the BSCS project has made it possible for FUNBEC to draw heavily upon its expertise particularly in evaluation techniques. (Richard Tolman, James Robinson and Hulda Grobman.) Collaboration between these consultants and FUNBEC staff members over several years has produced the report, "An Evaluation of Biologia." This resource base arrangement has built in FUNBEC a formidable evaluation capability arming it for an advance on many fronts in Brazilian education.

In taking these three steps in bahalf of these projects, namely, reinforcing the competencies of their staff specialists, providing vitally needed items of capital equipment, and investing in their intellectual capital, the Ford Foundation has ensured the problem-solving adequacy of these projects. That quality, together with their sound organizational structures and effective working links, endows them with sound organizational health out of which they are able to excel as centres of innovation in science education.

I summarize these foregoing examples of the Ford Foundation action in channelling technical assistance to specific targets in these five science education projects to build-up their organizational heath as follows:

IN INSTITUTION-BUILDING WITH A PROJECT WHOSE MISSION IS TO GENERATE INNOVATIONS IN EDUCATION, THE FORD FOUNDATION HAS HAD THE MOST SATISFACTORY RESULTS WHEN IT HAS DIRECTED ITS TECHNICAL ASSISTANCE PRINCIPALLY TO TARGETS THAT BUILD UP THE ORGANIZATIONAL HEALTH OF THAT PROJECT, VIZ.:

1. TO REINFORCING THE SPECIALIZED COMPETENCIES AMONG ITS STAFF MEMBERS, ESPECIALLY IN FIELDS THAT ENABLE IT TO ACCEPT THE NEWER KINDS OF CHALLENGES POSED BY THE CHANGING CONDITIONS IN THE SCHOOLS OF A COUNTRY;

2. TO SUPPLYING SUCH MATERIAL REQUIREMENTS FOR SUCCESSFUL CURRICULUM DEVELOPMENT IN THE SCIENCES AS LABORATORY EQUIPMENT, WORK-SHOP TOOLS, AND MACHINERY FOR PREPARING THE INSTRUCTIONAL MATERIALS (INCLUDING PRINTED MATTER) FOR CONDUCTING TRIALS IN SCHOOLS; AND

3. TO BUILDING UP ITS "INTELLECTUAL CAPITAL," MEANING, IN PARTICULAR, HOLDING OF RELEVANT DOCUMENTS AND LIVING STORE OF IDEAS

AND INFORMATION (MAINTAINED THROUGH CON-
STANT CONTACT WITH SUITABLE SOURCES OF
THESE—ESPECIALLY OTHER CURRICULUM DE-
VELOPMENT CENTERS).

E.3.   *The dimensions of time and money*

The last of my questions about the Foundation's aid-giving during the institution-building phase with these projects looks into the way time and money were handled. From the case histories, I quickly discover in how astute a manner the Foundation
has, in fact, handled these interwoven dimensions. Thus, frequent and close attention
to a recipient's spending of the funds allocated under a particular grant item has
occurred under the name of "monitoring" a grant item. As for its handling of time, the
Foundation has frequently had occasion to display timelines in meeting needs arising
suddenly to plague a recipient, or to be flexible and shift a deadline so that a recipient
would not be penalized in some unconstructive way. To these two examples, I must add
a third: the long-term perspective taken by the Foundation on its aid-giving with these
projects. It has shown great perseverance in its mission of supplying the technical
assistance related to institutionalization until full institutional form and strength have
come to these projects.

To provide corroborating evidence of this astute handling of time and money
by the Foundation, I draw upon some examples from the case histories. The first
illustrates the Foundation's practice of monitoring a grant item as a way of benefiting a
recipient. Through this device, the Foundation officers have frequently prodded a
grantee to move in some direction which they believed relevant to his goal. At other
times, they have used this to challenge a grantee to enter new and untried areas of
endeavour.

Repeated references in the case histories to the monitoring of grant items by
Foundation officers show how they used this technique to achieve a variety of purposes; from applying subtle pressure on a grantee to change some defective practice in
his performance, to inviting him to move out into new areas of endeavour. The Argentine case history illustrates both of these uses of monitoring. At one point, the Buenos
Aires office of the Ford Foundation found it necessary to modify the budget provisions
in its grant to INEC, reducing the provision for in-service courses and shifting funds to
an item for INEC-CICE cooperation on evaluation, an emphasis in INEC's work very
much favoured by the Foundation officers. Then, in that same modification, the Foundation specified that $14,000 should go to exploratory efforts in curriculum develop-
ment by INEC in collaboration with the new education ministry officer, Dr. Mignone,
whose creativity Foundation officers wished to encourage. These efforts by the Foundation to promote changes in the direction of a grantee's work succeeded well; INEC-
CICE cooperation soon took on added vigor, culminating in the release of the IPS
evaluation report, while INEC and Ministry of Education collaboration led to several
new curriculum development projects.

In another example, this one from the Brazil case history, the Ford Foundation again used control of funds under a grant item to influence the direction taken by a
recipient in his work. There, when new leadership had come to FUNBEC's helm
following the enforced departure of Isaias Raw, the Foundation awarded a fresh grant
in which it included an item of $15,000 earmarked for the exploration of potential new
areas of project development. Here again, the tactic succeeded. FUNBEC took the
"challenge" funds and used them to open up an entirely new area of curriculum development—a geography course is interweaving the study of science with social and
cultural concerns.

204

To this practice of monitoring the funds allocated under a specific grant item, the Foundation added the "Monitoring of time" as a way of influencing or assisting recipients. By this latter phrase I refer to astute management of the time element in grants, giving recipient a chance to improve his performance or avoiding penalizing him unproductively when circumstances may have prevented him from meeting a deadline. Both timeliness in response to needs among the recipients and flexibility in handling deadlines have marked these Foundation efforts to "monitor" time in behalf of its recipients.

Perhaps the most dramatic instance of timely action on the Foundation's part in behalf of a project occurred in the case of AUB/SMEC in Lebanon. There, the Foundation had to act with precipitate speed to rescue from total loss its previous investment over many years in the Arab science educators. Despite its valiant efforts to train these 'leaders' and place them at the avail of countries in the Middle East, authorities there, especially in Lebanon, showed little or no inclination to group them into a unit that could hold them in the Middle East and utilize their talents for innovative work in education. In 1969, as time was slipping rapidly away, the Ford Foundation stepped in with the swift and timely action of granting funds to the American University in Beirut for the purpose of creating SMEC. Through that action AUB was able to form a viable, critically-sized unit that held those science educators in Lebanon and provided them a suitable base from which they began to make their impact felt on science education, not only in Lebanon but in Arab countries throughout the Middle East.

Illustrating the attribute of flexibility in the Foundation's aid-giving is an occasion that arose in the course of the struggle to launch a programme of assistance to the project in Argentina. Although the Foundation first awarded a grant to the National Council for Scientific and Technical Research for an augmented programme in science education improvement as early as 1965, it was not until two years later that activities could commence under that grant. The Foundation displayed great patience during that long interval, keeping its grant in abeyance, while Angel Hernaiz worked diligently behind scenes to bring about the necessary government decree which finally permitted activity to begin. Incidentally, I see this display of patience as a direct manifestation of the resident status of the Foundation's representative in Argentina. Only in this position could a donor agency have followed the day-by-day changes in a country so racked by political and civil turmoil, and thereby have shown patience with its beleaguered recipient until conditions allowed him to accept a grant.

The time-connected attribute in the Foundation's aid-giving that has held the greatest significance for the development of these projects, however, was perseverance in aid-giving over a period of time long enough to allow the projects to reach maturity as centres of innovation, self-sufficient if not self-supporting. The lifetime of that support is at least a decade in the case of these five projects. It is only now, as a matter of fact, that the Ford Foundation is asking the question, in relation to its aid to these projects, "Has the time arrived to consider discontinuing the aid-relationship?"

F.   *New needs bring new opportunities to assist*
Although the analysis of the Foundation's own aid-giving experience with these projects yields a resonably defensible reply to that question about terminating assistance, that reply is being challenged by recent developments in countries where these projects are located. There, rapidly altering socio-economic conditions are causing a rising tide of children to flood into the schools, largely from sectors of those societies that have hitherto had little or no opportunity for schooling. At the same time,

those schools are feeling growing pressures to provide children a form of instruction that will fit them for participation in the modernization of their socieities. This means an emphasis on science and mathematics instruction, of course. But, because those children are largely from the lower income and rural strata of their societies, that instruction, to be effective, must be guided by an understanding of cultural and linguistic factors that apply to the learning behaviour of the children.

Quite understandably, then, educational authorities in those countries are turning to these successful science education projects to request their aid in preparing the required course of instruction. To respond to such requests, these projects find that they must supplement the competencies of their staff members with added specializations in fields such as psychometrics and linguistics. They are also aware of a need to collaborate with specialists in such applicable disciplines as sociology and anthropology. It is these needs that are posing the challenge to that tidy reply that perhaps aid-giving can now be terminated. Just at the moment when the Foundation had considered its aid-giving mission with these projects to be at an end, these new and urgent needs for technical assistance are asserting themselves.

That the Foundation is responding to this challenge, the case histories leave little doubt. In the Philippines, for example, it has decided to award additional study grants to UPSEC staff members to enable them to pursue advanced study and research, in this way acquiring competencies related to such assignments as curriculum development in science for rural and agricultural communities as well as science for primary schools.

This evidence from the case histories indicates a definite willingness on the part of the Ford Foundation to reconsider the question of terminating its aid-giving, at least with some of these projects. It suggests that the Foundation is finding new and more profound grounds upon which to justify its grants of technical assistance. These grounds include, first of all, the fact that, in most of these countries, these projects are the only truly competent groups of curriculum development specialists, at least in science and mathematics. Then there is the undeniable fact of the relevance of the output of these projects, now that they are moving into solving problems of rural or agricultural and especially primary school science education. What they are now doing is making a demonstrable contribution to the modernization process in the cultural and economic sectors of the societies of those developing countries where they are working.

Moreover, the Ford Foundation is not unaware that it can now realize exceptionally high rates of return on relatively small but well-aimed investments in these projects. This is a consequence of their unusually sound state of problem-solving adequacy—itself a product of previous Foundation investments in these projects, as I have just pointed out in the analysis.

For all these reasons then, the Ford Foundation appears intent on continuing its efforts to meet selected needs for technical assistance among at least some of these science education projects. As a revised reply to that question on terminating aid-giving, it is not only surprising, especially in view of the criteria adduced above, but also highly creative and responsible.

206

REFERENCES

1. For sake of brevity I shall employ this term "aid-giving" in referring to the programmatic activity of meeting technical assistance requirements of a project.

2. Personal communication to the author from F. Champion Ward, Ford Foundation, New York.

3. 28 September 1960 Memorandum from Robert C. Wickham to Alfred C. Wolf.

4. Adapted from Lester Pearson, "Partners in Development," N.Y. Publ. 1969, pp. 6, 127.

5. 17 June 1966 memorandum from S. Widdicombe of the Rio de Janeiro office of the Ford Foundation to Harry E. Wilhelm of the New York Headquarters of the Foundation.

6. 10 November 1970 memorandum by Dr. William D. Carmichael.

7. August 1973 letter to author from Augusto Tenmatay, the Ford Foundation, Manila.

8. The term "resource base" means, in the Ford Foundation lingo, an organization, institution or programme that can provide a range of related services—consultants, training opportunities, etc., to one of its recipients.

9. 7 January 1968 letter from Isaias Raw to the Ford Foundation office in Rio de Janeiro.

10. These criteria appear in a 5 March 1969 memorandum from K.N. Rao, New York, to William Carmichael, Brazil.

11. The programme in Turkey requires special and separate comment.
For, provided the Ford Foundation still intends to bring each project to a state where a creative centre of innovation has been enduringly implanted in the educational system, then its task in Turkey remains unfinished, but for a different reason. Provided that Turkish authorities want the Foundation to continue assisting them, then the Foundation has an obligation, it seems to me, to continue channeling technical assistance either to the ailing Science High School to restore it to its originally-intended function as a centre for generating innovations, or to the build-up of some new institution that would have this same purpose.
Incidentally, none of this comment is meant to bring into question the importance of the continuing assistance that the Ford Foundation is providing to the dissemination activities of the Science Education Development Commission (SEDC) through the skilled consultant services of Dr. Uri Haber-schaim.
(See Turkey Case History and also Chapter 1 of this analysis).

12. 28 Jan. '71. The Ford Foundation, Rio de Janeiro, interoffice memorandum of Peter Hakim to D. Carmichael.

13. Hulda Grobman in Brazil Case History

14. 10 April 1963 letter from Harvey Hall to Clark Bloom.

15. It is interesting to note that BSCS is one of the few national-level science curriculum projects in the U.S. that has survived beyond the 1960's era. U.S. science educators may find it useful to ponder the extent to which institutionalization of BSCS has bestowed survival value on it, and provided the US with a most important national asset to be shared with educators abroad.

Epilogue

Provided that I have been sufficiently skillful in my workmanship, this public review—the case histories together with the analysis—should succeed in giving a wide view to the experiences and accomplishments that have marked the course of these innovative projects across the past decade or two. In this epilogue, I would like to say a word to those who may find this information useful—science educators, ministry of education officials, and officers of donor agencies. I would like to invite them to explore the implications of these recorded events and to derive conclusions for their own areas of work and responsibility. For they alone can determine whether and how any of this information may be applicable to their situations.

Perhaps I could go a bit beyond merely inviting these interested individuals and orgnaizations and suggest at least some of the possible directions in which I see these implications leading, in this way stimulating their own explorations of these implications. For example, I could describe several urgent and unresolved issues in science education brought to light by the experiences of these five projects under review.

First and foremost there is a gnawing realization that reliable and significant measures of the effectiveness of innovations in science education for the school rooms of developing countries still escape the science educators. As the record shows, not one of these Ford Foundation projects has been able to demonstrate that effectiveness in any conclusive way. Fortunately, more sophisticated psychometric work is underway in these developing countries that may soon yield the longed-for reliable and useful indications of educational effectiveness of the instructional materials and methods in the sciences prepared in these projects.

The experience of these projects indicates that educational research is needed to determine how a child's culture and social class influence his ability to learn science, that is, to learn it and thereby acquire those benefits from it (greater objectivity, sound reasoning ability, etc.) that the science educators claim should accrue to him.

Preliminary research findings by several of these projects are disturbing in suggesting that the children now flooding into the schools from rural and lower socio-economic strata of the societies in these countries fail to learn science concepts under strategies of science instruction brought in from "Western" societies. Furthermore, the experiences of these science education projects under review point strongly to the growing struggle by curriculum development groups to be able to discern the "world-view" held by children from the so-called deprived sectors of the society in a developing country. That struggle will require, if it is to culminate in success, that curriculum development groups collaborate more fully with rural sociologists, linguists, anthropologists, and specialists in child development.

Now, I ask myself, what would a government official in the Ministry of Education of a developing country be likely to seek in this review of these innovative projects? Perhaps no issue preoccupies him more than that of how to meet mounting costs of education in his country. It would not surprise me, then, to have him look in this study for some clue to the cost of producing a new science course for his schools. Let me picture a situation in which he may very well find himself.

Perhaps a group of well-informed and well-meaning science educators—the local science teachers association, for example, has just devoted a two-year period to a study of the kind of science course that country ought to offer to pupils in its junior secondary schools. They have specified the course aims and objectives, the general corpus of knowledge to be learned, and indicated the distribution of topics over a two or three-year sequence, finally placing all this before this ministry officer as a forceful recommendation. He would naturally then seek information on the approximate cost of preparing such a course before he could respond to their recommendation. Does the review of the five Ford Foundation projects have anything to tell him in that situation?

First of all, if that Ministry official must begin from the very beginning (as was the case in Lebanon), then he must meet the cost of training at least four to five science educators up to the doctorate level in specializations related to curriculum development.

This study reveals that the Ford Foudnation invested approximately US $21,600 in such training for *each* of the five Arab science educators, or a total of US $108,000.

Next, he must pull these trained science educators together into a team much as AUB did when it formed SMEC. The cost of doing this, and of underwriting their activities for several years (assuming that it would require a several year period for the team to produce a course and submit it to trial use in schools) might be set at a sum similar to that of the first AUB/SMEC grant of US $167,000.

The total cost, then, to *produce* this course for his schools (not the cost of manufacturing and distributing multiple copies of text books to the classrooms or of conducting in-service training for teachers required to institute the new course in the schools) would amount to about US $275,000, based on the Lebanon project experience. Costs in the Brazil and Philippine cases were comparable.

Hopefully, by providing practical information on costs this way, this study can prove helpful to such a Ministry of Education official in his decision-making on innovation and change in his educational system and even in his effort to justify requests for technical assistance from donor agencies.

The last group for whom the findings and conclusions of this study may have implications are other donor agencies engaged, like the Ford Foundation, in meeting technical assistance requirements of projects for educational innovation and change in developing countries. To this group, I call attention to the conclusions on aid-giving which arose through my analysis of the performance of the Ford Foundation with these five innovative projects. Those conclusions have a wide applicability, it appears to me, to the aid-giving of any donor agency that aims to establish and sustain innovative work in education in the developing countries. How they apply, of course, those other agencies must themselves determine. For example, the conclusions point to certain organizational arrangements that appear to account for the high levels of effectiveness in the Ford Foundaton aid-giving. However, those arrangements are those of a particular agency with its particular aims, resources and constraints. They do not necessarily resemble the arrangements of another donor agency with different aims, resources, and constraints.

But, despite this specificity of the conclusions to circumstances in the Ford Foundation, they nevertheless do point to several highly important principles on sound aid-giving with innovative projects. These are lessons from experience that I would hope can by their study assist other donor agencies to reach higher levels of effectiveness in meeting the technical assistance needs of educational innovators in the developing countries. To these innovators, wherever they are found, I dedicate this study.

Announcing the annual publication of

a Summary of Research in Science Education
1973

Edited by **Mary Budd Rowe** and **Linda DeTure,** both of the
University of Florida, Gainesville.
ISBN: 0-470-74354-9   1975   92 pp. $4.95 paper
**Available to SCIENCE EDUCATION and JOURNAL OF RESEARCH IN
SCIENCE TEACHING subscribers at a reduced price of $3.95.**

This valuable research review analyzes and synthesizes research related to the teaching and learning of science completed during 1973. This review was developed in cooperation with the National Association for Research in Science Teaching. Appointed NARST committees worked with staff of ERIC Science, Mathematics, and Environmental Education Information Analysis Center to evaluate, review, analyze, and report research results. This review will provide research information for development personnel, ideas for future research, and an indication of trends in research in science education.

CONTENTS: Introduction. Purposes Served by the Review. Organization, Choice of Studies and Methods for Their Review. Other Reviews and Summaries. Learning: Introduction. Learning Studies Based on Theories Other than Piaget's. Piagetian-Based Studies. Behavioral Objectives. Formats for Instruction. Curriculum Evaluation. Tests. Physics. Science and the Handicapped. Education, Characteristics and Behaviors of Teachers: Teacher Education. Teacher Verbal Characteristics. Teacher Attitudes and Values. Values and Philosophy. Surveys. Summary and Conclusions. Index. References.

Books are available for a 30 day examination period. If the book is returned within that period, your bill will be canceled. Halsted Press will pay postage and handling for all orders accompanied by payment. In order for subscribers to receive the reduced price of $3.95, please send your order to the attention of Dept. SCI,

HALSTED PRESS,
A Division of John Wiley & Sons, Inc.,
605 Third Avenue,
New York, N.Y. 10016.